USERS' GUIDE TO INDUSTRIAL DIAMONDS

Users' Guide
to Industrial Diamonds

NORMAN R. SMITH

Technical Director
Diamond Products Division of Universal Grinding Ltd

HUTCHINSON BENHAM, LONDON

HUTCHINSON BENHAM LTD
3 Fitzroy Square, London W1

An imprint of the Hutchinson Publishing Group

London Melbourne Sydney Auckland
Wellington Johannesburg Cape Town
and agencies throughout the world

First published 1974

Set in Monotype Times, printed in Great Britain
on Aeroart paper by The Anchor Press Ltd, and
bound by Wm. Brendon & Son Ltd, both of Tiptree, Essex
ISBN 0 09 117050 8

Contents

Foreword

In the world of Industry as perhaps in any human activity there is a constant stream of information, sometimes general, sometimes highly technical, but all seeking to impart instruction in the art or science of some particular activity. Sometimes the information is accurate but incomplete in detail; all too often it can be found wanting.

In this book an acknowledged expert has assembled and clearly set out in logical progress basic data and the methods of applying them which so often receive insufficient attention in learned treatises.

Diamonds have become a world of their own and a complete industry has grown up devoted to their production and application to Industry. Many of the readers of this book, specialists in their own field, will not have realised to what extent the world we live in has become dependent on industrial diamonds, and the general reader would be astonished to learn to what degree he is fed, clothed, sheltered, transported, entertained, doctored and his life made generally pleasanter through products and processes which at some stage or another involve the skilled application of industrial diamond.

This book is entitled *Users' Guide to Industrial Diamonds* and no book was ever more accurately described. In it Mr. Smith has set out in detail the information which the designer and the production engineer must have to enable him to use to the best advantage one of the most valuable but often least understood materials available. The text is supplemented by drawings, diagrams and photographs and, what is so often lacking, includes bibliographical references which will enable even the specialist to extend his researches in his particular field if he so desires.

It has become a literary platitude to observe that a book fills a long-felt want. In this case that commonplace verdict is thoroughly deserved.

A. NORMAN HARLEY
President
The Gauge and Tool
Makers' Association
London.

Acknowledgements

In a minor key, industrial diamonds play a part in most human activity, but, in terms of geographical area, the consumption is generally proportional to the degree of industrial activity. The writer has been fortunate in being able to collect personally much of the information contained in the volume, but even more fortunate in having colleagues and collaborators who have actively participated.

Mr. R. Farrar, of L. M. Van Moppes & Sons Ltd., assembled much of the information in Chapters 1 and 11, and Mr. R. H. Phillips, B.SC.(ENG.), C.ENG., F.I.CHEM.E., made available details of diamond powder production and usage. Herr W. Rose, of Industriediamanten G.m.b.H.; Mr. C. A. Williams, of Impregnated Diamond Products Ltd.; and Messrs. E. N. Hallewell and D. S. Classey, of Diaform Ltd., were most helpful in supplying data for the chapter on Toolmaking; also M. P. Fricou of Precidia S.A., France, and Mr. E. M. Wilson, of the Diamond Division of Universal Grinding Ltd., for the Transport chapter. Examples of diamond usage in the electrical industry were supplied by Mr. F. J. Simpson, M.B.E., of British Diamond Wire Die Co. Ltd.; Mr. R. J. R. Cully, of Bryant Symons & Co. Ltd; and Messrs. P. M. Selby and T. K. Little of L. M. Van Moppes & Sons Ltd. Information appertaining to the Stone and Glass industries was provided by Mr. J. A. Newth, of Sharratt & Newth Ltd.; by Messrs. R. A. Haywood, J. F. Finnimore and L. F. Hankins, of Impregnated Diamond Products Ltd.; and Sig. R. Bolliger of L. M. Van Moppes & Sons S.p.A., Italy. The latter also supplied examples of diamond drilling in the Construction and Mineral industries. In Chapter 8, on Construction, examples were also supplied by M. P. Suied, of Forbeton S.A., France; M. G. Pittet, of Forbeton S.A., Switzerland; and officers of

Holemasters Ltd. in England. In the mineral field much information was supplied by the late Mr. A. E. Smith and Mr. R. O. Morris, M.A., F.G.S., M.I.M.M., of L. M. Van Moppes & Sons Ltd. M. H. Joire, of Drilling & Service S.A., France, was most helpful in commenting on the section dealing with oil field work. Information on the Swiss Watch and Jewellery industry was subscribed by M. J. D. Freinhofer, of L. M. Van Moppes & Sons S.A., Switzerland.

The author would also like to thank Mrs. M. E. Pegrum for her untiring help in the collation of the information and typing of the manuscript, and Messrs. M. Fehr and S. P. Edmund, DIPL.ING., M.SC., M.R.AE.S., for their help in translations of foreign documents.

The extracts from British Standards are reproduced by kind permission of the British Standards Institution, 2 Park Street, London, W.1.

1

The nature of diamond

DIAMOND is the hardest material known, but it is brittle, and tools will break quite easily if they are abused. The abrasion resistance varies with orientation, and some things are technically impossible or economically unjustified. Diamond has a very low coefficient of friction, a very low coefficient of expansion and a very high thermal conductivity. Diamond falls into two main categories: Type I and Type II, the great majority being Type I. Type IIb diamonds are semiconductors, whereas the others are extremely good electrical insulators.

These properties, and the others listed, give diamond a unique place in modern technology.

Diamonds are essential in general engineering; diamonds will drill oil wells but they will also play gramophone records; diamonds will saw marble and granite but they are also used in delicate ophthalmic surgery; diamonds will even decorate the crown of the Sovereign. Diamond has, indeed, some very special properties.

During 2,000 years of diamond mining, it is said that only about 130 tons have been recovered. To obtain this, however, some three thousand million tons of rock, sand and gravel have been sorted. The average diamond content of a diamond-rich ore is only of the order of one part in twenty million. To these natural sources must now be added synthetic grit production. Larger synthetic diamonds have been produced, but they are not available commercially, except as Polycrystalline Aggregates.

Pure diamond contains only carbon atoms. The carbon that is swept down the chimney and thrown away has the carbon atoms arranged in a random manner; if these carbon atoms are rearranged in a special manner, we have diamond.

It appears that even the carbon derived from toasted teacakes has

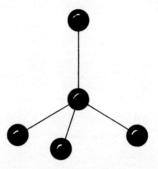

Diagram showing tetrahedral arrangement of carbon atoms

been converted into diamond! The first illustration shows this special arrangement; each carbon atom is surrounded by four near neighbours, forming a tetrahedron. These atoms are linked by chemical bonds, called co-valent bonds; these are represented by the lines. These bonds are very strong indeed, and this is why diamond is strong; to break the diamond the bond must be broken. This structure repeats itself, forming a giant molecule, as seen in the illustration below. Each of the four sets of bonds can be arranged so that they are parallel; if we cut through such a set of parallel bonds, a slice of diamond can be taken off. This process is called 'cleaving', and it can be repeated, rather like cutting cards. If this cleaving process is attempted when the bonds are not parallel, the diamond will smash, like glass.

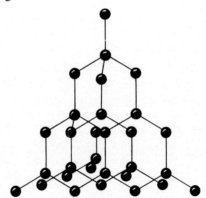

Atomic arrangement of carbon atoms in diamond—giant molecule

In the diamond industry, cleaving is one of the primary methods of reducing large stones to the required size, since it is quick and there is very little wastage. Obviously, the cleaver must know where these bonds lie in the diamond, since he must orientate it so that they are parallel. If we consider a simple shape, such as a cube, then these bonds will emerge from the corners and therefore, when cleaving a cube, the corners must be chopped off. There is no particular magic about cleaving diamond; in many respects it is rather like splitting wood. Everyone knows that wood can only be split along the grain; if we chop across the grain the fibres are simply smashed. So it is with diamond. In wood we have knots; when the split reaches a knot it will either go round it or stop there and the wood will then break or smash. In a real diamond we have something very similar, called naats, caused by local changes in the structure. When a cleavage crack reaches a naat, it will either deviate or the diamond will smash.

In wood, the grain and the knots are readily visible, but in a diamond these features are very far from obvious. Diamond cleaving is very specialised and highly skilled work; a mistake can be very expensive indeed. Not only has the cleaver to split the diamond, he has to produce a certain number of pieces to given dimensions, and very often these pieces must be cut so that they avoid inclusions, naats and so on.

When designing or using diamond tools, it must be recognised that these planes of weakness, i.e. cleavage planes, exist. Turning to

The diamond grain must not run parallel to the cutting force

wood again, no one would make a gangplank with the grain running *across* the plank, the grain would be arranged to run along the length of the plank. Similarly, when designing and using diamond tools, the grain must not be allowed to run parallel to the cutting force; if it does, the diamond will cleave.

It must be appreciated that diamonds can only be cleft by slicing through the interatomic bonds, and that this can only be done when these bonds are arranged so that in any one plane the bonds are parallel. It follows that no matter how the outer shape of the diamond is altered, the four cleavage directions remain unchanged. Thus, if all the corners of the cube are removed, we are left with an octahedron. In this octahedron, the cleavage directions are exactly the same as in the cube, and it can be seen that this means that we must cleave an octahedron parallel to the octahedral faces.

Now consider the polishing directions in diamond, since this is a useful way of studying the variations in abrasion resistance with respect to orientation. When we speak of diamond polishing, we are referring to a micro grinding operation; the process is used to cause a change of shape, it has nothing to do with polishing in the sense of making 'shiny'.

Generally, diamonds are polished on a scaife, which is a 300 mm. (12 in.) diameter cast iron plate rotating at about 3,000 r.p.m. Diamond powder dispersed in olive oil is rubbed on to the surface of the plate, and the diamond to be polished is applied to this surface. Polishing a cube face parallel to the edge will be very fast, i.e. the stock removal rate will be relatively high. If polishing continues on the same cube face, but this time the face is rotated a few degrees so that it is no longer parallel to the edge, polishing will be slower. If such tests are continued—increasing the angle that the edge makes to the polishing direction—it will be found that polishing becomes slower and slower until it stops altogether when polishing in a direction parallel to the face diagonal is attempted. If rotation of the diamond is continued, it will be found that, once the diagonal has been passed, polishing becomes easier again and the pattern repeats.

The results of such a test can be plotted as shown. Thus, we see that polishing is very easy parallel to a cube edge, but quite impossible along the diagonal. This change in hardness, or, more correctly abrasion resistance, is why diamond polishing, like cleaving, requires specialised knowledge. Once again, we must mention naats. We all

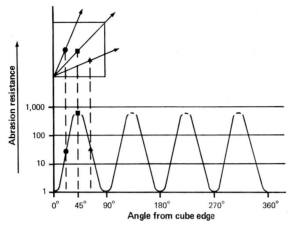

Variation in abrasion resistance in the cube plane

know that knots in wood are more difficult to cut and sandpaper than the surrounding wood. So it is with naats in diamond, and the polisher must try to avoid them. As with cleaving, if we knock pieces off our cube diamond, we do not change the polishing directions. If we knock all the corners off the cube, we are left with an octahedron and, since it is known how this lies in the cube, it can immediately be seen how to polish the points of an octahedron, i.e. in the direction of the ribs. Polishing from face to face would be virtually impossible.

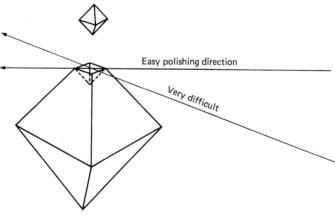

Variation in abrasion resistance on an octahedron point

The octahedron faces, or planes, are incredibly resistant to abrasion in all directions, and one never even attempts polishing in this plane. Quite naturally, this leads to requests for tools having the working face in this plane, but it must be remembered that this is also a cleavage plane.

The ribs of the octahedron can be polished, provided that we polish *across* the ribs. As the polishing direction tends towards the direction of the rib, polishing becomes harder and harder, and, again, we don't even try to polish stones parallel to the rib. If all the ribs are polished, generating new faces, we are left with a dodecahedron, and, since we know how this lies in the octahedron and how the latter lies in the cube, the appropriate polishing directions begin to make sense.

Unfortunately, from this point on, matters become increasingly complex, since polishing does not have to be undertaken only in these well charted planes, and a shift of only 1° or 2° off the plane alters the polishing directions very markedly. There have been various attempts to represent polishing directions by plotting hardness vector diagrams on a sphere, and, whilst we use stereographic projections in the laboratory, in the diamond polishing shop one relies almost entirely on the operator's skill and experience. There are devices for determining the best polishing direction on a particular face, such as the friction orientation device described by Yarnitsky, and a very similar one is used in the Van Moppes laboratories. These depend on the fact that the best polishing direction is also the direction of highest friction.

It should now be clear why diamond cuts diamond. When the scaife is loaded with diamond powder, some of the particles will have their hardest faces uppermost; if a soft direction on the stone we want to polish is addressed to these particles, then, in effect, something soft is being cut with something that is harder, so polishing is possible. If an attempt is made to polish a stone in its hard direction, nothing happens, because there is nothing harder on the scaife to do the cutting. This is why the tool designer is advised to consult his proposed supplier at a very early stage. When sawing, the same problems arise, and diamonds can only be sawn in certain directions; needless to say, diamond saws must be used.

It is worth noting that, when speaking of 'soft' directions, the term is purely relative. The 'soft' direction in diamond is still incredibly hard, and can only be cut with diamond.

Friction, as mentioned, changes with orientation. Generally, it can be stated that the coefficient of friction is very low, i.e. ·05, and this is independent of lubrication. However, in very high vacuum, i.e. 10^{-10} mm. of mercury, this value can rise to 1·0, and may be of importance when considering the operation of bearings in outer space. This rise in friction is due to the removal of adsorbed gases from the surface. If the friction is plotted as a function of orientation, the curves resemble those of wear resistance versus orientation.

How does a diamond wear; what is the wear mechanism?

Wilks and Wilks consider that it may be a cleavage mechanism. This can best be illustrated by considering wear at an octahedral point. In certain directions, the abrasive forces are resolved so that cleavage is favoured, and these directions are, in fact, the easy polishing directions. In other orientations, the cleaving forces will be small and these are the hard directions.

On the other hand, other workers have suggested a graphitisation mechanism. It was stated earlier in this chapter that one merely needs to arrange carbon atoms in a certain manner to obtain diamond. This is true, but how is this done?

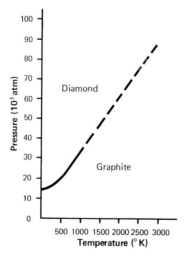

Carbon/diamond equilibrium diagram (R. Berman, Oxford University)

B

The carbon/diamond equilibrium diagram shows that diamond is unstable at ordinary pressures and temperatures. Carbon would much prefer to exist in the form of graphite at atmospheric pressures and, if the temperature is raised, this makes matters worse. Therefore, when synthesising diamond, very high pressures and temperatures are used so that the carbon forms in the diamond stable region of the diagram. After synthesising, the pressure is released and the temperature dropped, and, although the carbon remains as diamond, it is unstable. If the temperature is now raised, but not the pressure, the diamond will revert to graphite at approximately 1,700°C. There is another indirect transformation possible below this temperature.

It has already been shown that the friction is highest in the easy polishing directions. Since the heating effect is dependent upon the friction between the sliding contacts, it follows that this heating effect will be greatest in the easiest polishing direction. From this it might be deduced that the polishing, or wear, is due to graphitisation. In experiments with diamond sliding on glass, carbon has been found in the wear debris, but not diamond.

In yet other experiments, Seal has found wear debris which was neither carbon nor diamond. A diamond slider was caused to track over a diamond plate at very low speeds and under light pressure. The wear debris resembled adamantine, an organic chemical.

Obviously, it cannot be said that there is *a* wear mechanism; it depends on the conditions. A diamond dressing tool will wear in a different manner to a gramophone stylus. At present, research programmes are in progress which are aimed at studying the problem with special reference to diamond turning and boring tools.

Reference has been made to temperature rises in diamond. Diamond is, in fact, an extremely good conductor of heat; at ordinary temperatures it conducts heat much better than copper. This is very important in tool applications, since it helps to preserve edge quality, and, coupled with a very low coefficient of expansion (about the same as Invar), it helps to preserve dimensional accuracy.

Any discussion on the thermal properties of diamond must lead to the classification of diamond and the properties associated with each class. Natural diamond can be divided into two main groups: Type I and Type II, most diamonds being Type I. It must be remembered that the atomic model is, in fact, only a model, and a static model at that. In reality, the diamond molecule is a hive of activity and, in the vast majority of cases, it is very far from perfect. These imperfections, or defects, are many and varied. Of these, the most important is undoubtedly due to the presence of nitrogen. Nitrogen atoms are very similar to carbon atoms, so they can, and do, replace carbon atoms in the growing diamond. If these nitrogen atoms are dispersed at random throughout the crystal, there is what is known as a Type Ib diamond. These diamonds are extremely rare, being about 0·1% of all natural diamonds. Whilst the nitrogen atom is similar to carbon, it is not the same, and it therefore gives the crystal some special properties. Thus, a perfect diamond is colourless because it absorbs no visible light, but a Type Ib diamond, because of its nitrogen atoms, absorbs some of the blue component in visible light, and, therefore, such diamonds have a green-yellow colour. Natural diamonds in this form are extremely rare, as already stated, but it is worth noting that almost all synthetic diamonds are of this form, i.e. Type Ib. Since approximately 98% of all natural diamonds contain nitrogen atoms, the question arises why aren't they all green-yellow? The reason is that in most cases the nitrogen has diffused through the crystal and formed into platelets. When this happens, the properties of the diamond change, and this type of diamond, containing nitrogen platelets, is known as Type Ia. These diamonds no longer absorb visible light, but they do absorb ultra-violet light. If Type Ia diamonds are irradiated with ultra-violet, they absorb it.

Basically, the diamond is absorbing energy which it does not require; electrons are being excited to higher energy levels and they will try to get rid of this extra energy and drop back to their normal state. They do this by giving out light, but this is of a longer wavelength than that absorbed, i.e. it will be in the visible part of the spectrum. This is why such diamonds glow, or fluoresce, when irradiated in ultra-violet light.

Diamonds which do not have nitrogen platelets, and therefore do not fluoresce in ultra-violet, are called Type II. There is no sharp division between the two types, one merges into the other, but those diamonds classified as Type II constitute only a small percentage of all natural diamonds.

The Type I/Type II classification is done by sorting in ultra-violet light and in infra-red, since the absorption in infra-red also varies with Type I and Type II diamonds.

The thermal conductivity of Type II diamond is much greater than that of Type I; at ordinary temperatures it is about five times better than copper. This property may make Type II diamond very useful in semi-conductor devices, since one of the problems is to conduct heat away via a heat sink.

The vast majority of all diamonds are very good electrical insulators. However, this brings us to another subdivision in the diamond classification, Type IIb diamond. These diamonds are semiconductors and are extremely rare. Such diamonds have been used in some very interesting applications (see Chapter 11).

In this Chapter it has only been possible to touch on some of the more interesting properties of diamond; Chapter 11 describes how some of these properties can be applied.

REFERENCES

Occurrence, Mining and Recovery of Diamonds—Dr. A. A. L. Linholm.
The History of Diamond Production and the Diamond Trade—Dr. Godehard Lenzen.
Making Diamonds—H. J. Milledge. Chemistry Background Books. Published for the Nuffield Foundation by Longmans/Penguin Books 1968.
'Directional Grinding Hardness in Diamond'—R. M. Denning. *American Mineralogist*, Vol. 30, Pages 108–117, 1953; and Vol. 40, Pages 186–191, 1955.
'The Hardness and Wear of Diamond During Grinding and Polishing'—J. Wilks and E. M. Wilks *Physical Properties of Diamond*—Ed. R. Berman. Clarendon Press, Oxford, 1965.
'New Approach to Parameters in Diamond Polishing'—Y. Yarnitsky, *Science and Technology of Industrial Diamonds* Vol. II—Ed. J. Burls, Industrial Diamond Review Information Bureau.
(1964) *Nature* 201, 1279. F. P. Bowden and A. E. Hanwell.
(1959) *Phil. Mag.* 38, 158. J. Wilks and E. M. Wilks.
(1958) *Proc. Roy. Soc.* A187, 381. F. P. Bowden and H. G. Scott.
Industrial Diamond Review 25, 111, 1965. M. Seal.

2

The range of diamond-bearing products available to the user

THE RAW MATERIALS

NATURAL diamond is mined over considerable areas of Africa and its coasts (e.g. Congo [Kinshasa], South Africa, Ghana, Sierra Leone, South West Africa, Angola, Tanzania, Central African Republic, Ivory Coast), in Brazil and the U.S.S.R. To a much less extent there is also production in Australia, India and Venezuela.

'Conventional' synthetic diamond is produced in sizes up to about 600 micron. Made by subjecting graphite to high pressures and temperature in large presses, this material is manufactured by the International General Electric Company of New York Ltd.; by De Beers Industrial Diamond Divisions in South Africa and Ireland; by Komatsu and Ishi-Ken in Japan and by ASEA in Sweden. There is also a small production in China, Czechoslovakia and West Germany according to the *Mining Annual Review* June 1971.

'Explosion-formed' synthetic diamond is presently available commercially in sizes only up to about 60 micron. This material is manufactured by E. I. Du Pont de Nemours & Co., Inc. in the U.S.A.

The total production of natural (industrial) and synthetic diamond is reported in each case as about 40 million metric carats (0·2 of a gramme = 1 carat). The resulting manufactured industrial products are probably marketed to the ultimate user for a total sales value of about £150m. The natural production is reported to contain a further 25%–30% of material eventually used as gems, but all the synthetic is used in industry.

According to a De Beers report, 36% of the material (by weight) is utilised in diamond grinding wheels, 20% in saws, 18% as a loose abrasive and 13% in drill bits with an equal proportion in tools and dies.

In terms of the size of each diamond or diamond particle, application is broadly on the following lines with considerable overlap between the ranges in respect of their uses:

Approximate size range

Micron	Carats	Diamond available	Examples of application
0–40	–	Natural and synthetic powder	Fine grinding, lapping and polishing
40–1500	–	Natural and synthetic grit	Bonded in metal or resin to grind, drill and saw hard metals, glass and stone/rock and concrete
mm.			
1·0–3·8	0·01–0·5	Natural whole diamonds	Drill bits, glass cutters and multi-stone abrasive wheel truers
3·8–4·8	0·5–1·0		Single point truing tools and shaped tools
4·8–6·0	1·0–2·0		Single point truing tools and plunge cutting tools
6·0–8·7	2·0–6·0		Heavy duty truing tools and large plunge cutters

In addition to the diamond content, diamond bearing tools and products consume a wide variety of metals. In terms of world consumption the quantities are very small, but, of course, are of paramount importance to the diamond industry. Examples are:

1. *Mild or stainless steel* for tool shanks in truing and machining tools.
2. *Iron* for matrices and lapping plates for diamond shaping.
3. *Alloy steels* for mould making and for highly stressed tool bodies such as those used in oil and other mineral drilling.
4. *Bronze* for grinding wheel bodies and in powder form for sintered matrices.
5. *Aluminium* for wheel bodies and resin backing fillers.
6. *Nickel, tin, copper and zinc:* in matrices and beryllium copper for sintering and casting. Nickel is also used in diamond abrasive products made by electrodeposition and electro-forming.

Resins are used to bond diamond grit and cloth as a backing for diamond coated belts, sheets, discs or rolls.

THE PROCESSES

Synthetic diamonds are produced under conditions of extreme heat and pressure, generally in tungsten carbide containers. The processes developed by the various manufacturers are covered by a number of international patents. In the case of the 'explosive' process used by Du Pont, the largest particle size available commercially at present is of the order of 60 microns, and is of a polycrystalline structure. Other synthetic material is available up to about 1,500 microns.

The recovery of natural diamonds from their surrounding rock or 'blue ground' follows fairly conventional, if rather refined, mining practice. The last stage in the case of diamonds of normal sizes below about one inch consists of passing the concentrate, suspended in water, over a grease-covered vibrating table. Diamond has a strong affinity for grease and remains attached to the table. The other material is carried away by the water. The diamonds and grease are periodically scraped from the table and the diamonds are finally recovered by melting the grease. A preliminary classification by quality and size is then made before the recovery is passed to a central office for more detailed sorting.

The main property of diamond which comes to mind is, of course, its hardness. On Mohs' hardness scale, diamond is rated at 10. The difference between diamond and corundum at 9 was said to be greater than between 9 and gypsum at 1.

In 1940, Chauncy G. Peters and Frederick Knoop reported that by indenting hardness methods they had established the following relations between the minerals on Mohs' scale and other abrasive materials:

Sample	*Knoop hardness number*
Gypsum	32
Calcite	135
Fluorite	163
Albite	490
Crystalline quartz according to axis	710–790
Topaz	1250
Regular alundum	1620–1635
Green silicon carbide	2130–2140
Moulded boron carbide	2250–2260
Diamond	5500–6950

Other properties:

Material:	Pure carbon (C)
Atomic weight:	12
Specific gravity } Diamond crystal }	3·40 to 3·52
Specific gravity } Brazil carbon }	3·01 to 3·52
Melting point:	$3700°C \pm 100°$
Compressibility:	{ $0·16 \times 10^{-6}$ sq. cm./kg. { $0·18 \times 10^{-6}$ sq. cm./kg.
Thermal conductivity: at 20°C	{ Type I 9 watts deg.$^{-1}$ cm.$^{-1}$ { Type IIa 26 watts deg.$^{-1}$ cm.$^{-1}$
Max. at $-190°$C	{ Type I 24 watts deg.$^{-1}$ cm.$^{-1}$ { Type IIa 120 watts deg.$^{-1}$ cm.$^{-1}$
Thermal resistance:	0·69 cm. deg./W.
Thermal expansion:	$1·45 \times 10^{-6}$ for 28° to 105°C

The layman's mental picture of rough diamond is of the octahedron form. Many, however, are not of this shape. It is true that most industrial diamond applications could be accomplished with a diamond of this shape. There are, however, many applications where some other form is more appropriate. In fact, almost all forms of diamond, with the aid of experience and research, can be usefully employed.

The result of recent investigation tends to show that some processing of the diamond before setting makes a much more reliable natural product than ever before.

Diamond crystallises in the cubic system, the simplest forms of which are the octahedron and the cube. The crystal can be cleft along planes which lie parallel to the triangular faces of an octahedron. In the cube this cleavage plane is such that a crystal corner

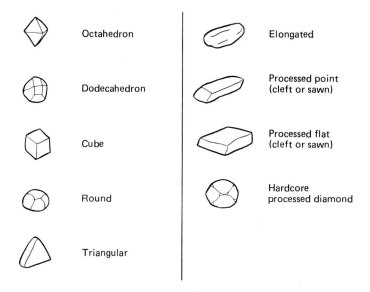

Octahedron	Elongated
Dodecahedron	Processed point (cleft or sawn)
Cube	Processed flat (cleft or sawn)
Round	Hardcore processed diamond
Triangular	

Industrial diamond shapes. The more common shapes used, but many are so misshapen as to be impossible of classification within these descriptions

would be removed by the cleaving process, leaving a triangular face in place of the corner on the main body of the crystal. One of the components of the cleaver's art is the ability to determine the direction of the cleavage plane in a rough stone which may have very little resemblance to the ideal shape.

The cleavage planes are parallel to the triangular faces in triangular shape diamonds and, of course, to the existing cleft faces on cleft points or flats. So-called long stones are usually misshapen octahedra or dodecahedra and the grain structure follows the same pattern. Along these cleavage planes diamonds offer great resistance to abrasion. The economic manufacture and use of industrial diamond tools often depend on the ability to recognise this structure.

Among the papers presented at the First International Congress on Diamonds in Industry, Paris, 1962, that by Dr. Eileen M. Wilks, of the Clarendon Laboratory, University of Oxford, dealt with the hardness of diamond. After drawing attention to the variable nature of diamond, she emphasises that, not only do different diamonds have appreciably different structures and mechanical properties, but that different parts of the same stone may differ appreciably. She goes on to quote the following values for the average depth of cut made by a diamond bonded wheel in the principal directions on diamond. They are presented in order of increasing hardness:

Face	Direction of abrasion	Depth of cut value
Dodecahedron	Parallel to axis	10·0
Cube	Parallel to axis	8·5
Octahedron	Towards dodecahedron	3·9
Octahedron	Towards cube	2·1
Dodecahedron	90° to axis	1·8
Cube	45° to axis	1·1

It will be seen that, in the experiments reported, the depths of cuts in the hardest and softest directions varied by a factor of about 9.

For very critical orientation of rough diamonds it is sometimes necessary to use X-ray methods to determine the grain direction accurately.

Type I and Type II relate to differences in light absorption in the ultra-violet and infra-red spectra, they also vary in fluorescence and structure.

An increasingly rare form of industrial diamond is known as 'ballas' because of its predominantly spherical shape. Although used to some extent in its whole state, it is generally cleft before being used as an abrasive wheel truer. 'Carbonado', or carbon for short, is another rare form found mainly in Brazil. It takes the form of a polycrystalline mass not obeying the crystal structure laws of normal diamonds. Its use lies mainly in the field of rock drilling, but it is also used in some very specialised abrasive wheel truing operations.

Atomic scientists have also tried to improve diamond properties by radiation. The treatment can certainly influence the colour of gem stones and attempts have been made to remove flaws, or 'strain centres', from industrial diamonds which may be the cause of subsequent trouble in grinding or setting operations.

The measure of weight now used by the diamond industry is the metric carat which equals one fifth of a gram. Industrial diamonds are normally specified in the smaller sizes by the number of diamonds which weigh one carat. In the larger sizes the actual carat weight is specified. The dividing line varies with local habit, but, normally, is in the region of one third to a half carat. The full size range used varies from about 600 diamonds per carat to 10 or 15 carats per diamond.

Industrial diamonds are normally available in the following broad categories:

1. Crushing boart, which is low grade material usually of indeterminate shape and unspecified size. This is used for crushing and grading as powder or grit for use in various grinding, cutting, lapping and kindred operations.
2. Small whole stones of regular shape in the 200 per carat to 0·50 carat size range, used for rock and masonry drilling bits. They are also used for multiple diamond wheel truing tools.
3. Generally larger and more specialised qualities and shapes, used for single point abrasive wheel truing tools; diamond tipped turning, boring and milling tools; diamond drawing dies and a multitude of less important applications. The weight range per diamond is of the order of 0·10 carat to 10 or more carats per diamond.
4. The diamonds not falling within the previous three categories are less numerous and relatively of small total value. They are nevertheless of real value to the community. They form the working areas of penetrators for testing the hardness of metals, tracer points for measuring surface finish, knife edges for microtomes, bearings for very accurate scientific instruments, ruling tools for diffraction gratings, the conical tips of modern gramophone needles and glass cutting tools.

TRANSFORMATION TO A USABLE PRODUCT

Having been produced synthetically or recovered from the earth and its eventual use determined, diamond may go through several processes before it is used in an industrial operation.

Powder and grit production

Virgin boart is put through a refined version of the normal mining techniques for reducing rock or ore to the required size. Ball and hammer mills are used to reduce the size to particles between mesh 10 (holes and wires to the linear inch) and something less than one micron. This is normally undertaken in various stages of which the first is often carried out by the mining company and is referred to as fragmentation. The 'fragmented' boart is then distributed to the producers of the finally crushed and graded diamond powder.

The diamond particles are then graded on sieves in the same way as other powders and grits used in the abrasive industry. This process is generally considered to give sufficiently accurate separation down to a minimum of 400 mesh (400 holes and wires to the linear inch) or approximately 40 microns. For grain sizes smaller than this, however, sedimentation, elutriation in gases or liquids and centrifuging methods are employed. All of the latter methods are based on the principle of using the mass of the individual particles to effect its own separation. The more advanced producers also separate varying particle shapes to suit specific needs.

In the synthetic material the particle shape and friability can also be controlled in the course of the manufacturing process. In order to assist in the retention of the particle in the eventual bond the diamond particles are in some cases also coated with a layer of nickel or copper.

The basic particle size ranges utilised are the subject of a number of national standards, and a European standard has been established by the Fédération Européenne des Fabricants de Produits Abrasifs, and the International Organisation for Standardisation (I.S.O.) also has a draft in circulation.

The following table shows the relationship between the more commonly used gradings. It is taken from 'Some Aspects of Wheel Formulation in Ceramic Grinding' by D. M. Thomas, M.I.M., which was presented by the Diamond Machining of Ceramics Symposium, in London, September, 1971:

B.S. mesh fraction (B.S. 410:1963)	New FEPA equivalent	Approx. average* particle size	Particles per carat
16/18	D1001	0·048	100
18/22	D851	0·040	200
22/25	D711	0·033	350
25/30	D601	0·028	600
30/36	D501	0·024	1,000
36/44	D426	0·020	1,600
44/52	D356	0·017	2,500
52/60	D301	0·014	4,500
60/72	D251	0·011	8,000
72/85	D213	0·009	12,000
85/100	D181	0·008	20,000
100/120	D151	0·007	30,000
120/150	D126	0·006	60,000
150/170	D107	0·005	100,000
170/200	D91	0·004	160,000
200/240	D76	0·0034	250,000
240/300	D64	0·0028	420,000
300/350	D54	0·0024	800,000
350/400†	D46	0·0020	1,300,000

* Particle size is difficult to define as particles are of an irregular shape. The figure quoted approximates to the diameter of a circle (in millimetres), the area of which approximates to the projected areas of the particle.

† The 400 mesh sieve does not appear in B.S. 410:1963.

Lapping compound

Diamond powder is also mixed with various carriers for use as a lapping compound on hard materials. The U.S.S.R. has issued a standard in respect of their range of such compounds under the reference GOST 16877/71.

Processing small diamonds for drilling

A number of processes are in use to improve some of the natural diamonds available for this work. The result of these refined milling processes is to round off the diamond shape and improve the surface quality. In removing the surface asperities, weak stones are also crushed to powder and eliminated as far as the original purpose is concerned.

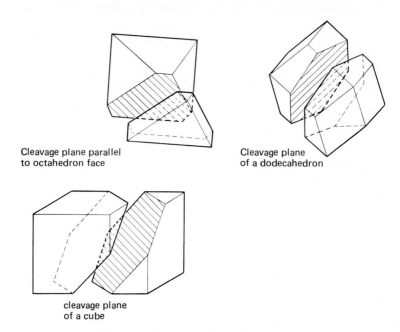

Cleavage plane parallel
to octahedron face

Cleavage plane
of a dodecahedron

cleavage plane
of a cube

Cleavage planes of simulated diamond forms

Cleaving

In order to improve the shape of a diamond for its eventual purpose it may be split along a cleavage plane. Extreme care and skill are needed if such operations are to be successful. A small incision is made at one end of the desired split. This is produced by a hand tool of which the edge is the natural sharp juncture of two cleavage planes of another diamond. When the incision is considered large enough the diamond in its shellac filled cup is positioned in a jig so that the incision is uppermost. A steel knife blade edge is then inserted in the groove and tapped with a boxwood mallet. If the cleaver's judgement is accurate the diamond will then split along the selected plane with very little loss in weight. The directions in which the diamond can be thus split are, of course, limited by the occurrence of the natural cleavage planes as described earlier.

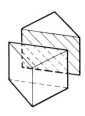
Cube sawn in a
dodecahedron plane

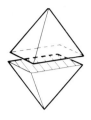
Octahedron sawn in a
cube plane

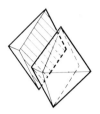
Octahedron sawn in a
dodecahedron plane

Cube sawn in
a cube plane

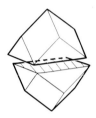
Dodecahedron sawn in a
cube plane

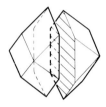
Dodecahedron sawn in a
dodecahedron plane

Sawing directions in simulated diamond forms

Sawing

This is undertaken for reasons similar to those applicable to cleaving. The possible directions of sawing, however, are different from those for cleaving. Sawing is generally undertaken on lines approximately parallel to a line drawn between four of the corners of an octahedron. This is described as sawing in the cube plane. They can also be sawn in the dodecahedron plane which is at right-angles to an octahedron edge. The saw used is a phosphor bronze blade, usually 0·127 mm. (0·005 in.) thick and 75 mm. (3 in.) in diameter. The edge is charged and re-charged with diamond powder applied with the aid of a small hand held roller. The operation is normally carried out by specialist sub-contractors who have batteries of the small sawing machines and of which several machines can be operated by one man.

Bruting

This operation was introduced to form the major diameter on a normal gem stone. It is also used, however, to rough cut cone and spherical forms on industrial diamonds. The stone is held in a brass 'dop' with a special shellac cement. The internal thread at the back of the 'dop' locates on the threaded spigot of a special chuck. The latter incorporates a friction plate which enables the 'cutter' to centre the diamond by lightly tapping the outer ring of the chuck which is mounted on a simple lathe. The cutting tool consists of a sharp piece of diamond mounted in a similar way to the workpiece, but then attached to a wooden handle held by the operator in a wooden rest. Under this rest is a tray in which the diamond 'swarf' is collected.

Shaping and lapping

In the terminology of the gem industry this operation is generally referred to as 'polishing'. As in the production of tools, however, most of the time is occupied in achieving the correct shape, the term is, in the author's opinion, no longer applicable. The machine used is a cast-iron lap of controlled porosity and driven at about 3,0C0 r.p.m. In the diamond industry this is generally referred to by the Dutch name 'schyf', but is also written as 'scaife'.

For some shaping operations the diamond is still held in a brass cup or dop with an easily softened lead-tin alloy. This was the basis of all 'gem polishing' for many years. The copper stem of the dop is held in a steel clamp attached to a wooden tong. (This is a slight modification of the original spelling 'tang.') The assembly is used to hold the diamond face in contact with the lap. The abrasive used is a fine diamond powder suspended in light oil.

Whenever possible, industrial diamonds are now preset in sintered metal powder inserts which permit positive location in appropriate jigs to control the shaping process. For producing flat faces, this is generally still the most useful method if carried out by skilled operators who understand and make maximum use of the grain structure. Attempts have been made to utilise a high voltage current between diamond and lap to increase the rate of stock removal, but, due to control difficulties, it has not been generally adopted. Higher peripheral speeds are used in some cases and, in others, diamond impregnated cup wheels have replaced the conventional 'schyf'.

In the case of holes to be produced in diamonds for wire drawing dies, the flat cast-iron lap is replaced with wire of suitable diameter which revolves and reciprocates to maintain the diamond and oil abrasive medium between the carrier and the workpiece.

Grinding

Where the diamond grain structure has to be ignored, as in the production of curved surfaces on the working areas of diamonds, then a bonded diamond wheel is generally utilised. In order to avoid grooving the wheel face, machines used for these operations generally incorporate a traversing motion of the grinding spindle. The work is often optically controlled by a microscope attached to the grinding machine having appropriate radius graticules incorporated in the eyepiece.

The swivelling motion about the centre-line of the workpiece to be ground is operated manually so that the operator can 'dwell' on high spots occurring in the radius due to variation in grain structure. In the case of conical and spherical grinding, the diamond is, of course, suitably mounted on a rotating workhead.

Other shape changing operations

In addition to these conventional shaping methods, for special requirements, such as in the diamond die industry, electrolytic, ultra-sonic and laser beam methods are utilised.

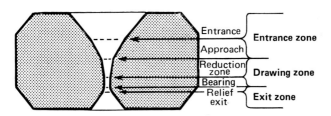

Diamond die profile nomenclature

C

Setting, bonding, moulding and coating

For some specialised applications, shaped diamonds are still hand set. This method falls into three categories:

1. *The brazing method* which requires a recess cut into a mild steel shank by drilling and filing. The recess or slot is made to be a close fit with the appropriate faces of the diamond, steel wedges are inserted to retain the diamond in position and the whole assembly is brazed together. To expose the working areas of the diamond without damaging the often delicate edges requires the very skilled use of a file.

2. *The clamping method* which uses some form of screw pressure between two jaws also formed to fit the back areas of the diamond.

3. *The casting method* is not very commonly used today. The diamond in such cases is held in a recess at the bottom of a mould. This may be done with a spring clip or by vacuum. Metals such as monel, brass, beryllium, copper, bronze and similar alloys are then cast around the diamond and formed in the refractory mould.

Powder metal setting is normally utilised in current diamond tool making including drill bits and metal bonded grinding wheels and saws. The methods adopted fall into two broad categories. In the first a mixture of some of the metal powders listed earlier is moulded around the diamond or mixed with the diamond powder. The compact thus formed is pressed and heat treated to form the required dimensions and other physical properties. The alternative is similar up to the point of forming a 'green' mount around the diamond under pressure. At the heat treatment stage, however, a further solid metal is introduced and melted to 'infiltrate' the green diamond bearing element. In many cases this also serves to attach this element to the main steel shank. It is widely used in drill bit manufacture.

In the last year or two, under the trade mark 'Resimet', a metal powder base has been used for diamond grinding wheels and into which a resin infiltrant is introduced. This bond offers the superior diamond retention qualities of the metal bond with the fast cutting properties of a resin bond.

Resin bonds: for resin bond diamond grinding wheels, phenol-formaldehyde resins are in normal use, but polyimide resins have also been used for several years. The methods used are basically the same as for manufacturing resin bond wheels containing other abrasives. The diamond grit is mixed with the resin powder and hot moulded to form the working area of the wheel. The backing or centre is then added and can be of resin or metal.

In many cases the diamond bearing element is attached to the shank, body or blade in the course of the heat treatment and pressing processes to which it has already been subjected. Where this is not so, however, the two components are soldered, brazed or bolted together, or, in the case of resin bond wheels, commercial adhesives are used. The assembly is then machined to final dimensions by turning, milling and grinding. In the course of doing so surplus brazing is also removed.

Electro-deposition is used to form envelopes for whole diamonds or to attach diamond grit to metal bodies. It is also used to produce accurate profile truing diamond devices.

Direct adhesion is extremely difficult to achieve with diamond. A chemical bond between diamond and metals which can be utilised as setting materials can only be achieved under very stringent conditions. For this reason this method is normally used only where large numbers of identical diamond bearing units are being produced. One such case is the diamond stylus or gramophone needle.

Whichever type of mounting is used, the practice is normally to use an oversize steel shank. In subsequent machining operations the position of the diamond can be corrected where necessary. It is easier to remove considerable amounts of steel than small amounts of diamond. In order to avoid accidental damage to the diamond edges, optical centering devices are used on lathes and milling machines wherever possible.

Extraction and servicing

To realise the full life potential of many diamond tools it is necessary to remove the diamond content after a period of use. The tool is then remade after either reshaping the diamond, selecting a new natural point or, as in the case of drill bits, removing substandard diamonds and replacing with new ones. The process normally adopted to remove the diamonds from the metal mount or bond is electro-chemical. The tool is suspended in an electrolyte and made the anode of an electrolytic cell. This disintegrates the metal setting and releases the diamond. In its simplest form the metal surround is reduced to a minimum by machining and the remaining metal merely dissolved in acid.

Inspection

As far as is practicable, inspection devices are built into production equipment such as radius grinders, lathes and milling machines. They usually take the form of microscopes and optical projectors which are also widely used in final inspection. Another optical aid, developed within the industry by Mr. M. Fehr, is the reflecting goniometer. This permits the measurement of the angles between polished flat surfaces without removal from the jig or tool holder and does not rely on having a well defined profile as is required for projection. In some cases final inspection also includes test applications under simulated working conditions. Two examples are plunge cut machining tools as used in watch case turning, and hardness testing indenters with which trials are made on specially made test blocks.

The hardness of mounts and matrices is checked on the normal Rockwell, Vickers and similar instruments.

Static and dynamic balancing are undertaken on diamond abrasive wheels, saws and rotary truers where appropriate.

THE RESULTING TOOLS

In terms of weight utilised, diamond grinding wheels, used on tungsten carbide, corundum, glass, ceramics, stone and other hard materials, form the largest product group. This type of grinding wheel is also proving economical on grinding some alloy steels under particularly exacting conditions. In this field, the alternative synthetic abrasive, cubic boron nitride, has also been found to be superior in certain instances. Diamond wheels and hones are reported as consuming about 35% of the total of the combined production of natural and synthetic diamond.

The next group on the same scale is diamond saws for carbides, transistor materials, ceramics, refractories, glass, fibre glass, stone, concrete and other hard to cut materials. Consumption here is of the order of 20%.

Diamond powder and grit, as a loose abrasive or in the form of lapping compound, are of about the same order.

Drill bits for prospecting, mining, oil-well drilling and concrete are about equal in consumption to tools and dies used for abrasive wheel truing, machining, glass cutting, gauging and wire drawing. These two groups together consume the balance of about 25% of the total industrial diamond production by weight. Consumption here, however, is confined for practical purposes to natural diamond and, in terms of sales value of the finished tool, represents a greater proportion; it is probably of the order of 40%. In these products the diamond value per carat is generally higher than for grit and the labour content also larger in proportion than is the case with impregnated products.

DIAMOND GRINDING WHEELS AND HONES

Diamond powder impregnated tools made by users

Before bonded diamond products were offered commercially by specialist diamond tool makers, some users found that single layer diamond abrasive surfaces could be usefully employed. These generally took the form of a soft copper or aluminium alloy base machined to the required form and then having the requisite diamond powder grade rolled into the surface. Sometimes the surface was grooved to hold the abrasive. The diamond grit was generally mixed with light oil or petroleum jelly to make it adhere to the surface whilst rolling with a hard steel roller which pressed the particles into the copper. The rolling operation tended to crush at least some of the weaker grains and the effective grain size of the finished tool was therefore less than the nominal grain size of the charge.

Small centreless grinding wheels are made by rolling diamond powder into the plain copper surface of the grinding wheels used in 'rondelling' sapphire bearings and can also be used for grinding other hard materials in disc or rod form. The grinding wheels are generally of the order of 100–150 mm. (4–6 in.) diameter with lengths to suit the workpiece. Bull-nosed cup wheels and peripheral wheels were also made on copper or aluminium alloy bases by this process for use in the optical lens industry. They have now been largely superseded by sintered metal bond tools.

Lapping plates are made in the jewel bearing industry for bringing the bearing blanks to uniform thickness. A copper plate of say 200 mm. (8 in.) diameter is used. The diamond and oil sludge is sometimes rolled in with a tapered steel roller on a converted shaping machine. The axis of the roller and the direction of shaping head movement are at an angle to one another. The result is a combined rolling and skidding action which is said to provide a better anchorage for the diamond powder. Smaller lapping plates made in a similar way but using a mild steel or soft cast-iron base were at one time widely used for the resharpening of tungsten carbide tipped tools on cylinder reboring machines used in automobile engine reconditioning. These have now been mainly superseded by bonded diamond cup wheels.

Diamond broaches are made mainly for use in the jewel bearing industry. A number of formulae exist for their manufacture of which one consists of the following mixture by weight: Diamond powder 10 parts, borax $12\frac{1}{2}$ parts and calcined bauxite 1 part. After thorough mixing, the amount to be treated is placed on a steel plate which has been heated at the centre to about 800°C. The mixture is blended further with a spatula until it is of a brown colour. Sufficient to make one broach is then withdrawn towards the outer and cooler part of the plate. There, whilst still plastic, it is rolled into rod form with the spatula. Diameters from about 8 mm. (0·30 in.) upwards are made to suit the recess size required in the jewel bearing.

Diamond charged mandrels are referred to in some literature for grinding very accurate small holes in hard materials. It is claimed that such tools for holes of less than about 6 mm. ($\frac{1}{4}$ in.) diameter have the advantage of being much more rigid than conventional grinding points using aluminium oxide or silicon carbide and not needing such high speeds. Speeds even lower than 7·6 metres per second (1,500 surface feet per minute) are satisfactory with diamond charged mandrels as compared to 25–30 metres per second (5,000 or 6,000 surface feet per minute) for conventional grinding wheels.

The mandrel is made from soft cold-rolled steel. The length of the diamond charged part should be about half of the length of the hole to be ground, but should not exceed about 4·5 mm. ($\frac{3}{16}$ in.).

The shank should then be undercut below the diamond charged diameter for a length sufficient to clear the hole. The diamond powder is moistened with oil and spread on a hardened steel plate (at least 65 R.C.). The mandrel is then held with the working area about 3 mm. ($\frac{1}{8}$ in.) above the plate and struck sharp blows with a hardened hammer. This method is said to be preferable to rolling as it results in a more random placement of sharp cutting edges and better grit retention. From the author's experience, this hammering technique is sometimes replaced by the use of two glass strips to one of which the diamond paste is applied and the mandrel is then rolled between them.

Diamond charged form grinding wheels are sometimes made particularly for short run form grinding carbide tools in the gauge and tool making industry. A copper disc is used and the required form is machined on the periphery. This may be done on a lathe for simple forms or with a Diaform attachment on a grinder for more complicated and accurate forms. A diamond turning tool replaces the chisel truer used normally. A hard steel roller is then ground with the mating form to that on the copper disc. The latter is then smeared with grease and mounted on a fixture which allows it to be turned by hand through a crank attached to the spindle. The jig also has a spindle to carry the hardened steel roller, which is pressure loaded, in contact with the copper blank. Diamond powder is applied to the greased rim and, by rotating the crank, is pressed into the surface which is subsequently cleaned with carbon tetrachloride.

Slitting discs are probably the most common type of tool made in this way. Electrolytic copper or phosphor bronze discs are used for the base of the smaller sizes up to about 150 mm. (6 in.) diameter. In thickness they are normally from 0·5 mm. (0·020 in.) up to about 2·5 mm. (0·10 in.). In larger sizes, tin plated steel sheet is sometimes used. The blades are ganged together on a mandrel and slots milled in the periphery to a depth of say 1 mm. (0·040 in.). About twenty blades can be mounted together and are clamped at each end with flanges slightly smaller in diameter than the blades. The slots are then filled with a paste of diamond powder and oil and the assembly mounted on a lathe. The peripheral surface is then swaged with a steel roller pressed against it by screw pressure from a mounting on the cross-slide of the lathe. Rolling is continued until the diameter of the pack of blades has been reduced to the diameter of the flanges.

Such discs are, of course, a heavier version of those used in diamond sawing. They are used extensively in cutting sapphire boule for synthetic watch jewels and record player styli, for cutting ornamental semi-precious stones, glass and, in the larger sizes, in Idar Oberstein for the famous German agate industry.

Resin bonded wheels

Abrasive wheels, hand laps and hones of diamond powder in resin bonds are made commercially by specialist producers mainly for use in tungsten carbide grinding operations. In the U.S.A., for instance, about 75 % of all wheels used in this work are resin bonded. In Europe, the proportion of resin bonded wheels used appears to be less. Generally, grit sizes in the 100 to 4C0 mesh range are used in this bond. Much research has been undertaken to develop better diamond grit characteristics for this type of bond and, for most applications, metal coated synthetic grit has proved superior.

The process of manufacture can be outlined as follows:

a. Prepare a steel mould having in it the form in which the finished wheel is required. One or more plungers or movable members are required by means of which pressure can be exerted.

b. A mixture of diamond powder and resin powder incorporating a filler is then spread evenly in the area of the mould which will form the working face. The filler is selected from a range of metal powders, carbide powders, aluminium oxide or other hard powders. The proportions of diamond and resin depend on the diamond concentration required in the finished wheel. The total amount of the mixture will determine the depth of impregnation.

c. The heat and pressure cycle appropriate to the resin used then follows.

d. In some processes operation c. also moulds the wheel backing or centre, for which purpose further resin powder has been added to the diamond charged area in the mould. In other cases the backing is made separately and the two bonded together afterwards with a suitable adhesive. A third alternative is the use of aluminium backing plates or centres to which the resin bonded diamond ring is attached.

e. In all cases the working area is then ground to be concentric and true with the bore and other locating faces and then balanced.

In addition to these tools, resin bonded hand laps are made to 'touch-up' hard metal tool edges *in situ*. This is useful where the damage sustained in use is slight and set-up time can be saved by not having to remove the tool from the machine to take it to the tool grinder.

Sintered metal bond wheels

The method of manufacture follows in principle the same lines as that used for resin bonded tools. The resin powder is replaced with metal powder and, of course, higher temperatures and pressures are needed. The metal bonds vary widely in composition, the most common range being the bronze group. Iron, cobalt, tungsten, nickel and many other metals in smaller amounts are also utilised to modify bond characteristics.

Similar manufacturing methods are used to produce tube drills for glass, ceramics, stone, carbides and other hard materials. The range also includes milling cutters for glass.

Dimensional standards

Resin, metal and the less used vitrified and ceramic bonded grinding wheels made by these methods have been covered by national standards, but it is hoped that the standards published by the Fédération Européenne des Fabricants de Produits Abrasifs will be adopted not only by the member nations: Austria, Belgium, Denmark, France, Germany, Great Britain, Italy, Luxemburg, The Netherlands, Norway, Portugal, Spain, Sweden and Switzerland, but also more widely in countries using the metric system and, ultimately, by the International Standards Organisation (I.S.O.).

The existing standards are:

Area (prefix)	Reference	Product
Britain (BS)	2064:1953/9	Straight cup
		Double cup
		Dish
		Taper cup
		Peripheral
		Chip breaker
		Bull nose cup wheels
West Germany (DIN)	58741/2–10.67	Diamond tools for optical use
	58744/4– 4.69	Optical trepanning tools and blades
	69110 –11.70	Diamond optical inserts
	32072	Diamond grinding wheels and points
U.S.S.R. (Gost)	16167 – 70	Peripheral wheels O/D only
	16168 – 70	Small peripheral wheels (solid impreg.)
	16169 – 70	Straight wheels (with diamond on walls as well)
	16170 – 70	Straight cup
	16171 – 70	Double cup
	16172 – 70	Taper cup wheel
	16173 – 70	Flaring cup (O/D impreg.)
	16174 – 70	Flaring cup (face impreg.)
	16175 – 70	Dish AT (straight face impreg.)
	16176 – 70	Dish A1T (Taper peripheral)
	16177 – 70	Dish A3T (Taper face)
	16178	Dish A4T (Taper underside)
	16179 – 70	Vee form grinding wheel
	16180 – 70	Half-round convex peripheral
Poland (PN)	62/M 59340	Peripheral
	62/M 59341	Plain cup
	62/M 59342	Double cup
	62/M 59346	Taper cup
	61/M 59347	Dish
U.S.A.	USAS B74.1–1966 revision of B74.1–1957	U.S.A. standard identification code for diamond wheel shapes— sponsored by the Grinding Wheel Institute and approved by the U.S. Standards Institute

In addition to these standardised products falling fairly strictly within the description of diamond grinding wheels, the range of metal bonded diamond tools includes milling cutters for the preliminary shaping of spherical surfaces on lens and flat surfaces on prisms. Subsequent semi-finishing operations on lens surfaces are carried out with diamond pellets mounted on convex and concave metal carriers. The milling tools and the drills are also covered by B.S. 2064:1953/9.

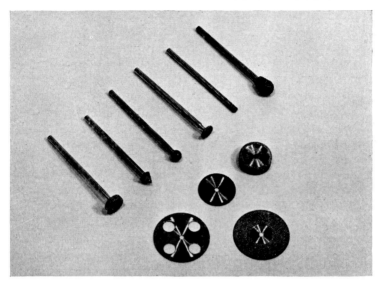

Examples from a range of electro-metallic grinding tools designed for use in dentistry, but also useful in other fields for grinding, slitting, slotting and surfacing hard materials such as ceramics, metallic carbides, refractories, porcelain, tiles, carbon and glass

Electro-metallic coated tools

One of the earliest uses of this type of tool was in dentistry, but the small tools designed for this work are now also used in industry and many other tools made by this process are available.

A metal base is machined to the final dimensions of the tool required making allowance for the layer or layers of diamond powder with which it is to be covered in the required areas. This allowance must not only take into account the number of layers but also the the diamond particle size. For instance, the allowance on a single layer of sieve 60/72 powder is of the order of 0·21–0·25 mm. (0·008–0·010 in.) and for two layers of sieve 300/400 powder 0·07–0·1 mm. (0·003–0·004 in.).

The layer of diamond is held temporarily in contact with the metal base whilst the assembly is submerged in an electrolyte. A coating of electro-deposited metal is then formed around the diamond particles and adheres to the metal base. In doing so, it also holds the diamond in position. The process is stopped when the metal coating is thick enough to hold the diamond grains securely for the job on which the tool is to be used.

Most of the range of diamond tools covered by B.S. 2064 can be made by this method as well as in the bonds shown in the specification. Such wheels, however, do not have the same cutting characteristics and, therefore, cannot be considered as an alternative in all operations.

Electro-deposited tools are also made in the form of very thin wall hollow drills suitable for glass drilling, as diamond coated files for machine and hand filing hard materials and for band sawing hard and abrasive materials.

Diamond hones and hand laps

The manufacturing processes used in diamond hone production follow closely those used in diamond wheel making. The resulting tools can advantageously replace conventional silicon carbide or hones containing other abrasives in the case of very long runs, or where the material being honed does not respond to honing by the alternative tools.

The main advantage of diamond hones is their longevity, which materially reduces machine downtime due to the need for changing hones. They are also capable of fast stock removal and can be used at lower pressures, thus developing less heat and reducing the risk of distortion of workpieces.

Metal bonding is normal for diamond hones but resin, vitrified and electro-deposited bonds are available and the processes of manufacture are very similar to that of diamond wheels except that the final balancing is, of course, unnecessary.

Although honing is used on the outside of cylindrical and on flat surfaces, it is generally more applicable to the finishing of bores.

The size range of diamond hones has therefore to be such that they can be accommodated in the expanding head of the honing machine and can at the same time be contained within the bore to be honed.

British Standard 2064:1953 covers only hones having a length of 2 in. (51 mm.) or more. Many hones are, however, in use of much smaller sizes to suit specific needs in the production of components for diesel pumps and injectors, sewing machines, automobiles, refrigerators, electric motors and many similar assemblies.

The sizes covered by the British Standard are:

| Length | | Width | | Overall thickness | |
mm.	in.	mm.	in.	mm.	in.
50	2	3	$\frac{1}{8}$	3	$\frac{1}{8}$
50	2	4	$\frac{5}{32}$	2·4	$\frac{3}{32}$
50	2	5	$\frac{3}{16}$	5	$\frac{3}{16}$
75	3	6	$\frac{1}{4}$	6	$\frac{1}{4}$
100	4	8	$\frac{5}{16}$	6	$\frac{1}{4}$
100	4	11	$\frac{7}{16}$	8	$\frac{5}{16}$
100	4	11	$\frac{7}{16}$	9	$\frac{3}{8}$

In order to determine whether an application is suitable for the use of diamond hones and then to determine the characteristics of the hone to be used, the following factors should be known: 1. The workpiece dimensions and material specification, including its hardness, which affect the working area and bond to be recommended. 2. Whether the surface to be honed is continuous or interrupted and in what way this may also influence the hone working area. 3. The stock to be removed, the tolerance allowed and the surface finish both at completion of the previous operation and after honing are relevant to the grain size, concentration and bond to be used. The latter factors with information on the time allowable for honing may also decide whether the desired result can best be achieved in one, two or even three separate stages. 4. The quantity of components envisaged will influence the overall economy of the operation and in some cases may be taken into account in deciding on the depth of impregnation to be recommended. 5. Honing machine

Diamond impregnated honing inserts

characteristics also influence hone requirements: the maker and his type number should be known and the particularly relevant characteristics are: the number of spindles and their speed range both in revolutions per minute and reciprocations; the head pressures and expansion range available; the method of holding the workpiece and the coolant used.

The hone itself varies not only in outside dimensions, but also in the depth of impregnation employed and which is, of course, a major influence on life span. As the cost of hone manufacture is very little influenced by this variable, it is only the additional cost of the diamond content which is involved in using the maximum depth compatible with the amount of expansion available on the honing head. The maximum depth of impregnation should, therefore, be used provided the number of components is sufficient to consume at least one set of hones. The number of hones per set is, of course, determined by the number of segments in the honing head. The type of bond and the diamond concentration to be used are determined by an assessment of all the relevant factors outlined, but are also helped by having, as a background, details of conventional hones if they have been used previously and the results obtained with them. The grain size of the diamond is influenced mainly by the amount of stock to be removed and the final finish required.

It will be appreciated from the number of factors involved that there is no simple formula from which diamond hone specifications can be determined. The following notes can, therefore, be taken only as a very general guide, needing confirmation after considering all aspects of any particular application.

The hone head should be designed to take hones of about two thirds to three quarters of the workpiece length. The width of a diamond hone can generally be less than that of a normal hone. This not only reduces the cost of the hone but also reduces the pressure needed in operation.

This can be particularly important in thin wall workpieces. Roughing or preliminary honing operations usually call for diamond grades in the range mesh 85–100, 100–120 or 120–150. The normal range of honing operations calls for grit sizes 150–170, 170–200 or 200–240. Very fine finishes call for mesh grades 240–300 and 300–400 or finer in the 20–40 micron range. The range of materials for which diamond honing is generally applicable is as follows: heat treated steels, cast-iron, tungsten carbide and other hard metals, ceramics and glass. On these materials, finishes in the 2–50 micro inch range can be obtained.

Some of the most widely used diamond honing machines are made by Maschinenfabrik Gehring K.–G. of Germany, Micromatic Hone Corporation who manufacture in the U.S.A. and in England, Delapena & Son Ltd. and Chaphone Engineering Development Ltd. of England, Éts. Buchly of France and Sunnen Products Co. of U.S.A.

Typical working conditions, for example, on a Gehring vertical honer are of the following order: Diamond hones should be attached to their retaining shoes with an adhesive such as Castolin. To obtain the most consistent results the working faces of the diamond hones mounted on the head can then be ground to approximately the diameter of the workpiece bore. Some machine builders suggest that, to avoid a tendency to glaze the hone, this should be done without a coolant. A 30 or 46 L aluminium oxide wheel is recommended. This operation, or the alternative of chamfering the hone edges, is more important on wider hones, say 10 mm. (approximately $\frac{3}{8}$ in.) wide or more.

Specific working details and case histories are described in the chapters dealing with industries in which diamond honing is used, but the following is intended to provide guidance of a general nature: The length of reciprocation should be set at about one third of the hone length.

The speed of reciprocation is in the 10–12 metres per minute range (approximately 33–39 ft. per minute). The spindle speed should be set to give 35–45 metres per minute (approximately 115–148 ft. per minute). Hone wear rate normally increases as speed is lowered below this range. Working pressures are of the order of 3·5–6 kilograms per square centimetre (approximately 50–85 lb. per square inch). For roughing this may be increased to 11–12 kilograms per square centimetre (approximately 156–170 lb. per square inch) but should be associated with a low viscosity lubricant. Conversely, lower pressures are used for finishing with higher viscosity lubricants. Examples of lubricants used are Honilo 10 and 50 (Castrol), Sultran D (Mobiloil), HP1 (B.P. Co.), Somentor 28 (Esso) or Macron 11 (Shell). For very fast stock removal and where finish is of secondary importance, paraffin is used.

Factors which may cause loading or glazing of the working face of the hone and consequent reduction in cutting efficiency are:

a. Lubricant not being properly directed on the hone face.
b. The use of a lubricant having an excessive viscosity.
c. The honing pressure being too high.
d. Attempting excessive stock removal for the hone specification being used.

When a hone becomes loaded, the surface should be dressed with a medium abrasive stone.

The diamond impregnated element of a hand lap is also made in the same way as a honing tool, but is provided with a handle. They are mainly used for minor improvements or repairs to the edges of tungsten carbide tool edges.

Diamond coated cloth

Diamond grit bonded in this way is available for belts, sheets, discs and rolls, but is not in great demand.

Diamond saws

Most diamond saws are of the metal bond type, but some resin bond continuous rim saws are also used. In addition to these, made for sale to users, there are other types still made by the users themselves in the same way as other surface coated products described earlier.

The two main categories are segmental saws for stone and refractories and continuous rim saws for glass and ceramics. Both are of the sintered metal bond type. The third has a diamond and metal rim electro-deposited either on the periphery or on the inside diameter of the thin annular saws mostly used in the slicing of germanium and silicon for transistors.

The segments of saws in the first category are sintered individually and subsequently brazed on to a steel centre with pre-machined slots in the periphery. The surplus brazing alloy is removed and the blade tensioned and cleaned. The bonds used are, of course, in general harder and more abrasion resistant then the grinding wheels previously described. The diamond grit sizes are also coarser. The saws range from about 0·30 m. to 2 m. in diameter (12–72 in.). Similar segments are also brazed to straight steel blanks for use as reciprocating stone saws.

Standards for segmental saws have been established:

Area (prefix)	Reference	Product
Britain (BS)	2064:1953/9	Stone saw diameters in increments of 2 in. (50 mm.), from 8–20 in. diameter (200–500 mm.) and then 2 ft. (0·6 m.), 2 ft. 6 in. (0·75 m.), 3 ft. (1 m.), 3 ft. 6 in. (1·1 m.) and 4 ft. (1·25 m.)
U.S.A.	USAS B74.1–1966 revision of B74.1–1957	General saw configuration
U.S.S.R.	Ukrainian SSR Gosplan catalogue of synthetic diamond products	Segmented disc saws in diameters 300, 400, 500, 630, 800 and 1,100 mm.
Europe (FEPA)	Standard for Diamond Saws (Metric)	

The continuous rim type saws are normally sintered in one unit with simultaneous attachment to the steel centre. Comparatively large furnaces and presses are therefore required for their production. The relevant standards in this field are:

Area (prefix)	Reference	Product
Britain (BS)	2064:1953/9	Cut off wheels (metal bond) 75–350 mm. (3–14 in.) diameter
U.S.A.	USAS B74.1–1966 revision of B74.1–1957	U.S.A. standard identification code for diamond wheel shapes—sponsored by the Grinding Wheel Institute and approved by the U.S. Standards Institute
U.S.S.R. (Gost)	10110–62	Cut-off wheels 50–320 mm. diameter
Poland (PN)	56/M–59105	Diamond saws 75–150 mm. diameter

Generally, these standards are considered to include not only sintered rim saws, but also electro-deposited. Apart from the U.S.S.R., national standards have not been established for annular or internal cutting saws. The U.S.S.R. standard quotes the following sizes:

D

| | Diameter | | Cutting | Blade |
	Outside mm.	Inside mm.	thickness mm.	thickness mm.
U.S.S.R.	206	83	0·20	0·10
(Ref. AKBP)	257	105	0·22	0·10
	257	105	0·24	0·12
	257	105	0·27	0·15

The use of these tools in the cutting of semiconductors is dealt with in Chapter 5 on Electrics and Electronics.

Diamond powder, grit and compound

As a loose abrasive, the material is available in the sizes covered by the national standards to which reference is made earlier in this chapter.

The choice of the correct grade depends on the material being worked, the degree of finish required, the time allowed for the process and the method of application. Because of the wide variation between individual requirements, it is not possible to be more specific, but the following broad outline will serve as an initial guide:

SUMMARY OF MAIN USES

Material	Operation	Examples of components	Grades used PS—sieve sizes PM—micron sizes
Diamond	Sawing Rough polishing Fine polishing General polish	Gems and shaped tools	PS 300/400 PM 20/40 PM 0/2 PM 0/40
	Piercing Reboring Polishing	Wire drawing dies	All micron sizes, depending on the operation and die size
	Grinding Roughing Polishing	Drawing dies	PS 240/300 and PS 300/400 PM 8/25 and PM 20/40 PM 4/8 and PM 6/12
Hard metals including tungsten carbide	Grinding Roughing Polishing	Heading dies	PS 300/400 PM 4/8 PM ½/3 and PM 0/2

	Polishing	Tool tips	PM 6/12 to PM ½/3 on soft lap
Metals	Polishing	Metallographic specimens	PM 4/8 and PM 0/1
Synthetic sapphire and ruby (corundum)	Sizing Countersinking Piercing Oliving Polishing Glossing	Bearings and escapements	PM 4/8 PM 8/25 to PM 4/8 PM 1/5 to PM 6/12 PM ½/3 and PM 2/6 PM ½/3 and PM 2/6 PM 0/1 and PM 0/2
	Sizing Polishing	Gramophone needles	PM 4/8 and PM 6/12 PM ½/3 and PM 2/6
Steel (hardened)	Lapping Polishing Fine polishing	Gauges	PM 20/40 and PM 0/40 PM 6/12 PM 0/½ and PM ½/1

Diamond powder is accurately size graded and great care should be taken to keep it so, or serious trouble may occur in use. Containers should always be closed with the correct lid when not in use. This prevents the ingress of dirt and other foreign matter. The powder should preferably be tipped from the container and not spooned out as contaminants may be present on the spatula or other tools used for this purpose.

If some form of tool is essential for transferring powder, then one should be kept specially for each grade and stored in a clean place, away from others used for different grades. Each grade of diamond powder should have its own laps, mandrels and other bases set aside and marked for that grade. The working areas of such bases must be kept free from extraneous matter. A consistently satisfactory degree of finish can only be obtained by this attention to detail. When transferring the work from one grade of diamond powder to a finer grade, it is essential that all traces of diamond from the previous operation be removed and rigorous cleaning methods are necessary to ensure this removal.

Large users of diamond powders, having a grain size of less than about 50 microns, usually find it more economical to buy the powder in bulk and make up pastes, suspensions or tools to suit their own needs. This is current practice in diamond die and tool making, in the manufacture of jewel bearings and in some units of the glass working industry.

Where the use of the material is not on such a large scale or where the use is intermittent, the purchaser often finds it more convenient to buy the powder ready mixed as a lapping compound. Typical examples of this practice occur in metal mould finishing for plastics production, the preparation of metallographic specimen surfaces, the finishing operations on the working surfaces of tungsten carbide drawing dies and tools, and semiconductor lapping.

The compound was earlier supplied in collapsible tubes but glass or plastic syringes are now more common in 2 or 5 gram packs. The disposable plastic syringe has the advantages that no replacement cartridge is needed, the danger of glass breakage is avoided and there is no contamination risk due to using the wrong nozzle.

In order to facilitate identification of grade by the user, the compound is sometimes prepared in a series of colours—each identified with a particular diamond grain size.

Generally, the concentration of diamond in the compound is higher in the larger grain sizes, which are in turn normally associated with heavier stock removal. It should also be remembered that there are less particles per weight unit in coarser grades than in finer ones and, thus, less cutting points.

A typical commercial lapping compound, such as 'Dialap', is offered in the following alternatives:

Colour code	Order code	Micron	Concentrations	Application
Grey	$\frac{1}{4}$/1	$\frac{1}{4}$	1	Superfine finishing,
	$\frac{1}{2}$/1	$\frac{1}{2}$	1	metallographic polishing
	$\frac{3}{4}$/1	$\frac{3}{4}$	1	on soft material
Blue	1/1	1	1	Fine finishing and
	$1\frac{1}{2}$/1	$1\frac{1}{2}$	1	metallographic polishing
	2/1	2	1	on hard materials
Green	3/2	3	2	Finishing
	3/1*	3	1	
Yellow	6/3	6	3	General purpose polishing
	6/4	6	4	
Red	8/4	8	4	General purpose lapping
	8/5*	8	5	
Brown	14/5	14	5	Fast lapping
	14/4*	14	4	
Mahogany	25/5	25	5	Stock removal and
Purple	40/5	40	5	roughing steel
	45/5	45	5	

Orange	60/6	60	6	Stock removal and
White	90/6	90	6	roughing hard metals

Concentrations marked * are not normal concentrations, but are usually available from stock.

To use this material effectively, one or more of a series of accessories are usually needed depending on the nature of the work:

Lapping sticks may be needed in a range of sizes having sections of say:

Rectangles		Rounds	
mm.	in.	mm.	in.
3 × 3	$\frac{1}{8} \times \frac{1}{8}$	3	$\frac{1}{8}$
3 × 6	$\frac{1}{8} \times \frac{1}{4}$	4·5	$\frac{3}{16}$
4·5 × 4·5	$\frac{3}{16} \times \frac{3}{16}$	6	$\frac{1}{4}$
6 × 6	$\frac{1}{4} \times \frac{1}{4}$		
8 × 12·5	$\frac{5}{16} \times \frac{1}{2}$		
8 × 19	$\frac{5}{16} \times \frac{3}{4}$		

These are available in two forms. The hard sticks are made of resin impregnated multi-ply wood and are useful for fast stock removal. The soft sticks are slower acting and produce finer finishes.

Felt cones are used with small powered rotary hand tools such as the 'Derota' unit described later. They are usually supplied with 3 mm. ($\frac{1}{8}$ in.) diameter shafts. The more commonly used sizes are:

Cone number	Diameter		Length	
	mm.	in.	mm.	in.
1	19	$\frac{3}{4}$	28·5	$1\frac{1}{8}$
2	16	$\frac{5}{8}$	28·5	$1\frac{1}{8}$
3	12·5	$\frac{1}{2}$	28·5	$1\frac{1}{8}$
4	9·5	$\frac{3}{8}$	20·5	$\frac{13}{16}$
5	9·5	$\frac{3}{8}$	16	$\frac{5}{8}$

Felt bobs are similar to the felt cones, but the flat ends are more suitable for lapping larger flat areas. They are normally used in the following sizes:

Bob number	Diameter		Length	
	mm.	inches	mm.	inches
1	19	$\frac{3}{4}$	40	$1\frac{9}{16}$
2	16	$\frac{5}{8}$	35	$1\frac{3}{8}$
3	12·5	$\frac{1}{2}$	25·5	1
4	9·5	$\frac{3}{8}$	14	$\frac{9}{16}$
5	6	$\frac{1}{4}$	11	$\frac{7}{16}$

Wooden cones and bobs are also available in two hardness grades.
Nylon brushes, foam fabric, special microcloth polishing cloths and silicon carbide paper discs are also offered as additional accessories.

Power units, such as the Derota, consist of an electric motor, a foot operated speed control and a flexible shaft. To the latter can be fitted a rotary handpiece in which felt bobs or cones can be inserted. Alternatively, the flexible shaft can be used to drive a work head which converts the rotary motion to a reciprocating one. The head has a variable stroke from zero to 6 mm. ($\frac{1}{4}$ in.), this being achieved by an adjustable eccentric. The final drive incorporates a stiff spring which acts as a shock absorber in the event of the tool being forced against an obstruction. This prevents the work or the tool being damaged under such circumstances and enables lapping to be carried out to the bottom of a blind hole or up to a shoulder.

Lapping fluid is a very important component in the successful use of diamond compounds. Most manufacturers offer a fluid made up to suit their own formulations of compound base. The fluid is used to lubricate the work and spread the compound evenly over the area required. This fluid is supplied in aerosols.

DRILL BITS

From the point of view of manufacturing techniques, there are two broad categories in use. They vary only in the type, size and positioning of the diamond content. The surface set bit was developed from the old hand-set bit where each diamond was peened into its individual seating. This method was replaced by powder metal setting. In the second category, coarse diamond grit is used. This is mixed with the powder in the same way as for a metal bonded diamond grinding wheel. From that point, however, the process follows the same course as the surface-set bit. They are designed to be fully used without resetting.

The differences between bits used in mining, in the oil-fields and in construction are of dimension and proportion.

The core bits used in mining are generally covered by the following standards:

Area (prefix)	Reference	Product
Britain (BS)	4019 Part I 1966	Core barrel assemblies, casing and casing barrel assemblies and drill rods
U.S.A. (DCDMA)	Bulletin No. 3 (last amendment 1970)	Core barrel assemblies, casing and casing barrel assemblies and drill rods
Canada (CDDA)		Core barrel assemblies, casing and casing barrel assemblies and drill rods
Europe (Metric)	Craelius (trade name of Svenska Diamantberg-borrnings A/B Stockholm, Sweden)	Core barrel assemblies, casing assemblies and drill rods
U.S.S.R. (Gost)	9431–60 (not specifically diamond bits)	

Coring bits used in the oil-fields are not made to any national standards nor are solid bits except that the taper threads on the latter are usually required to conform to the standards of the American Petroleum Institute specification for rotary drilling equipment (eighteenth edition of March 1963). Copies of this are available from the Director of the Institute, Division of Production, 3C0 Corrigan Tower Building, Dallas 1, Texas.

The specification of the diamond bearing areas is dealt with in Chapter 8 and states the tolerances on outside diameters.

Coring bits for use in the oil-fields are made in outside diameters to suit borehole conditions as the work progresses. Inside diameters and thread connections are made to suit individual core barrel manufacturers' designs.

Oil well coring and drilling bits are generally of the surface set type, but some designs incorporate both surface set and impregnated areas.

In the case of diamond tube drills used in the construction industry, a supplement to B.S. 4019 has recently been issued to cover this range as B.S. 4019: Part 2: 1973.

The comparatively thin wall tubular drills or trepanning tools are made by the same methods employed for diamond core bits used in mineral prospecting and in the oil-fields. The range of sizes in common use is from about 19–160 mm. ($\frac{3}{4}$–$6\frac{1}{4}$ in.) O.D., but larger sizes are available.

Drill bits in this range are available in both surface set and impregnated formulations. More details are given in Chapter 8.

GLASS CUTTING TOOLS

Among the diamond tools using whole diamonds, this is, no doubt, the best known. The selected 'vitrier' diamond is located by eye in a carbon mould and sintered into a powder metal compact. This in turn is machined to position the diamond in relation to the steel block with which the normal 'English Pattern' glass cutting tool is provided. The working face of the diamond is then 'manipulated' to finally establish its correct position in the steel block before the latter is attached to the steel spigot, protruding from the brass ferrule, and in turn the wood or plastic handle to which it is attached. Where the cutter is required to operate on an automatic cutting machine, the operation of course stops at the steel shank.

ABRASIVE WHEEL TRUING TOOLS

Tools of this general description fall into six broad categories:

1. Single diamond.
2. Indexing single diamond.
3. Multi-diamond.
4. Bonded diamond grit.
5. Cone and chisel shaped.
6. Rotary and block.

They generally have the following characteristics:

1. A single diamond selected as appropriate under all the conditions appertaining to the job in hand. This is usually mounted

A selection of traditional diamond glass cutting tools:

A and B are standard English hand type cutters

C is a tube cutter for bores from 6 mm. ($\frac{1}{4}$ in.) to 25 mm. (1 in.) diameter and for lengths up to 750 mm. (30 in.)

D is an all metal 'rack' type continental hand cutter

E is a circle cutter. These are available for diameters from 50 to 900 mm. (2 to 36 in.)

F illustrates a continental pattern with taper shank and wood handle

G is a 'writing' diamond for engraving and general marking work

H represents an alternative continental pattern with a notched head and wood handle

in a sintered powder metal insert held in turn in the recess of a mild steel shank of dimensions to suit the socket on the grinding machine. The actual means of mounting may also be by way of hand fitting and brazing directly into the mild steel shank or by casting metal around the diamond. Such tools usually bear a serial number for subsequent identification when resetting becomes necessary. The weight of the diamond is also marked on the shank in metric carats (0·2 gram). The reduced diamond weight after each period of use is marked on the shank at each subsequent resetting. The exact point in time at which the tool should be returned for resetting depends mainly on the work requirements.

They should never be retained in service beyond the point at which the abrasive wheel begins to grind away the metal setting surrounding the diamond.

Normally, such tools are returned to the maker for resetting, but, in the case of very large users, diamond tool makers are willing to licence them to carry out this service themselves. This is only to be recommended if the volume of such resetting work in the user's plant is sufficient to justify having at least one man properly trained and specialising in this work. Unless the resetting is in the hands of someone who really appreciates the needs of this apparently simple operation, considerable economic risks are taken. Apart from possible damage in the actual extraction from the shank on subsequent resetting, a fault in the mount surrounding the diamond may result in breakage when put to further use. This may result in the loss of a diamond worth £50 or £100. As the manufacturers usually make only a nominal charge for this skilled service, the risks are not worth taking.

2. To facilitate the regeneration of the natural point on single point truers where this factor is important, such tools are made with indexing tool holders. In their simplest form such tool holders are hand operated by various ratchet and locking devices. Mechanically operated units are made to be actuated by stops at the end of each truing pass. On machines fitted with hydraulics the latter can be extended to actuate the diamond indexing mechanism. The use of either type, which is automatically operated in the machine cycle and thus

reduces the human element, certainly results in lower diamond cost per dressing and greater consistency in grinding wheel performance.

Where the conditions required are particularly exacting, the rough diamond is formed to a cone to ensure a consistent contact area between diamond and wheel at each index position from the first truing traverse.

3. In the third group the truing medium consists of a number of small but whole diamonds, some or all of which contact the abrasive wheel at the same time. Some such tools were rather laboriously made before powder metal setting techniques

Alternative diamond setting patterns for multi-diamond truers used on plain wheels

were developed. The diamonds were comparatively large and such tools could be made only with one diamond layer. The adoption of powder metal diamond setting methods extended the possibilities to the use of much smaller diamonds and the manufacture of multi-layer compacts to extend the life of such tools.

The normal range of diamonds used in tools of this type is from a small of about 0·02 carat to a large of 0·5 carat. The total weight per tool varies from about 0·10 carat to 5 carats. For plain truing the diamond bearing insert is usually a cylinder from about 6 mm. ($\frac{1}{4}$ in.) to 18 mm. ($\frac{3}{4}$ in.) diameter with lengths of the same order. Rectangular forms are also used, especially where some adjustment of the angle between the tool cutting face and the abrasive wheel periphery is desired. Such tools should be specified in cases where fairly heavy wheel loading is expected, but, due to comparatively fine grain size, the final truing must be accomplished with small diamond contact areas. With these tools the leading diamonds remove the loaded wheel areas and the following diamonds, slightly offset from the wheel, are used to provide a shallow finishing cut simultaneously.

4. The small whole diamonds used in the tools described in paragraph 3 are normally set in predetermined patterns, each stone being positioned individually in the course of building up the complete powder metal compact before heat treatment.

The fourth group of wheel truing tools consists of crushed and graded diamond powder mixed with metal powders and sintered. The diamond particles are not individually set in a pattern but are distributed evenly throughout the matrix in the same way that an abrasive wheel consists of abrasive grains and a bonding agent. The particle sizes of the diamond powder used must be related to the grain size of the wheel to be trued. The relation should be of about the following order:

Abrasive wheel grain size range		Diamond particle size	
Mesh	Micron	Mesh	Micron
46–80	400–200	25	600
80–180	200–95	50	300
180–300	95–55	100	150
Finer than 300	Minus 55	200	80

The metal matrix used is normally rather harder than that used in multiple whole diamond truers, but the dimensions of the diamond bearing inserts are of the same order. The total diamond weights used vary according to the area of wheel to be trued at each pass and normally range from about 0·5 to 5 carats. The concentration or weight of diamond per unit of volume of the diamond bearing area can also be varied, but is normally of the order of 3–5 carats per cubic centimetre.

5. The production of a cone truer follows the same pattern as a single point truer, but the diamond shape is finally 'bruted' or cut to the required cone angle and radius. In the case of a chisel, the processes consist of:

a. Selecting a diamond having a cross section appropriate

Chisel type diamond truing tools

to the included angle and radius of the profile required. Setting requirements must also be considered. The smaller the angle and radius the smaller the diamond cross sectional area to avoid wastage of the valuable material and unnecessary expenditure of time in reducing the diamond to the size required. The diamond is also selected so that, when set and ground to form the most wear resistant grain structure, it coincides as far as possible with the centre of the radius. This is normally the area in which the greatest wear occurs.

b. The stone is sintered into a flat powder metal compact.

c. The diamond bearing 'blade' is then brazed into a slotted steel shank. The slot is now made to standard dimensions and no longer has to be filed to suit the diamond contour.

d. The flanks of the shank are ground to the angle required on the finished diamond profile and, at the same time, the required diamond areas are exposed for shaping.

e. The oversize shank, complete with diamond bearing blade, is inserted in a square carrier and axially located by the flats ground on it during the previous operation.

f. The square carrier is located in a vee guide attached to a pantograph jig on the diamond lapping bench. The diamond chisel flanks are then formed on the diamond charged cast iron lap. At the end of this operation the distance between the lapped flats at their nearest point is sufficient to ensure that, when the required radius has been ground, it will be tangential with the flanks.

g. The square carrier is now transferred to an oscillating head, optically controlled grinding machine. The carrier locates in a vee block on a swivelling base, which then passes the diamond across a diamond powder impregnated cup wheel along a path which results in the required radius being ground on the tool. The operator controls the accuracy of the radius by constant inspection through a microscope fitted to the machine. The eyepiece of the microscope is fitted with graticules corresponding to the radii required.

h. The steel blank is finally machined on a combined lathe/ milling machine which enables diameter and locating flat to be machined in one set-up. The shank is then marked with its serial number and finally ground to ensure the accuracy of the shank when fitted to the user's grinding machine.

Tools in these categories 1–5 inclusive are supplied in steel shanks to the following national standards:

Area (prefix)	Reference	Product/comment
Britain (BS)	2002:1953/9	Dimensions of diamond truing tools
	(Recently reissued in metric as 2002:1973)	
U.S.A. (ASA)	B67.1–1958	ASTME/IDA
W. Germany (DIN)	1820:1941	Diamond shanks and mountings
India	Y5–61	Indian Railway Board
U.S.S.R. (Gost)	607–56	Shanks and diamond content
Poland (PN)	62/M 59531	Taper shanks
	62/M 59532	8 mm. dia × 25 mm. long
	63/M 59534	Pyramid diamond in 6 mm. Ø × 25 mm.
	63/M 59541	Multi-diamond in taper shank
	63/M 59547	Impregnated types
Czechoslovakia (CSN)	224918	Diamond truing tools

6. Rotary and block truers—this development finds its optimum field of use in long run mass production. Because it is undoubtedly the most consistent form of abrasive wheel truing yet devised, it will also find an increasing use in plain truing. The adoption of higher speeds in production grinding with increases from the conventional 25 metres per second (5,000 ft. per minute) to speeds of the order of X2 or X3 will still further increase interest in this method of truing.

The area of contact with the wheel is a cylindrical surface of evenly spaced hand set small whole diamonds or random set coarse grade diamond powder. These cutting elements are held in sintered powder metal carriers or are held on the surface by electro-deposited metal. This diamond bearing unit is mounted on a rigid spindle which, in its simplest form, is in turn carried in precision but very free running bearings held

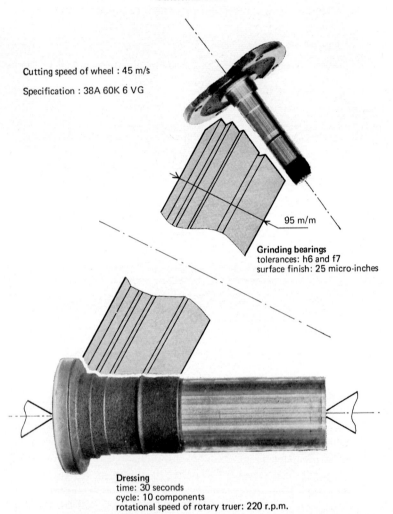

Differential shaft

Cutting speed of wheel : 45 m/s

Specification : 38A 60K 6 VG

95 m/m

Grinding bearings
tolerances: h6 and f7
surface finish: 25 micro-inches

Dressing
time: 30 seconds
cycle: 10 components
rotational speed of rotary truer: 220 r.p.m.

*Diamond rotary truer, grinding wheel and workpiece in their relative positions
on an angle head grinding machine* (Precidia S.A.)

in a yoke. The latter is located on the grinder by a shank inserted in the usual diamond truing tool socket. The assembly is adjusted on the socket axis so that the rotary truer carrying spindle is appreciably out of alignment with the running axis of the grinding wheel spindle.

On traversing the assembly, the rotary truer starts to revolve as it approaches the wheel edge. It is induced to do so by contact with the zone of air and coolant carried round by the abrasive wheel. This avoids the harsh initial contact which would result from the stationary rotary truer touching the revolving wheel. When the two are in contact, the angular setting results in a 'scrubbing' action. This is an essential part of the operation.

Unlike a metal 'crush roller', which has no peripheral movement in relation to the grinding wheel, a differential is essential when using a diamond rotary truer. Due to the hardness difference between the diamond content and its surrounding metal matrix, a pattern would otherwise be imposed upon the wheel. Small recesses would be formed in the abrasive wheel surface by the diamonds.

To ensure that this important speed differential between abrasive wheel and rotary truer is maintained, most of the latter are mounted on power driven spindles. For plain truing they are usually between say 40–80 mm. (about $1\frac{1}{2}$–3 in.) in diameter by 25–50 mm. ($\frac{1}{2}$–1 in.) wide. They may be traversed across the wheel face whilst being driven on an axis which is either parallel to the grinding spindle, at 90° to it or any angle between these. The direction of rotation may be the same or opposite to the wheel so long as the speed differential is not eliminated.

The rotary truer characteristic that has so far been found most important is the ability to make them with profiles and thus be used as plunge truing devices. Case histories are quoted in Chapter 4 on the Transport Industry.

For use on surface grinders, both plain and profiled block truers can also be made. All of these products can be produced in sintered or electro-formed types. Selection depends on the accuracy required, the batch size and the machine type.

A relevant British Standard is being drafted to cover the

E

interface with the machine tool. The working areas are generally in the range of 75–150 mm. (3–6 in.) in diameter and 12–100 mm. (0·5–4 in.) in length. Greater length can be provided by gang assembly on a common mandrel.

MACHINING, ENGRAVING AND BURNISHING TOOLS

The broad categories of this group are:

a. Diamond tipped boring tools for finish boring such items as automobile bearings, electric motor bearings and similar components. They are generally used on special purpose machine tools.

b. Diamond tipped turning tools for finish machining aluminium pistons for internal combustion engines, copper commutators and many plastic components. Some are used on standard high precision lathes and many on specially designed machine tools. Both groups a. and b. are traversed across the component with a shallow cut to produce finishes of the order of 10–20 micro inches.

c. Diamond plunge cutting tools which have been mainly developed to produce small brilliantly finished areas on watch cases, rings and cufflinks. These are invariably used on machines developed specifically for these operations. They are also used in grooving and parting off operations in other fields.

d. Diamond tipped milling cutters used mainly on the same components as group c., but also used for machining such items as aluminium cylinder heads for aero engines and the mating faces of pump components.

e. Diamond faced burnishing tools used on continuous surfaces to improve surface finish.

For groups a. to e. the method of manufacture follows approximately the same course. The diamond is selected not only for its intrinsic good quality but also to have a shape and size approximating to the finished diamond required. The grain orientation must be appropriate not only to the requirements of shaping it but also to its ultimate function. In satisfying all these often contradictory requirements the occurrence of ideal stones is reduced to a minimum. Despite the resulting rarity value of the diamond content, the average diamond cost factor in a normal tool is not more than about 25%. The normal weight range used in these tools is of the order of $\frac{1}{2}$ to 1 ct., but much larger diamonds are used where the length of cutting edge requires it.

The position of the top face is then marked by the shaping supervisor and a preliminary locating flat lapped in that position. This flat is then used as the datum for setting in a powder metal insert of rectangular form. The latter in turn locates the diamond in relation to the jigs used to finish lap the flats and radii which form the eventual cutting edge. The finished diamond bearing insert is then brazed in a suitable slot in the oversize shank which is finish machined to the required size. At the same time the diamond cutting edge or burnishing area is correctly positioned in relation to the shank.

In order to facilitate recording the life of such tools they invariably bear a maker's trade mark and serial number.

There is a very high proportion of these tools which are made to non-standard dimensions, particularly in the watch and jewellery industry to meet the requirements of fashion (see Chapter 10).

However, Standards do exist and are used in some industries. The British Standard is also due for revision and conversion to metric.

Area (prefix)	Reference	Product/comment
Britain (BS)	1120:1943/54	Diamond boring and turning tools
	(Now reissued in metric form as B.S. 1120:1973)	
U.S.A. (ASA)	B67.1—1958	ASTME/IDA
U.S.S.R. (Gost)	13288	Diamond turning and boring tools

WIRE DRAWING DIES

The processes involved in diamond drawing die production can be summarised:

Selecting die stones: Selecting diamonds is the most important feature in diamond die manufacture, since the quality of the stone determines the life of the die and no subsequent manipulation can rectify any error of judgement in this respect.

Shape: Whilst true octahedra and true dodecahedra rarely occur, the majority of crystals incline to one or the other but with such an infinite diversity of irregularity that one can say that no two stones are exactly similar. Many crystals are, in fact, shapeless from a diemaker's point of view, although they may be economically cut into brilliants. Twinned crystals (maacles) have a weakness at the 'seam' and should not be used for dies. The ideal shape is rhombic dodecahedron.

Colour: The internal structure of white and yellow stones is generally good and these therefore make the best dies. Many of the brown stones are visibly laminated under magnification and for this reason are to be discarded. Whereas the pigment is uniform in yellow and brown stones, stones which are white internally (or, more correctly, colourless) are often highly coloured superficially. This pigment on the surface can be in minute spots, indiscriminate blotches or it can completely cover the stone so that, when the colour is sufficiently dense, the stone cannot be examined internally. Two other types of diamond which defy examination are those with a crystalline crust (commonly called coated stones) and the water-worn stones from river diggings which have been worn dull.

Purity: It is comparatively simple for the expert to recognise and discard stones unsuitable from the point of view of shape and colour, and when this is done there remain whole, closed, blocky crystals approximating the dodecahedron of either white or yellow colour and with sufficiently clear surface to permit internal examin-ation. The quantity of such stones represents a very small proportion of the diamonds produced and this percentage is further reduced by internal examination for carbon spots, flaws, fissures and inclusions of all kinds. This final examination involves great discrimination and experience since good quality die stones are virtually flawless and certainly purer than the majority of diamonds used for jewellery purposes.

Flatting: The flats on the top and bottom of the diamond are cut on a schyf. The diamond is held in an adjustable dop so that the correct cutting plane, according to the particular orientation of the diamond, may be more readily found. In the case of diamonds used for small diameter dies, a third facet (known as the 'window') is cut on the side, through which the progress of manufacture is observed, angles controlled and size measured under the microscope.

Drilling: The drilling machines vary in design, according to the phase of drilling and size of hole being excavated, but fundamentally the action is the same (because of the impact of the grains of powder on the diamond caused by the rapidly oscillating movement, it is more of a chiselling action than drilling). The diamond is carefully centred on the revolving spindle which oscillates against the drilling needle, also revolving at high speed. The needle is suitably ground and charged with the correct grade of diamond powder for each stage of the operations for drilling the entrance, approach, reduction zone and the drawing duct. The needle is in all cases ground *in situ* and for the small diameters is ground under the microscope built into the drilling machine. For the very finest diameters (0·05 mm. (0·002 in.), down to 0·0063 mm. (0·00025 in.)) the drawing duct is pierced electrolytically and in this process the stone is held just beneath the surface of a suitable electrolyte and a pointed platinum alloy needle inserted into the finely drilled reduction zone. The circuit is completed by a second electrode in the solution, and with suitable electrical controls arc voltages down to 40 volts can be used. In this field ultrasonics, lasers and high voltage discharge techniques are also used.

GAUGING AND TRACING POINTS

In this field most applications have their own precise diamond requirement which cannot be varied if the apparatus is to function.

The diamonds in this range, most commonly known in engineering, are the indenters or penetrators used in hardness testing apparatus. The diamond working area takes the form of a polished cone or pyramid depending on the apparatus used and not on the choice of the user.

Pyramid and conical diamonds, generally of smaller included angle, are also used as the tracer point in surface measuring instruments.

Spherical diamond anvils are used on many measuring and controlling units on cylindrical and internal grinders. Some gear and thread grinders use flat faced diamond anvils to 'feel' the position of the grinding wheel working face and actuate mechanisms that compensate automatically for grinding wheel wear.

The main methods and equipment used are the same as for diamond cutting tools. The actual jigs used are, of course, modified in view of the differences in the geometric form required and, in the case of the cone and spherical forms, the workpiece has to revolve in the course of shaping, grinding and lapping.

In the latter operation the grinding and lapping must take place in several grain directions and thus with varying rates of stock removal. Because of this, the diamond tool manufacturer has to be extremely watchful to avoid a tendency for such conical and spherical forms to become lobed.

Especially good optical equipment is necessary to measure the vital meeting place of the four component facets on micro indenters and tracer points for surface measurement.

The more commonly used diamond indenters for hardness testing (Edgwick, Avery, Rockwell, Vickers and Firth)

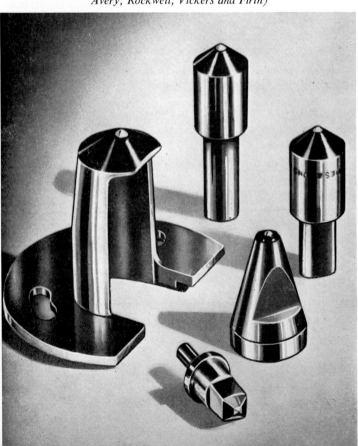

This extensive range of diamond products is utilised in an even wider range of industries, and some of these are described in the remaining chapters.

REFERENCES

British Patent 1,279,413 (Resimet)—Impregnated Diamond Products Ltd.
British Patent 1,007,814—Cincinnati Milling Machines Ltd.
Mining Journal Annual Review—June 1971.
De Beers *Abrasives for Industry*—1.11.70.
'Some aspects of wheel formulation in ceramic grinding'—D. M. Thomas, M.I.M., Diamond Products Division of Universal Grinding Ltd., September 1971.
Physical Properties of Diamond—R. Berman and Ed. R. Berman, 1965.
Fédération Européenne des Fabricants de Produits Abrasifs:
    FEPA Standard for Diamond Saws.
        Standard for Diamond Grinding Wheels.
        Standard for Diamond Grain Sizes.
U.S.S.R. Gost 17006—71 Diamond Annular Wheels.
        Gost 9770—61 Diamond Grinding Wheels.
        Gost 13288/9/90/1/2/3/4/5/6/7—1967—Diamond tipped turning and boring tools.
        Gost 2999—59 Vickers type Pyramind Hardness Testers.
        Gost 9017—59 Diamond tracer points.
        Gost 607—56 Diamond Dressing Tools.
        Gost 9206—59.
Polish PN62/M59531/2/4—Shanks for Diamond Truing Tools—single diamond.
        /M59541/7—Shanks for Diamond Truing Tools—multiple diamond.
        PN61/M–59100 and 59107.
British B.S. 1987:1953—Diamond Grain Sizes.
U.S.A. ANSI B74.16—1965.
Germany DIN 848—1965.

3

Toolmaking

IT is intended to take the title definition in its broadest sense. Although often part of the activity of another engineering complex, toolmaking has a distinctive character of its own, and, for the purpose of this chapter, includes not only conventional tool, die, gauge and fixture making but also machine tool building both as a separate entity and as part of other manufacturing activity.

The main diamond products used in toolmaking are:

1. Diamond wheels in resin, metal and electro-metallic bonds.
2. Abrasive wheel truing tools, mainly of the single point, chisel and cone type.
3. Diamond indenters, gauge anvils and tracer points.
4. Diamond powder as a loose abrasive or lapping compound.

Diamond grinding wheels for the field are covered by the standard specification of the Fédération Européenne des Fabricants de Produits Abrasifs, in the U.S.A. by USAS B74.1—1966 B74.1—1957, and the U.S.S.R. by Gost 5674—70 in respect of taper cup wheels.

CARBIDE AND CERAMIC TOOL GRINDING

Tungsten carbide and ceramic edged tools for use on lathes, milling machines and shapers invariably rely on diamond grinding and lapping wheels to produce the edge quality required. These tool tips rely on diamond powder at a very early stage. The metal pressing dies in which they are cold formed have diamond compound lapped working surfaces. For many non-standard forms the cost of dies to the specific shape required is not justified. In such cases the pressed carbide powder form from the nearest shape available is shaped in its green state by clean cutting, long life, electro-deposited diamond slitting discs, twist drills and grinding wheels. After sintering, further corrective shaping may be carried out on profile grinders using diamond discs or formed wheels. The final grinding and lapping of the new tool edge and its subsequent resharpening constitute one of the major consumers of bonded diamond powder products. Most of the wheels used are from the cup type alternatives, but peripheral wheels and chip-breaker wheels are, of course, also used.

In order to decide which wheel specification is to be used, the following factors must be known:

a. Type of operation—roughing, finishing or super-finishing.
b. The material to be ground—type of carbide or ceramic.
c. Machine specification—freehand tool sharpener, controlled cutter tool grinder, tool and cutter grinder for milling cutters or normal surface grinder.
d. Spindle speed—in order to obtain optimum results from the diamond wheel, this needs to provide a peripheral speed in the range of say about 10 to 30 metres per second (approximately 2,000 to 6,000 feet per minute). Some idea of what this means in terms of revolutions per minute for various wheel diameters is shown in the following table of approximate speeds:

| Mean diameter of | mm. | 50 | 100 | 150 | 200 | 250 | 300 |
wheel working face	inches	2	4	6	8	10	12
10 metres per sec. or 2,000 ft. per min.	R.P.M. 4,000	2,000	1,330	960	750	630	
20 metres per sec. or 4,000 ft. per min.	R.P.M. 8,000	4,000	2,660	1,920	1,500	1,260	
30 metres per sec. or 6,000 ft. per min.	R.P.M. 12,000	6,000	3,990	2,880	2,250	1,890	

e. Machine condition—for freehand grinding, only the state of the wheel spindle is in question, but, on machines employing table or wheel head movements, the state of the slides and feed mechanism is also important.
f. Working conditions—traverse speed to be used, depth of cut required, type of coolant.

The final choice must depend on the sum of all of these factors, but the following guide in terms of wheel characteristics is generally accepted in the field of tool shaping with diamond wheels.

Grit sizes in the range of 85 to 150 mesh are for high rates of stock removal, but produce a coarse surface (probably 10–20 micro-inches). For most applications this must be improved by lapping with finer grit sizes to achieve a satisfactory edge quality. Sizes from about mesh 150–200 provide edges adequate for most machining operations (probably 6–12 micro inches), but are improved by subsequent hand lapping. Wheels containing diamond powder in brackets between 200 and 400 mesh are used for very accurate dimensional requirements, for fine edges (surfaces of say 4–8 micro inches) needed for critical finishing and for very thin edges. Generally, the finer the edge quality the longer will be the tool life. For surface finishes less than 4 or 5 micro inches, diamond grain sizes in the 6 micron range may be required.

Most wheel manufacturers offer a choice of at least two or three, and sometimes more, hardness grades of metal and resin bonds. The harder metal bonds are used for cutting off wheels and for grinding with heavy pressures. Medium hardness bonds, normally of the bronze type, are for most hand and machine grinding operations on tool tips. Softer and 'porous' metal bonds are used for deep cuts where the operation borders on milling characteristics rather than grinding.

Hard resin is recommended for high dimensional accuracy followed by medium grades for most machine grinding as for milling cutter grinding. The field for soft resin grades is for grinding large contact areas and superfine finishes.

Diamond concentration relates to the weight of diamond powder per unit of volume in the diamond impregnated area of the tool. It is generally between one and five carats per cubic centimetre ($16\frac{1}{2}$ and 82 carats per cubic inch) and is referred to by terms such as 'low' (25C or 30C), 'medium' (50C), and 'high' (75C or 100C) within the bracket mentioned, normally 100C is equivalent to 4·4 cts. per cm.[3]. Assuming that the same pressure per particle is required to obtain effective cutting action, it will be clear that the choice of concentration depends on total cutting pressure and the area of contact between work and wheel. The larger areas of contact occur on normal cup wheels when grinding and regrinding lathe and shaper tools. For these, medium or 50 concentration is normally the

AMERICAN DIAMOND WHEEL SHAPE CODES

TO ASS 7413 - 1961

CUP WHEELS

D6A2

DOUBLE CUP WHEELS

D9A3

TAPER CUP WHEELS

D11A2

DISH WHEELS

D12A2

CUTTING DISCS

D1A1R

PERIPHERAL WHEELS

D1A1

INTERNAL GRINDERS

Supplied with or without
spindle. DW. With spindle
D1A8. Without spindle.

FLARING CUP WHEELS

D11V9

Diamond wheel shape codes to ASS 7413–1961; some of the main types used in tungsten carbide tool grinding

maximum required. In the case of small face or line contacts, such as those which occur in milling cutter grinding with flaring cup or saucer wheels and in surface grinding with peripheral wheels, higher concentrations are preferred.

The thickness of the diamond bearing area is referred to as the depth of impregnation. This dimension is usually in the range 1 to 5 mm. ($\frac{1}{16}$ to $\frac{1}{4}$ in.), but in carbide grinding the lower half of this bracket is usually specified.

The cost of manufacture of a diamond wheel is not much influenced either by diamond concentration or depth of impregnation, but the final selling price is affected considerably by the cost of the diamond content which in turn does depend on these two factors. From the point of view of ultimate economy on continuing work, the greater depths of impregnation are best. The choice of concentration depends on the application and it does not follow that a higher diamond content resulting from this factor will prove to be a long term saving.

The wheel specification having been determined by weighing all these factors, the following conditions should be observed in its use.

The machine should be maintained in good condition not only as regards the grinding spindle but also the flange against which the wheel locates. This assembly should not only be true but also be in static and dynamic balance. It is recommended that the diamond wheel be mounted on its own arbor and remain there throughout its life. The wheel periphery should be true within 0·0127 mm. (0·0005 in.). Conditions leading to vibration in use accelerate wheel wear and may also necessitate expensive retruing operations. Feed mechanisms should be checked regularly to avoid accidentally applied excessive cuts being taken with consequential wheel damage. Where the work is clamped or otherwise held rigidly, the arrangements should be as foolproof as possible to guard against the same contingency.

A coolant supply is not always possible as, for example, in the case of milling cutter grinding with resin bonded wheels, but, where it can be used, considerable wheel economies result. Experimentally, it has been shown that, under otherwise similar conditions, wheel cost per unit of carbide removed is of the order of 7 for dry grinding, as compared to 3 for a wick applied coolant and 2 for a really copious flood coolant. Mist coolant can be usefully employed where other methods are not acceptable. The foregoing relates to resin bonded wheels. Metal bonds must always be used with flood coolant.

Whilst, in some cases, vitrified bond diamond wheels are used for grinding steel tool shanks and carbide tips simultaneously, it is recommended that, wherever possible, the steel should be undercut with an aluminium oxide grit abrasive wheel such as, say, a 60K cup wheel. If the tip has been badly damaged, it is sometimes more economical to rough grind before applying the diamond wheel. A silicon carbide cup wheel about 60J is suitable. If the amount to be removed in the roughing operation is not excessive, however, medium hardness metal bond diamond wheels 85/100 grit are recommended for freehand applications or a softer metal bond and the same grit size for machine controlled grinding.

Normally, only light pressures are needed for the wheels to function properly and premature glazing is avoided. Heavy pressures are not only detrimental to the diamond wheel but also to the carbide insert being ground. Local overheating may result which, in certain cases, may also result in surface fissures and consequent premature failure of the tool. If the pores of the wheel do become loaded with the carbide cuttings, the abrasive properties of the surface can be restored by light dressing with a soft abrasive stick.

The foregoing is still generally true, but the advent of polyimide resins has resulted in resin bond diamond wheels being designed specifically for heavy cuts under flood coolant conditions. These are particularly applicable to mass production operations such as the 'cam grinding' of 'throw-away' tungsten carbide tool tips.

There have also been considerable developments in other diamond wheel characteristics in the last few years.

When considering carbide grinding, it is necessary to define the material to be ground. These are cemented carbides, usually referred to as tungsten carbide, although this material is only the major constituent of the final hard metal. Sintered carbides consist of small hard carbide particles which range in size from $\frac{1}{2}$ micron to 10 microns. These are bonded or 'cemented' together with a matrix of a tougher metal, normally cobalt.

Varying the proportions of the carbide particles and bonding metal, adding alloying elements and changing the grain size of the carbide particles can produce a considerable range of hardness values and physical properties in the final product.

First marketed in 1927 by the Krupps factory in Germany, the early cemented carbides were known by the trade name 'Widia'. This material had been developed by K. Schroter in an attempt to improve the materials for wire drawing dies. The product at that time consisted of tungsten carbide particles mixed with 6% cobalt and sintered at about 1,600 degrees centigrade.

At present carbides of many other metals, including titanium, tantalum, niobium, chromium and vanadium are used, each bonded with cobalt while, mainly in America, a form of carbide is used consisting of titanium carbide having nickel/molybdenum as the bonding material. The introduction of this new hard material caused immediate problems in shaping and grinding. Grinding with conventional abrasive wheels was found to be a costly and technically unsatisfactory method and so the natural step was to attempt it with diamond. As in many other cases it was at this moment that an industry so small as to be insignificant had tremendous potential and opportunities created for it by the technical advancement of another.

The use of diamond to grind hard materials had been known for centuries and, as far back as 1824, diamond bonded wheels were used by Pritchard to produce diamond microscope lenses. These wheels were, in fact, made by hammering diamond particles into iron bodies. By the middle of the century, diamond wheels of this single layer type were in fairly common use and it is known that, to produce small diamond wheels, various grain sizes of diamond were hammered into coins made of copper.

As the first recorded use of diamond impregnated wheels dates from 1932, it is highly probable that the early carbides were ground with the 'hammered' type of diamond wheels mentioned above. Impregnated diamond wheels first became available in 1932. These were resin bonded wheels. The earliest types available were developed and patented by Mr. L. E. Van Moppes and Mr. A. C. Wickman in England. These original 'Spedia' wheels were offered in coarse, medium and fine grain sizes only.

Although more free cutting and versatile than metal bonded products, resinoid wheels are more easily damaged by physical blows or overheating of the bond caused by abuse during working.

Although resin bonded wheels were the first impregnated type marketed, the possibilities of metal bonded diamond wheels had been known for some time. In 1883, Paulin Gay, of Paris, filed a patent describing a method of manufacturing abrasive materials by incorporating quartz, emery or other gemmiferous substances in a metal or metal alloy matrix.

Many patents followed citing various metals and techniques, mostly involving cold pressing and sintering or infiltration methods. These techniques are still in use, but the wheels produced have a tendency to be erratic in performance and unreliable from a repeatability aspect.

The development of a hot pressed 'fully densified' metal bonded wheel was the work of a Belgian, Pierre Neven, during the 1930's. Due to the impending war in Europe, his staff and the machinery moved to England in 1939 where work was continued at Gloucester. This company became Impregnated Diamond Products Ltd. and the trade name 'Neven' is still used in conjunction with the 'UNI' of the parent company, Universal Grinding Ltd.

Metal bonded wheels are more durable than resin bonded wheels but are usually slower cutting. They are normally used with flood coolant to reduce the heat generated during grinding, as overheating can crack the carbide.

The wheels are used for cylindrical, centreless, surface and internal grinding, also for slitting carbide, but the major application in this field is the off-hand grinding of tungsten carbide tipped turning tools.

Having produced resinoid and metal bonded diamond wheels capable of grinding carbide, it then fell to the manufacturers of diamond wheels to improve the efficiency of the product. In general terms the demand was, and still is, for diamond wheels which grind faster, cooler and give a higher efficiency from the diamond. To achieve this, it is desirable to know how the diamond wheel works.

It has been stated by Chalkley and Thomas that, when considering the ideal wheel, the following circumstances prevail:

'The ideal grinding action can be described as one that operates at the desired cutting rate at which the diamond wear and bond wear proceed evenly and equally.

'An equilibrium surface state is set up such that, at a steady rate of debris production, the clearance between the diamond "face" (the surface represented by the protruding diamond points) and the bond "face" will allow for the escape of the debris and the correct degree of wear of the bond matrix. At a certain stage in the wear of a diamond particle it will be levered out of its socket, but fresh diamond points will be uncovered as the matrix wears and, overall, an equilibrium condition exists.

'In other words, the conditions enable the wheel to become "self-dressing", and this must be the basic aim in designing diamond wheels for continuous and trouble-free use. Too great a change in the conditions can cause this state of surface equilibrium to alter, leading to premature loss of diamond (and to short wheel life) or to overlong retention of blunted diamonds (and a hard grinding action requiring a dressing action on the wheel to renew its surface).'

Premature diamond loss from the bond was very much the case with early resin bonded diamond wheels. The natural diamond being used was extremely tough and tended to be regular in shape unless specially selected. The individual faces of the diamond were also quite smooth.

This meant that the physical grip of the resin on the diamond left much to be desired. When blunting of the diamond point took place, the increase in pressure on the socket usually caused the diamond to be pulled out.

An additional problem was, and is, that, in the commonly used phenol formaldehyde resin, the physical properties of the resin start to deteriorate if the temperature rises over 230 degrees centigrade and this also allows the diamond particle to be more easily pulled out of the bonding. Excessively hard working of a resin wheel can cause extremes of temperature at the grinding face. The resin then becomes burnt or 'charred'. In this condition the diamond wheel wear rate is extremely high. A major step forward was made in 1957 when it was announced that synthetic diamond, first produced in 1955, was commercially available.

The first synthetic diamond was most suitable for use in resin bonded wheels, possibly more by accident than design. The physical appearance did little to inspire confidence. In attempting to describe the product in non-technical terms, it was only possible to say that it looked like small, variously coloured, irregular shaped pieces of coke. However, carbide grinding trials immediately showed the superiority of the new diamond over its natural counterpart. The characteristics which gave synthetic diamond its superiority in this application were:

1. Irregularity of shape and coke-like texture.
2. Friability.

The irregular shape allowed the resin to give a better grip on the diamond crystal, holding it in the bond for longer periods. This tendency was also enhanced by the friability of the diamond.

When grinding, the diamond becomes blunted or 'glazed'. Friable diamond has the property of fracturing under pressure which allows the blunted portion to break away. In practice, this reduces the tendency for the diamond to be pulled from the socket, and leaves a new sharp point to continue working.

Further increases in the performance of resin bonded wheels have been achieved by the development of 'metal clad' or 'armoured' diamonds. These are synthetic diamonds to which a metal coating has been added, usually by the electroless deposition process. For wet grinding the diamond recommended is nickel coated. The coating is 55% of the total weight and the thickness of coating obviously increases the effective particle size. The coating on a 150 grade diamond is approximately ·013 mm. (·0005 in.) thick.

For dry grinding the diamond recommended is more friable and is coated with a composite material, mainly copper. The weight of the metal coating is 50% of the total weight and, again, the coating thickness gives a larger particle size. In use the coated diamond of both type has given significant increases in performance for the following reasons:

1. The increase in particle size and surface area allows the resin to achieve a better grip on the particle. This is also assisted by the fact that metal/resin adhesion is normally better than diamond/resin adhesion.
2. The coating forms an envelope around the diamond. Should fragmentation of the diamond occur, the broken particles are likely to be held by the coating and so retained in the wheel to continue working.
3. The primary feature claimed by the diamond manufacturers is that the cladding acts as a heat sink. This helps the resin retain its physical properties by dissipating the heat generated at the grinding point more efficiently.

It is known by diamond manufacturers and wheel makers that

F

wheels using coated diamond need more power to drive them. This can be a disadvantage on lower powered machines. There are also indications that coated diamonds are less suitable than uncoated synthetic diamond on applications where braze material is encountered.

The position at present is that coated diamonds give greater efficiencies in many carbide grinding applications. This has been established by testing. There appears to be no reason why the different coatings should give significantly different results. Much work needs to be done to establish where performances are different and why.

The advent of synthetic diamonds suitable for use in metal bonded wheels had understandably less impact in the carbide grinding field than that caused by the original type.

The synthetic diamond produced for metal bonded wheels needed to be tougher to match the harder characteristics of the metal bonds. This meant that, although much improved in shape and physical characteristics, the synthetic diamond, to some extent, resembled its natural counterpart. It did, however, show improvements over natural diamond for many applications and is used extensively in plain cup wheels.

Another significant development is the metal/resin combination bond recently patented by Impregnated Diamond Products Ltd., of England, and sold under the registered trade name 'Resimet'. In this formulation the diamonds are first firmly held in a porous metal structure produced by cold compacting and sintering technique. This skeleton is then infiltrated with resin which strengthens and improves the resilience of the diamond bearing area. The resulting product has many of the virtues of both metal and resin bonds. It shows to particular advantage in cases where dry grinding cannot be avoided.

One factor which is sometimes not given sufficient attention when considering carbide grinding efficiency is the effect of coolant. Grinding tests by Hughes showed remarkable results when testing six soluble oil coolants against plain water. The wheels were resinoid peripheral wheels containing De Beers' synthetic diamond. Two diamond types were used, unclad synthetic diamond and nickel coated synthetic diamond, in three grain sizes. The operation was surface grinding carbide.

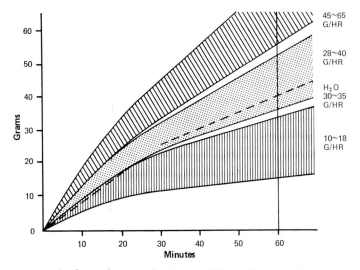

Coolant selection related to carbide stock removal:
Diagonal shading—Neat oils
Spotted shading —Finely dispersed soluble oils
Vertical shading —Soluble oils at normal dilutions

From the results it was apparent that, with the unclad diamond, the use of water as a coolant gave a lower performance efficiency. However, when using nickel coated diamonds, water became the second most efficient coolant for the same operation. An explanation of why this happened was not forthcoming. Selection of the correct coolant is also important when grinding carbide with metal bonded wheels. This was shown by Chalkley who compared the different grinding rates (grams/hr.) of a metal bonded plain cup wheel in a plunge grinding experiment. The test simulated off-hand tool tip grinding and the carbide was oscillated against the wheel face at a fixed pressure.

Various coolants were used on this operation. The results showed that soluble oils at normal dilutions reduced the grinding rate, measured in grams of carbide removed per hour, compared with water. The finely dispersed soluble oils were about equivalent to water. This indicated that they were useful merely as corrosion inhibitors.

The most effective coolants on this operation were neat oils. These ranged from paraffins to heavy oils. The extreme viscosity types gave performances at the lower end of the neat oil band. The best performances were achieved by the middle viscosity oils which in some cases doubled the grinding rate achieved using water.

These two sets of results show that the use of a suitable coolant can drastically alter both the speed of working and life of diamond wheels. Obviously, there is a great deal of work to do in this field, both by the coolant manufacturers and diamond wheel makers. If, and when, this work is carried out, the results could lead to considerable increases in carbide grinding efficiency.

DIAMOND FORM GRINDING IN CARBIDE TOOL DIE MAKING

Diamond grinding plays an important part in the production of all forms of carbide dies. Press tools for razor blade manufacture, drawing dies for wire, coining dies, heading dies for screws, bolts and rivets. As in tool grinding, peripheral and various types of cup wheels are used as well as internal grinders and slitting discs, but, in this field, precision form grinding is also of great importance. In its simplest form, this profile grinding can be undertaken with 'rolled in' preformed diamond wheels, as described in outline in Chapter 2.

The method employed by Toolmasters (Manufacturing) Ltd., of Hillingdon Heath, England, to make such wheels was developed to produce extremely accurate press tools such as lamination dies for the electrical industry. It was developed with the aid of Diaform pantograph truing equipment. It is claimed that accuracies of less than ± 0.0125 mm. ($\cdot 0005$ in.) can be achieved, thus permitting complete interchangeability of ground details. They quote, as an example, a form of 6 mm. ($\cdot 25$ in.) wide and 4·5 mm. ($\frac{3}{16}$ in.) deep on a 125 mm. (5 in.) diameter wheel. This would require about 3 carats of diamond powder. For roughing: mesh 100/120 would be recommended, and for finishing: 170/200. The sequence of operations would be:

1. A carbon disc is formed to rough out by normal electro-erosion method. To do this, the normal diamond truing

chisel on a Diaform is replaced with a diamond turning tool having the same cutting profile as the chisel.

2. Using a similar head mounted Diaform set-up on the surface grinder, form an aloxite wheel with the reverse form to that required on the workpiece.
3. Mount a steel roller on a small hand operated or motorised workhead which is in turn located square against the back plate of the magnetic chuck.
4. Use the formed wheel to grind two identical forms in the steel roller. The first form is to be used for initial rolling and the second for finish rolling.

> *Note:* These rollers should be made of H.S.S. or H.C.+I.C. (NEOR KE 970) and must be hardened to at least 63C Rockwell.

5. Remove the aloxite wheel and replace with a brass disc.
6. Remove the standard Diatipt chisels from the Diaform and replace with a carbide tipped turning tool for roughing and a Diatipt turning tool for finishing as in operation 1.
7. Using the same template as for the truing operation, machine the brass disc to the same profile. The latter is then compared with that on the roller to ensure accurate mating.
8. Clean the formed profile on the brass disc and coat evenly with an adhesive.
9. Brush the required grade of Diadust evenly over the profile which is to be used to form grind the carbide.
10. Use the first formed roller in contact with the Diadust covered brass disc with sufficient pressure to ensure that the Diadust is partly forced into the brass.
11. Lightly brush the brass disc with a solvent to remove the adhesive. The Diadust should have been sufficiently pressed into the brass not to be removed at the same time.
12. The second formed roller is then used to complete the final rolling in of the Diadust and to produce the required degree of accuracy.
13. Remove the fixture carrying the steel roller.
14. Locate components on the magnetic chuck and use the formed diamond coated disc to finish grind the form required.

To obtain optimum accuracy, the brass disc should not be

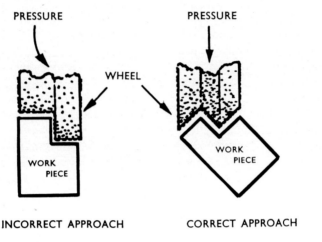

INCORRECT APPROACH   CORRECT APPROACH

Grinding operation—application of pressure when using a 'rolled-in' diamond wheel

removed from the machine until the grinding operation is completed. It should run at about 25–30 metres per seond (5,000–6,000 surface feet per minute) and a copious supply of coolant must be used. The wheel should be periodically cleaned with a brush dipped in paraffin.

Limitations: It is obviously not practicable to roll a vertical face. It is also necessary to maintain as near as possible equal pressure on opposing surfaces. This ensures positive location between the roller and the brass disc. As an example, if a square step is to be formed it is recommended that this should be approached at an angle of 45°. The form on the wheel would then be a 'V', which is an ideal shape.

Wheels of this type are often used to finish grind after roughing by the electro-erosion method.

For more sophisticated work and longer runs, commercially made wheels are now offered and utilise the method described in British patent specification 1,044,784. They are supplied ready for use and are available in diameters 75–200 mm. (3–8 in.), in widths up to 25 mm. (1 in.), for form depths up to 12 mm. ($\frac{1}{2}$ in.). They are recommended for use at 25–30 metres per second (approximately 5,000–6,000 surface feet per minute), with a flood coolant.

These carbide form grinding methods are both of the 'plunge grinding' type. The alternative is to use a vee form diamond wheel of predetermined radius and angle, and which, in turn, traces a path controlled by a pantograph/template or similar mechanism. The latter can be in the form of a complete machine, such as the Studer, Sheffield, Wickman and PeTeWe, or a unit which can be added to an existing surface grinder or similar basic machine.

One of these is the 'Cardiaform', which provides a reciprocating head for the vee wheel. This unit is attached to a Model 5 Diaform unit and can be used either on an existing surface grinder or on a purpose made base. This pantograph unit is available in 10:1 or 5:1 ratio and both employ a 75 mm. (3 in.) vee form wheel having a profile to suit the workpiece form. This wheel can be used on forms up to 25 mm. (1 in.) × 12 mm. ($\frac{1}{2}$ in.) in the case of the 10:1 pantograph, and 50 mm. (2 in.) × 25 mm. (1 in.) in the 5:1.

For heavier form grinding operations, the 'Copiform' employs the normal surface grinder spindle to carry a larger vee form diamond wheel and the basic machine movements to position the workpiece. The additional movements are provided by a 1:1 templete controlled mechanism and a built-in reciprocating motion infinitely variable in speed and adjustable for stroke length up to 150 mm. (6 in.). The indicator-stylus unit is mounted on the wheelhead of the grinder, and the base unit is designed to be adaptable to the table of most standard horizontal spindle surface grinders. Above the base casting is a cradle, fixed to the base at each end so that it pivots to a limited degree about its length.

The cradle carries the cylindrical ways on which the work holding fixture reciprocates. The sequence of operations is generally:

1. Select a diamond wheel having a radius less than the smallest radius required on the job.
2. Make a template of the required profile.
3. Set up a piece of graphite or plastic material in the vice on the Copiform table. This should be approximately 10 mm. thick.
4. Pulnge the diamond wheel into the graphite to a depth suitable for the form. The Copiform reciprocating mechanism should be used and care taken that the basic grinder crossfeed is not moved.

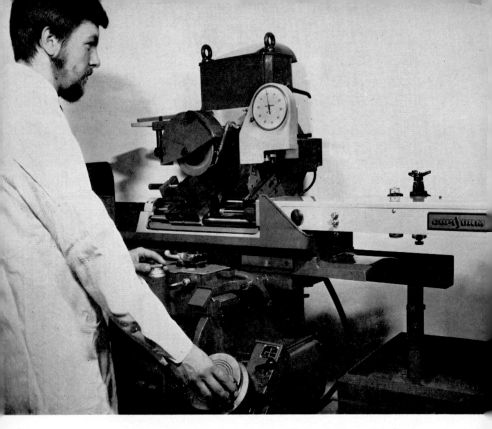

Vee form diamond wheel mounted on surface grinder fitted with COPIFORM device for profile grinding tungsten carbide (Diaform Ltd.)

5. Note the reading on the down-feed handwheel.
6. Move the grinding machine table so that the ground slot is under the stylus pin.
7. Use the movements at the back of the indicator stylus unit to position the blade of the stylus pin central in the slot.
8. Lock the indicator unit slides and lift the wheelhead clear of the graphite.
9. Treat the graphite with a wax release agent, form a pocket around the stylus blade and fill with quick setting epoxy resin.
10. The stylus thus formed is a replica of the form on the diamond wheel.
11. Set up the carbide workpiece in the Copiform vice.

12. Plunge grind the form in steps using the Copiform traverse.
13. Finish grind the whole profile following the template with the stylus and maintaining the indicator at zero.

The following case history is quoted by Toolmasters (Manufacturing) Ltd., of Hillingdon Heath, England:

Toolmasters used the Copiform to grind the stator forming sections which were part of a progression lamination tool manufactured in carbide. The carbide was purchased in a pre-sintered shape giving an approximate profile to that finally required. The templates to make the punch shape were made and the die templates were matched from these using plastic metal.

The form on the centre die section was accomplished in 25 hours' grinding and 74 grams of carbide were removed. The outer die sections were each produced in 20 hours with the removal of 127 grams of carbide. The complete form on the punches, to match with the dies, was accomplished in 40 hours for each piece, with the removal of 100 grams of carbide from each section.

The required cutting clearance between punch and die was 0·025 mm. and, when inspected, the actual overall tolerance achieved was 0·010 mm. The total weight of carbide removed was 554 grams, and the complete work was carried out using a single electroplated diamond wheel with a complete radius of 2·5 mm. The stylus was remade twice to eliminate any inaccuracies caused by wheel wear, but, in the final analysis, it was discovered that this was not really essential.

Both the plunge and pantograph methods are used to produce the profiles on form tools for turning and milling where appropriate.

In the case of wire, bar, tube and similar drawing dies, a greater variety of diamond using techniques are employed. In the green state (unsintered), diamond tools are used to pre-form by drilling, reaming and slicing. These operations are generally carried out with surface coated electro-metallic diamond tools, but turning and boring operations also employ normal diamond tipped cutting tools.

After sintering, both drawing dies and such items as heading dies may also be machined with diamond tipped boring tools. These operations are followed by conventional grinding with both resin and metal bond diamond wheels.

The final operations of smoothing and polishing are carried out with diamond powder which is either mixed with a carrier by the user or purchased as a commercially available lapping compound. The grades usually employed are in the scale from 8/25 micron down to 0/2 micron and for which the following are some notes on recommended practice:

Guidance notes for the general use of lapping compound: A specific working procedure can only be determined for each job when all the details are known and often only after some preliminary trials. The following notes, however, are applicable to most general work:

a. Clean the work thoroughly before starting and between stages with clean rags or paper tissue to prevent carryover of coarse grades to fine grades.
b. Use a separate lap for each grade or the work may be spoiled.
c. Apply compound to the lap when using a hand lap, but to the work when using a bob.
d. The choice of starting grade and type of lap, e.g. metal, wood or felt, depends upon the condition of the work and the amount of stock to be removed. For the quick removal of stock or deep scratches, a hard lap and a coarse compound are required. A good general purpose starting combination for removing deep scratches would be a grade such as Dialap 25/5 or 40/5 with a hardwood stick or a bob.
e. Apply a little compound and rub the work area with the lap, applying light pressure. The compound will blacken with cuttings; a little more compound may be added if necessary. When the lap becomes sticky, the work can be lubricated with lapping fluid.
f. After a few minutes, clean the work thoroughly with a clean rag or paper tissue. If the operation is complete, the area being lapped will be evenly abraded and free from the original work marks. If necessary, repeat the operation with the same grade.
g. Take a softer lap and a finer compound, e.g. 6/3 or 3/2, and apply as before, continuing to use lapping fluid.

h. Operation 'g' will produce a good general purpose polish. For a fine finish, use one of the grades 3/2 to $\frac{1}{4}$/1.

Carbide rolls, used to produce ribbon from beryllium silver-clad copper and other resistance wires, are also produced by a similar sequence of operations. The diameters, key way and side faces are pre-ground with metal bond wheels, followed by mirror finishing on a resin wheel and finally polished with 1 micron diamond powder.

Within the context of the application of diamond to tool and die making, it should also be remembered that diamond, as a loose abrasive and in the form of grinding wheels, is also widely used in the production of diamond tools and wire drawing dies.

ELECTROLYTIC GRINDING OF CARBIDE

Because of the high costs of grinding carbide with diamond wheels, many efforts have been made to develop cheaper processes. The most promising of these is electrolytic grinding which was a development of electrical discharge machining. An electrolytic grinding machine was built at Gloucester in 1950/51 by Sparcatron Ltd. A patent was filed in 1951 covering the use of a tool electrode containing particles of insulating material which projected from the surface of the tool.

These particles, which could be diamond, would maintain a gap between the tool electrode and the workpiece to prevent a short circuit and enable erosion of the workpiece surface to occur. Development of the process was taking place in many countries, principally America, but the machines were rather crude and development was slow until the early 1960's. The potential of the process for off-hand grinding of carbides was by this time becoming widely realised and several machines appeared on the market including the Sparcatron electrolytic off-hand grinder. This was shortly superseded by the Contelyt range of machines. In very basic terms the process operates on the principles of an electric cell. In this case the revolving diamond wheel is the cathode and the carbide work-piece is the anode. Passage of a direct current, normally around 12 volts, is made possible by the flow of an electrolyte between the wheel and workpiece. Protrusion of the non-conductive diamonds

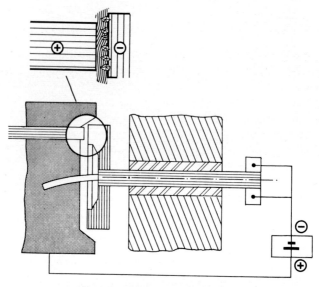

Electrolytic grinding with a diamond wheel

from the wheel face insulates the wheel face from the workpiece. The electric circuit is produced by connecting the positive lead from the D.C. supply to the grinding table and the negative lead to a brush assembly on the wheel spindle.

The spindle is insulated from the remainder of the machine. In operation, when the circuit is completed by the electrolyte flow between the wheel and workpiece, anodic oxidation takes place on the face of the workpiece. This oxide would become a barrier to the current flow and the process would eventually stop, but it is being continually swept away by the diamond particles.

The amount of mechanical grinding in the process is relatively small and, as the diamond wheel produces its best performance in a 'bedded in' or glazed condition, considerable increases in diamond wheel life can be achieved. The amount of mechanical grinding will vary with the wheel/workpiece pressure, but an increase in diamond wheel life of between 2 and 8 times can be achieved compared with conventional grinding. Such an increase is not the only advantage of the electrolytic process. Other advantages are:

1. Cool grinding—no heat cracks in workpiece.
2. Stress free surface on workpiece—longer tool life.
3. Carbide and steel shank ground without difficulty.
4. Good surface finish with faster grinding rate.
5. Lower pressures of operation—less operator fatigue.

Considering the advantages and eventual savings that can be made by using electrolytic grinding methods for carbide off-hand grinding, it seems that the only disadvantage, and the reason for its slowness in being accepted, is the high initial cost of the machine.

The electrolytic process is being used on vertical spindle machines for carbide surface grinding and for the production of throw-away tips. An electrolytic tool and cutter grinding machine is also available. It is possible to do electrolytic form grinding with electroplated diamond wheels and there has been a recent development in the production of close tolerance forms by electrolytic grinding. In this case the formed wheel being used is a reverse plated diamond roller which has had the nickel bonding etched back from the top level of the diamonds to give a gap through which the electrolyte can flow. It is possible to produce more accurate wheel forms with 'reverse plating methods' than with conventional direct plating on to metal blanks. Limits of down to ·0075 mm. (·0003 in.) can be achieved with reverse plated rollers and this accuracy is reflected in the finish ground article.

At present, thread forms have been produced with radii of ·25 mm. (·011 in.) and fairly high grinding rates have been achieved. This is still in the experimental stage and different grain sizes are being tried. It is felt that the normal system of using the largest grain size possible may not produce the most efficient grinding conditions in this case.

In some cases where electrolytic methods were applied to form grinding, difficulty was encountered in forming and reforming the special diamond wheels developed. This was finally overcome by mounting an electro-deposited vee form wheel on a Diaform pantograph unit and providing an air motor drive. This arrangement proved adequate to form and re-form the Copperdyne wheels.

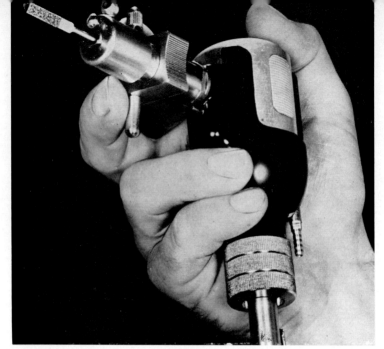

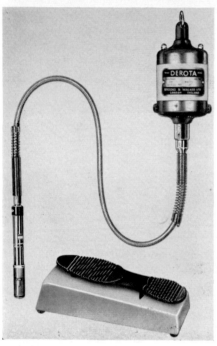

Power tool unit and
alternative heads for use in
diamond lapping. The straight
and contra-angle handpieces
are for rotary applications
and the reciprocating
head for situations where
this action is preferable
(Taylor Gauge & Tool Ltd.)

FINISHING OPERATIONS ON TUNGSTEN CARBIDE
AND CERAMIC TOOLS AND DIES

Where the shape permits and the surface finish requirements demand, impregnated hand laps and lapping compound are used. Much of this work is in the form of manual operation, albeit sometimes power assisted by the use of such power units as the reciprocating head Diprofil and the rotating Derota or similar equipment. As an indication of the factors involved in diamond lapping, however, the following conditions are quoted by Du Pont in a study of the parameters of lapping:

Test Piece:	C–2 Carbide as used for machining cast iron and non-ferrous metals. Good toughness and high wear resistance.
Machine:	Crane 300 mm. (12 in.) Lapmaster.
Lapping plate:	Cast iron with spiral grooves.
Lap speed:	60 r.p.m.
Pressure:	0·365 kg./cm.^{2} (5·2 p.s.i.).
Slurry concentration:	40 cts. per litre.
Dispensing rate:	20 drops per minute.

The stock removal rates on the C2 samples, having an area of 10·90 cm.^{2} (1·69 sq. in.), according to diamond particle size were:

Particle size (micron)	6		15		30	
	Du Pont synthetic diamond	Natural diamond	Du Pont synthetic diamond	Natural diamond	Du Pont synthetic diamond	Natural diamond
Stock removal Rate per hour over the quoted area	·075 mm. ·003 in.	·05 mm. ·002 in.	0·3 mm. ·012 in.	0·23 mm. ·009 in.	·45 mm. ·018 in.	·275 mm. ·011 in.
Surface/finish (micro inch AA)	2	2	4	4	7	6

Du Pont synthetic diamond gives a faster stock removal rate than natural diamond of the same grade, but the surface finishes grade for grade are very similar.

TOOL AND DIE STEEL GRINDING AND
LAPPING WITH DIAMOND

In normal production terms, diamond is generally only a factor in the sense of grinding ferrous metals in so far as it is used to form, true and dress conventional silicon carbide or aluminium oxide grinding wheels used in such operations.

However, diamond lapping compound is often used in steel mould and die finishing, and, recently, grinding wheels containing synthetic diamond and cubic boron nitride have proved to be economically justified in certain grinding operations on some alloy steels.

In the case of coining dies, they are first 'struck' from master working punches and then hardened and tempered. After one or two intermediate operations, diamond lapping compound is used, in a range from about 25 microns down to 1·5 microns, to produce a final finish of the order of 1 micro inch CLA. Standard fluid is applied as the lapping agent and water for cleaning the dies between grades. For the coarser compound grades, cherrywood laps are used, and balsawood for the finer grades. The original change from conventional abrasive (white bauxite emery) resulted in the employment of less time on the operation and a better finish on the coins.

Similar applications of diamond lapping compounds occur in hardened steel dies used in the injection moulding of plastics. The high mirror finish, achieved by finish lapping with diamond compound, is necessary not only to ensure the required surface finish on the ultimate component, but also to ensure its immediate release from the mould in the course of production.

Recently, a great deal of publicity has been devoted to the application of diamond and cubic boron nitride abrasive wheels to the grinding of alloy steels. So far it has been shown that such wheels can perform a number of operations in this field, but there are many less where an economic justification has been proved.

Where the economics have been proved, the material has been of the high speed steel or tool steel and case-hardening steels, with hardness values of the order of HRC60. The operations have been carried out on machines of greater strength and power than would normally be employed for comparable operations using more conventional abrasives. The operations, themselves, have generally been of a very high degree of form and dimensional accuracy and some internal grinding under toolroom conditions or fluting.

Cases have been quoted of considerable savings on machine tool bed grinding. In one case a reduction in time from 1 hour to 9 minutes was reported in the grinding of a cast iron lathe bed. The comparison was between a conventional silicon carbide wheel and a flaring cup wheel containing DXDA–MC metal clad synthetic diamond. The resulting finish of 0·5 micron (20 micro inches) was found satisfactory without further finishing operations.

DIAMOND TRUING TOOLS FOR TOOL AND DIE STEEL GRINDING

Many of the metal removal needs encountered in toolmaking are achieved by precision grinding. The efficiency of the aluminium oxide and silicon carbide grit wheels used depends to a great extent on the diamond truing and dressing devices utilised. In the tool and gauge making field, the predominance of skilled operators and the need for versatility result in the simple single point diamond truer still being the main tool for plain grinding.

The range of abrasive wheel variables is so wide that diamonds in all sizes from say 0·05 to 2 ct. or more can be economically utilised for appropriate wheels. Equally, the alternative shapes to the octahedron: the dodecahedron, cubes, round, triangular, long shapes and cleft or sawn material, all have their uses in this field. Qualities approaching the gem down to near blocky boart can be used according to the refinement, or otherwise, of the operation.

Many attempts have been made to correlate these factors in terms of the best diamond to be used under given circumstances, but so far without producing any universal formula.

Shanks for abrasive wheel truing tools are specified in the following standards:

U.K.:	B.S.2002:1953 (this has now been reissued in metric form as B.S.2002:1973).
U.S.A.:	ASA B67.1—1958 (A.S.T.E./I.D.A.).
West Germany:	DIN 1820—January 1941.
U.S.S.R.:	Gost 607–63 (Multi-point).

G

India: Y5–61 (Railway Board).
Poland: PN62/M59531/2.
Czechoslovakia: CSN 224918.

B.S.2002:1953 lists the wheel variables to be considered in selecting a diamond for wheel truing:

1. Type of abrasive.
2. Grain size.
3. Grade.
4. Type of bond.
5. Diameter and width of face.

The publication also lists the operating variables:

1. Angle of presentation.
2. Wet or dry truing.
3. Depth of cut and rate of feed (traverse).
4. Peripheral speed of wheel.
5. Type of material being ground and degree of finish required.
6. Whether plain or form grinding.
7. Type and general condition of machine.
8. Operator's skill.

From the author's experience, these variables affect diamond selection generally in the following ways:

Type of abrasive: The tougher silicon carbide requires a better quality and a more well defined cutting area than aluminium oxide abrasives.

Grain size: Grain sizes in the normal range of say 60–100 mesh (150 micron) from the point of view of plain truing do not materially affect diamond selection. Grain sizes coarser than 60 require progressively larger diamonds, but generally cheaper qualities are more economical. The cutting area and form are not so important. Conversely, mesh sizes smaller than 100 require progressively more well defined cutting areas and smaller diamonds should be used.

Wheel grade: Soft grades result in relatively slow diamond wear rates. The wear rate increases progressively as the hardness of the bond increases.

Type of bond: A vitrified bond is less critical of diamond truing requirement than resinoid. The latter generally is more economically trued with a good quality diamond having well defined cutting edges.

Wheel diameter and width of face: These factors determine the area of wheel which has to be traversed in one pass of the diamond truer. The larger this area the more diamond bulk is needed to resist the abrasion and heat. This preserves the parallelism of the wheel face as far as possible.

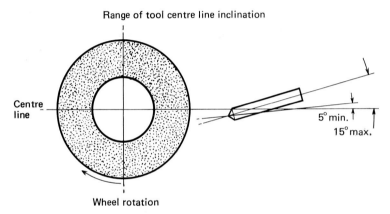

Recommended angular relation between diamond truing tool and abrasive wheel according to B.S.2002:1953

Angle of presentation (drag angle): The British Standard recommends that the point of contact between truing tool and wheel should be below centre-line and the tool centre-line inclined towards the direction of wheel rotation at an angle of 5°–15° from the same wheel centre-line.

Some authorities have recommended that a 'trailing' angle also be established in the direction of traverse. Whilst this may be advantageous as regards the regeneration of the diamond point, it does imply that the truing tool should be in contact with the wheel only in one truing direction. The truing time is thus materially increased and such a loss of machine time is seldom tolerated under production conditions.

Wet or dry truing: Dry dressing is to be avoided wherever possible from the point of view of diamond economy. Most dry dressing and grinding are, fortunately, confined to relatively small wheels such as very accurate form grinding on surface grinders, and, in such cases, small very wear resistant diamonds with well defined cutting points are recommended.

Depth of cut and rate of feed (traverse): Heavy cuts and high rates of traverse are associated with the rougher type of grinding which generally utilises coarser and larger wheels, thus qualifying for larger diamond truers. These can accept the high stock removal rates. One reason for deep cuts is the heavy impregnation of metal in the wheel surface that results from plunge grinding on roughing operations such as automobile crank grinding. In such cases the diamond truer not only has to contend with the abrasive and the bond of the wheel, but also the metal cuttings which have been forced into the wheel in the course of grinding. In many ways this is the most arduous task demanded from abrasive wheel truing tools. Shallow cuts and fine traverse feeds conversely are usually employed for fine finishing work and thus are utilised on finer grain wheels demanding smaller diamonds with well defined cutting faces.

Peripheral speed of wheel: Normally, truing with a diamond tool is carried out with the abrasive wheel revolving at its grinding speed. In the case of very critical truing operations, such as some thread grinding, wheel speed can be reduced for truing and, in doing so, prolong diamond life and improve accuracy.

Type of material being ground and degree of finish required: Ductile materials, such as stainless steel, tend to load the grinding wheel more than normal steels. This results in a greater number of truings or dressings in terms of components ground. The diamond thus wears more rapidly in terms of elapsed time. In order to avoid tools having to be changed too often with consequent loss of production, a better quality diamond is justified for finishing operations on such materials. The degree of finish cannot be determined by the diamond alone. The choice of grinding wheel, the condition and design of the machine, coolant filtration and rate of truing tool traverse all play a part in determining the surface finish obtainable. The relation between these factors and the diamond specification is broadly:

A sharp diamond will make the wheel act as if of a coarser grade.
A larger area of contact between wheel and diamond will improve finish, but reduce the stock removal rating of the wheel. A machine in relatively poor condition may give improved surface finishes if a small area of contact is provided between wheel and diamond, as the stresses set up in the machine will be less.
For fine finishes a copious supply of well filtered coolant is needed and is, incidentally, beneficial to the diamond but does not affect its specification. Varying rates of traverse can be compensated by the diamond to some extent. If the traverse rate is too coarse for the finish required, then a broader diamond contact area should be used. If a coarser finish is required with heavier stock removal, but leaving the traverse rate as before, then a narrower area of contact is needed.

Whether plain or form grinding: Very open forms can be considered as plain grinding, except that the included angle formed between the cutting tip of the diamond and the shoulders of the shank must be small enough to be accommodated within the form when using the control mechanism available. This need usually dictates that the rough diamond must also have a well defined cutting area.

Type and general condition of machine: The normal range of precision grinders, such as surface, universal and plain grinders, does not of itself have particular diamond truer requirements. Because of the necessity of entering a bore, however, internal grinders often have comparatively small diameter spindles or, at least, spindle extensions which are easily deflected. To combat this, the area of contact between diamond truer and abrasive wheel must be kept to a minimum and so reduce the pressure used in truing. Because the work pressure also needs to be minimal, the wheel must also be as free cutting as possible. If simple single point tools are to be used, small octahedrons are to be recommended.

The main component of machine conditions that directly affects diamond selection is vibration. This may be adversely influenced by basic lack of rigidity in the machine design; imbalance or wear in the wheel spindle or the wheel itself; uneven hydraulic or other feeds; or slideways that have been seriously worn. An out of balance workpiece or worn workhead may also result in uneven wheel wear and loading. In most cases one or more of these faults will also result in the workpieces being rejected until the machine is corrected. Where the work is not critical, however, but the machine condition results in rapid diamond wear, a larger diamond of lower quality can be the solution.

The Société Genevoise d'Instruments de Physique make their Vibrometer to measure the magnitude and direction of vibration in machine tools and this can often be used to advantage where bad truing results are suspected to be due to vibration. The vibrations transmitted to the instrument are measured in relation to an inert mass suspended like that of a seismograph. The movements are optically magnified by a microscope mounted on the housing and measured with a graduated eyepiece.

Rule of thumb diamond weight guide

Bearing in mind all the foregoing considerations, many straight-forward plain truing jobs can be economically carried out on the basis of the following guide, assuming the use of a medium quality single diamond truer:

Small wheels in vitrified and resinoid bonds with hardness ratings H–M and grit sizes 40–80, not exceeding 25 mm. (1 in.) wide face:

| Wheel diameter | | Diamond weight range |
millimetres	inches	carats
75	3	$\frac{1}{4}$
150	6	$\frac{1}{2}$
225	9	$\frac{3}{4}$
375	15	1

Larger wheels in the same range of grits and grades, but not limited in width, can be trued with diamonds of size range selected according to the following formula:

For metric wheel sizes: $\dfrac{\text{Diameter} + (2 \times \text{width})}{250}$

OR

In inch wheel sizes:

$$\frac{\text{Diameter} + (2 \times \text{width})}{10}$$

= Diamond weight in metric carats within a tolerance of approximately plus or minus 20%.

Summary of recommendations for users of single point diamond wheel truers:

a. Ensure correct wheel balance and rigidity of mounting.
b. Angle of presentation: the drag angle should be between 5° and 15°.
c. The cutting edge of the diamond should not be above the centre-line. Items b. and c. assist in point regeneration.
d. Depth of cut: in general this should not exceed 0·05 mm. (0·002 in.).
e. Adequacy of coolant system, where used. It is essential that the coolant should be turned on before the diamond makes contact with the wheel. Should the diamond be accidentally overheated it should not be quenched.
f. Adequate machine maintenance.
g. Systematic rotation of tool and regular examination to ensure withdrawal from use in sufficient time to permit economic servicing.
h. Reclassification, after servicing, in the light of the operating variables.

Grain structure as a factor in diamond truing

It is well known, to those experienced in the manipulation of diamonds, that the rate of wear of a given diamond varies according to the direction in which it is attacked. A diamond is most resistant to wear when attacked on the diagonal of a cube face. It is at its least resistant when attacked at 90° to the octahedron edge or rib.

Twinned stones or maacles are very wear resistant at the intersection of the grain structure.

These factors are utilised in a number of ways to improve diamond tool performance.

Scientific investigation and the use of X-rays have made it possible to recognise the best direction in which to orientate diamonds in relation to the work to be performed. Diamond truing tools have been made containing diamond sections presenting these optimum wear faces to the wheel to be trued. Under certain conditions, the life achieved with such tools is claimed to be up to six times that of an average diamond which has not been orientated. In practice this knowledge is not much used in production grinding for several reasons. In order to recognise the correct orientation, comparatively expensive equipment has to be installed. So that a constant area of contact is maintained in relation to the wheel surface to be trued, the diamond content of the tool must be cut from a larger and thus more expensive diamond. The waste which results adds further to the cost. Under ideal conditions the high priced tool may still be economical in terms of a ratio of wheel volume removed per unit of diamond weight or volume; this is not so under normal production grinding conditions. The adverse effects of coarse hard wheels; heavy metal loading; vibration; coarse feeds; lack of constant coolant supply and consequent overheating; deep cuts and general incidence of abuse result in the user normally paying more per truing than is the case with alternative diamond truing methods.

The measurement of diamond wear in terms of wheel volume removed

Several organisations have been associated with attempts to establish an average diamond wear rate in terms of volume of abrasive wheel removed in truing and dressing, notably the U.S. War Production Board research project undertaken for the U.S. Government and the later investigation undertaken by the Production Engineering Research Association in co-operation with the Van Moppes Group, as one of the association members. The former investigation was carried out by H. Whittaker and reported in his WPB Research Project NRC–507, WPB–9. This report quotes wear rates under the conditions of the investigation from 0.3×10^{-5} ct. per cubic inch to 30×10^{-5} ct. per cubic inch with an average of about 6×10^{-5}. The conditions which in practice were considered to give what might be called a mean wear rate were:

Wheel—aluminium oxide 46/60 M vitrified at 5,000 surface feet per min.

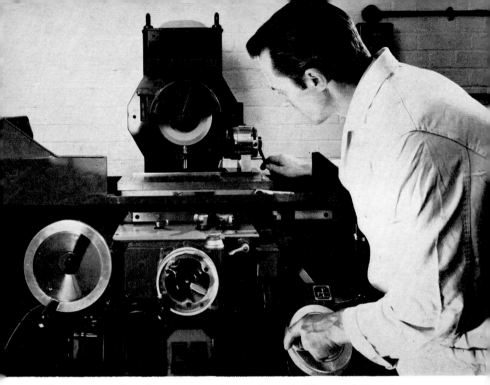

The tangent radius dresser mounted on a Jones & Shipman 540 surface grinder (Diaform Ltd.)

Feed 0·0015 in. per rev. at 0·001 in. depth of cut using a coolant.

On average the report quotes the wear rate of diamonds used in dry dressing as five times that when a coolant is used—varying between three and ten times. Diamonds were found to wear about twice as quickly when applied in their 'soft' grain direction as compared to their 'hard' direction.

The subsequent work added little to the earlier knowledge.

In addition to the operations coming within the scope of plain grinding, there is also a wide application of form grinding in tool-making. In its most elementary form, radius and angle fixtures of established design are used to control the path of the diamond truing tool.

In a more sophisticated form, combining both operations in one device, equipment such as the 'Tanrad' is now marketed commercially. This combination permits radii and flanks to be

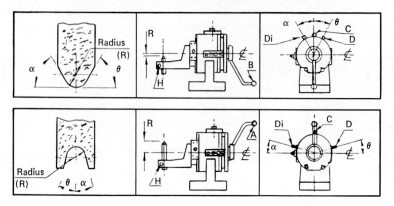

Typical tangent radius dresser settings showing from left to right: alternative wheel forms, diamond settings and stop positions (Diaform Ltd.)

dressed in one continuous movement, thus ensuring a perfect blend. This is often difficult to achieve when using separate devices for radius and angle dressing. The diamond tooling normally used on this equipment is small single point truers for open forms and chisels for forms in which these cannot be accommodated. The chisel profiles are usually of included angles of 40° or 60° and radii of 0·13 mm. (·005 ins.) or 0·25 mm. (·010 ins.).

Where more complex profiles are to be ground, the truing operation can be facilitated with the use of optical devices attached to the grinding machines. This enables the operator to follow the path of the diamond truing tool as it traverses the wheel at a magnification of 10:1. He is also thus aware of any change in the tool profile and can compensate accordingly.

The more generally accepted method, however, employs the pantograph principle to transfer the form from a 5:1 or 10:1 template to the grinding wheel periphery by controlling the path of a diamond chisel tool. Early tools of this type contained relatively large diamonds lapped on all faces with resulting sharp and rather easily damaged working edges. Such diamonds were relatively expensive and, because of their natural shape, difficult to mount securely. These difficulties were largely overcome by the development of diamond setting and grinding techniques that permitted the utilisation of 'naats' or 'twinned' diamonds of flat triangular form. The resulting tools are not only cheaper to produce, but also more wear resistant.

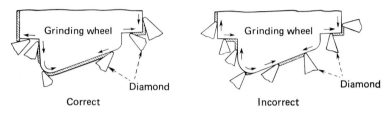

Directional traverse of the chisel diamond is an important factor in accuracy and tool life when using the Diaform pantograph form truing device

The use of such tools has been greatly facilitated by the intro-duction of a number of path control mechanisms of which by far the most widely used is the Diaform attachment. This is basically a pantograph mechanism, but which incorporates a number of patented features, several of which are designed to improve the utilisable accuracy and longevity of the diamond tipped chisel. Later models of this attachment are further improved in this respect by the incorporation of roughing and finishing diamonds on the same work arm to enable both operations to be performed on the same set-up.

Tandem Diatipt chisels form truing a grinding wheel under Diaform control

This method of precision wheel forming provides very material benefits, for example:

a. It requires very much less skill from the operator than earlier methods.

b. It is very flexible as only the template need be changed to true another form. The sixteen portable models can also be transferred at a moment's notice from one surface grinder to another.

c. The template can be easily retained in stock, a form once ground can be repeated at will to the same tolerances as before.

d. The wheel can be so easily re-dressed, the choice of wheel need be influenced only by the needs of the job to be ground. The comparatively hard wheels previously used to form-grind hardened steels were specified to maintain form as long as possible regardless of the metallurgical requirements of the work surfaces and their reaction to over-heating. For hardened steel, wheels formed with the aid of the Diaform need be only soft grades such as G or H and of a grit size appropriate to the form, the finish required and the stock to be removed.

For this type of operation aluminium oxide grit is generally recommended for high speed steel and hardened tool steel. In addition to being the most effective grinding medium, it also results in less diamond wear than a corresponding wheel containing silicon carbide grit. Vitrified bond is recommended. A typical wheel specification for normal form grinding is thus A 100 G.V.

A finer grit size may be necessary for small radii and sharp corners. Using Whitworth thread forms as a guide, the following table indicates the appropriate grit size:

Threads per inch	Wheel grit size
6–12	100–150
12–18	150–180
18–24	180–220

The products in which this wheel forming method plays a part are very diverse and include for example:

Grinding vee ways in machine tool beds.

Helical grooves in re-circulating ball nut shafts.

Circular form tools for electrical components.

Press tools for razor blades.

Straight and involute splines.

Work holders for turbine blades.

Relief compensated form tools.

Jigs on Hauser and Moore jig grinders.

Crushing rolls.

Special drill tip forms on the Rohde & Dorrenberg drill grinder.

Rolls for wire forming.

Cold extrusion dies for hand torch casings.

Press tools for electric shaver, typewriter, calculator, record player, telephone and radio valve components.

Rolling tools for automobile wheels, fenders and grills.

Punches and form tools for nuts, bolts and screws.

In the author's opinion, it is only grinding machines equipped with this type of wheel forming device that can economically use chisel diamonds. Other truing devices invariably use only one or two angles of approach in profile. The result is that the area of contact between diamond and grinding wheel increases rapidly as the diamond wears.

The Diaform attachments incorporate the unique feature of a rocking motion about the centre-line of the chisel radius. This motion is controlled by the operator, and, by using the flank to the maximum, the overall working form of the diamond is maintained for long periods.

It is necessary periodically to adjust the vertical height of the diamond edge in relation to the setting block. This compensates for the overall wear. This is, however, a simple adjustment carried out on the machine by means of the backing-up screw in the diamond block. With this height reset correctly, any malformation of the diamond radius can be located with the 0·0001 in. dial indicator provided. This can then be corrected by the operator concentrating his subsequent use in that area.

With specific relation to the use of chisel truers in the production of formed edge tools, such as milling cutters, broaches, routers and lathe tools, the 'R' series of these pantograph units has been

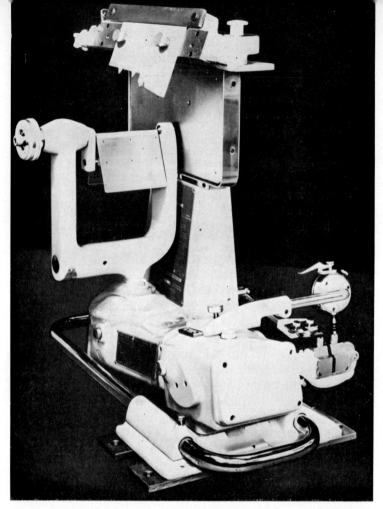

Diaform model ATR showing relief angle compensating device and positioning mechanism for the diamond chisel truers

designed to provide the modified form to compensate for rake and clearance angles. On these the template of the true form can be tilted to compensate for angles of front clearance and top rake and swivelled to compensate for side clearance angles. This produces the modified form on the grinding wheel, which, when used to grind a tool set at the clearance angles, produces the correctly compensated form on the tool edge. Lengthy calculations and the difficulties of making templates with developed ellipses for radii and rectified angles are eliminated. The device provides for front clearance angles up to 30° or side clearance up to 15°.

In addition to the uses of chisel truers on pantograph devices mounted on conventional grinding machines, they are also utilised on a number of specialised machines. For example, the scope of use of the slotting unit on popular jig grinders can be considerably extended and production times improved with such additions.

Model 5/1 Diaform and chisel truers on Rohde & Dorrenberg grinder

Special drill grinders, such as the Rohde & Dorrenberg, are also fitted in the same way.

In production form grinding, crush forming with metal rollers is an accepted method as an alternative to diamond, but it is, perhaps, ironical that, in many cases, diamond chisels on pantograph truers are used in the original grinding of the steel rollers. Because of the relatively short runs encountered in conventional toolmaking, neither crush dressing with metal rollers nor rotary truing with diamond is much used. However, an exception to this, quoted in the technical press, was the production of 'four in one' carbon steel pliers used in machine shops, in the electronics industry and in the home. The operation consisted of form grinding six cutting grooves varying in diameter from 0·69 mm. (0·027 in.) to 2·11 mm. (0·083 in.) and which when assembled had to match in pairs. The operation is carried out on a Gallmeyer & Livingston surface grinder in batches of 18 units. The 300 mm. (12 in.) diameter × 31 mm. ($1\frac{1}{4}$ in.) wide vitrified, aluminium oxide wheel is now dressed with a 56 mm. ($2\frac{1}{4}$ in.) diameter rotary dresser in place of the previous metal crush dresser, with some 15 % saving in production costs.

Another toolmaking operation using rotary truers, in some cases, is the grinding of drill flutes.

DIAMOND DEVELOPMENT AND THE MACHINE TOOL INDUSTRY

Machine tool builders have a twofold interest in diamond tooling. They use it in their own production and are influenced in their design work by the availability of appropriate diamond tooling. Gears, lead screws, beds and headstock spindles are, of course, ground on diamond trued wheels, and the antifriction bearings used rely on similar processes. High precision thread grinders, such as the Matrix, Lindner and Jones & Lamson, all depend on their built-in diamond truing devices. The same can be said of gear grinders, such as the Orcutt, Matrix, Gleason, Reishauer and the Maag with its special compensating device depending on diamond anvils.

Special lathes have been designed for diamond turning, such as the Bryant Symons (England), the Boley (Germany) and Petrazzini (Italy). Other more specialised machines have been developed for commutator turning with diamond tools and slicing germanium and silicon with 'annular diamond saws'. Honing machines, such as the Gehring (Germany) and Jones & Shipman (England), incorporate features based on the characteristics of diamond hones. For the jewellery industry, a wide range of machine tools has been designed, mainly in Switzerland and Germany, to utilise advantages of diamond machining watch parts, rings, cuff-links, bracelets and similar items. This range is described in more detail in Chapter 10.

More recently, makers of grinding machines for mass production precision form grinding have been influenced by the availability of rotary diamond truers and, in some cases, have patented various aspects of drive units incorporated in their designs. The advent of high speed grinding is also increasing interest in rotary truers not only for form grinding but also as a traverse unit for plain grinding.

The present interest in the use of grinding wheel surface speeds of rather more than double the conventional 25/30 metres per second does not in itself impose new problems on the truing equipment supplier. It does, however, intensify the problems which existed before, and which can be summarised:

1. Justification of initial investment and subsequent truing tool costs per final component.
2. To minimise machine down time during truing and in adjusting or replacing the truing device.
3. To maintain truing tool dimensional accuracy for the maximum time without adjustment in order to sustain wheel geometry.
4. To provide maximum consistency in contact area between truing tool and grinding wheel, and thus maintain stock removal and work finish factors of the abrasive wheel at the required levels.
5. To have sufficient wear resistance to minimise the effect of varying degrees of wheel loading.

Single point dressers usually satisfy the first requirement, but high speed grinding wheels adversely affect the other four factors in terms of elapsed time.

Their performance, however, can be improved by the use of indexing tool-holders. Multi diamond truers suffer from the same disadvantages.

Some improvement is achieved by the use of blade truers or with

H

stationary powder impregnated tools. The greater area consistency achieved with this tool, however, is generally at the cost of rather rapid longitudinal wear, which on wide wheels may result in taper, especially in heavily loaded wheels.

Many high speed production grinding machines have been designed primarily for form grinding, and these designs often include the use of rotary truers mounted on drive units incorporated in the machine design.

These rotary truers provide a consistent line contact with the abrasive wheel and a very large working area to minimise wear rate. An example of such an application is a multi-grooving job carried out on a Newall N.U. unit grinder using 660 mm. diameter (26 in.) A60RB wheels, operating at 51–61 metres per second (10,000–12,000 surface feet per minute). The multiple rotary truers are housed in a rigid belt driven plunging workhead, which is an integral part of the grinder.

Type	R/T R.P.M.	R/T size		Motor H.P.	Application
		Ø	W		
Heavy duty driven	600 approx.	70 mm. 2¾ in.	25 mm. 1 in.	⅓–½	Cylindrical and centreless
Medium duty driven	2,720	50 mm. 2 in.	6 mm. ¼ in.	⅛	Cylindrical centreless or heavy internals
Light duty driven	2,720	25 mm. 1 in.	3 mm. ⅛ in.	⅛	Mainly internal
Heavy duty free running	Depend on wheel speed & angle	63 mm. 2½ in.	16 mm. ⅝ in.	Not applicable	Mainly centreless on roughing operations

DIAMONDS IN GAUGING, TESTING AND MEASUREMENT

In this field, most applications have their own precise diamond requirement which cannot be varied if the apparatus is to function.

The diamonds in this range, most commonly known in engineering, are the indenters or penetrators used in hardness testing apparatus.

Heavy duty

Medium duty

Light duty

Free running

Examples of R/T drive units. Air motor drives are available as alternative power sources

The diamond working area takes the form of a polished cone or pyramid depending on the apparatus used and not on the choice of the user.

Pyramid and conical diamonds, generally of smaller included angle, are also used as the tracer point in surface measuring instruments.

Spherical diamond anvils are used on many measuring and controlling units on cylindrical and internal grinders. Some gear and thread grinders use flat faced diamond anvils to 'feel' the position of the grinding wheel working face and actuate mechanisms that compensate automatically for grinding wheel wear.

For softer materials the Brinell tests utilising steel balls as penetrators are used.

Equipment using diamond penetrators or indenters is used for harder materials. The commercial basis for the use of the cone indenters is the American Rockwell hardness tester. From this have developed the testers using similar diamond forms and made by: George H. Alexander and W. & T. Avery of England; Malicet & Blin of France; Briro, Wolpert and Reicherter of Germany; Galileo of Italy; Hauser of Switzerland and Gnehm from the same country; the Swedish Alpha Durometer and the Ultra-Testor made by Établissements Henri Benedictus of Belgium. The British application of this type of hardness testing is covered by B.S. 891 : Part 1 : 1962.

The alternative to the Indenter is the 136° pyramid and which is covered by B.S.427 : 1961 (Part 1) and 1962 (Part 2).

The U.S.S.R. Gost 2999 also relates to 136° pyramid indenters and varies only in detail.

Vickers type hardness testing instrument employing 136° square based pyramid diamond indenter, checking the hardness of the steel blank of a diamond core bit

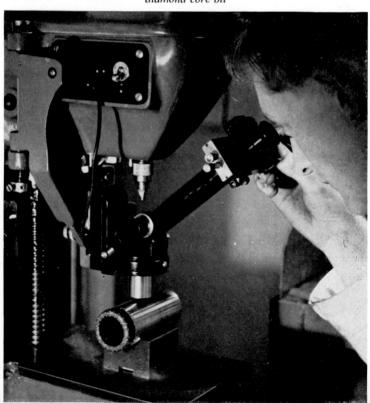

Because of the confusion that still exists in the relation between the various scales used in hardness testing, the following extract from British Standard 860:1939—Comparison of Hardness Scales—may be helpful:

'The most widely employed methods of measuring hardness are the "Brinell", "Diamond Pyramid" and "Rockwell" tests. There are individual preferences for using these, but cases are increasing where the same material is tested in different works laboratories by the three different methods. There has, in consequence, been a general demand for some means of correlating the most used A, B and C scales of the Rockwell test with those of the Brinell and Diamond Pyramid tests.

'Investigations show that there can be no general theoretical relationship between these scales, and empirical formulae devised from experiments only hold closely for materials of approximately similar composition and in a given condition. Variations in the empirical relationships result if the conditions as regards composition heat treatment and cold work differ appreciably, and also if different loading ratios are selected in the Brinell test. On the other hand, groups of materials similar as regards composition, cold work, etc., when tested by any of the above methods, may give fairly close comparisons.

'The following table is, therefore, a general approximation. It is issued solely as an indication of the order of the relationship between the three systems of hardness readings, and must not be used as a standard for the conversion of hardness values given on one scale in any British Standard to those of another scale.'

The National Bureau of Standards of the United States Department of Commerce developed the Knoop indenter and described it in their Research Paper 1220, 'A Sensitive Pyramidal-Diamond Tool for Indentation Measurements', by Frederick Knoop, Chauncey G. Peters and Walter B. Emerson. The development is covered by U.S. Patent Specification 2,091,995.

The pyramid form employed has an included longitudinal angle of 172° 30' and an included transverse angle of 130° 0'. The ratio of the diagonals is 7·11 to 1. The minimum lengths of the longitudinal and transverse edges are 0·7 mm. and 0·5 mm. respectively.

This type of indenter can be used over a wide range of materials, but it has been applied mainly in the micro-hardness testing field in the investigation of brittle materials such as glass, hard carbides, thin layers of metals and very small specimens.

APPROXIMATE COMPARISON OF HARDNESS SCALES ACCORDING TO B.S.860:1939

| Diamond pyramid scale (B.S.427: 1931) | Brinell (steel ball) scale (B.S. 240: 1937) | | Direct reading hardness test (Rockwell principle) (B.S.891: 1940) | | | | | |
| | | | C scale 150 kg. diamond cone | | A scale 60 kg. diamond cone | | B scale 100 kg. $\frac{1}{16}$ in. steel ball | |
(1)	Variations (2)	Adopted value (3)	Variations (4)	Adopted value (5)	Variations (6)	Adopted value (7)	Variations (8)	Adopted value (9)
20	15–25	20						
40		40						
60		55						
70		65						
80		75						
90		85						
100	80–100	95				43	47–61	54
120		115				47		65
140		135				50		77
160		155				53		83
180		175				56		89
200	175–205	195			58–60	59	93–95	94
220		215				60		97
240		235	18–23	20		61		100
260		255		24		63		
280		275		27		64		
300	280–300	295	27–33	30	65–68	66		
320		310		32		67		
340		325		34		68		
360		345		36		69		
380		360		39		70		
400	370–395	380	38–42	40	70–72	71		
420		395		42		72		
440		415		44		73		
460		430		45		73		
480		445		47		74		
500	445–480	460	46–50	48	73–76	75		
520		475		49		75		
540		490		50		76		
560		505		51		76		
580		520		52		77		

APPROXIMATE COMPARISON OF HARDNESS SCALES
ACCORDING TO B.S. 860:1939—*cont.*

Diamond pyramid scale (B.S.427: 1931)	Brinell (steel ball) scale (B.S.240:1937)		Direct reading hardness test (Rockwell principle) (B.S.891:1940)					
			C scale 150 kg. diamond cone		A scale 60 kg. diamond cone		B scale 100 kg. $\frac{1}{16}$ in. steel ball	
	Varia-tions	Adopted value	Varia-tions	Adopted value	Varia-tions	Adopted value	Varia-tions	Adopted value
(1)	(2)	(3)	(4)	(5)	(6)	(7)	(8)	(9)
600	515–550	535	52–56	54	75–79	77		
620		545		55		78		
640		560		56		78		
660		570		57		79		
680		585		57		79		
700	580–620	595	57–61	58	76–80	80		
725		605		59		81		
750		630		61		81		
800			60–64	62	77–83	82		
850				63		82		
900			63–67	65	78–84	83		
950				66		83		
1000			65–69	68		84		
1100				69		85		
1200				70		87		
1250					87–90	88		
1400				71	90–93	91		

Micro-hardness testers

The hardness testing applications described earlier in this chapter all relate to macro methods employed for ascertaining values of relatively large specimens. Micro-hardness testing is an additional facility to aid research in metallographic and mineralogical studies. It permits the determination of the hardness of the different constituents of a micro structure.

Instruments designed for this work usually employ diamond indenters of the Vickers or Knoop pyramid forms. The tolerances acceptable for the surface finish of the facets, the perfection of the edges at the intersections, the dimension of the final point and its concentricity in relation to the shank, are, however, more stringent than with such indenters needed for macro or normal testing.

Very much lighter loads are used in micro-testing and do not generally exceed 100 grams.

These factors, plus the incorporating of precise locating facilities on these instruments, also make them invaluable for hardness testing fine wires, needle points, delicate pivots, metal foils, watch and clock components, highly stressed aircraft parts and case hardened items.

Because of the light loads and small indentations to be measured, such specimens must have surfaces lapped plain and free from scratches or pits. As an example of the very small differences which have to be measured, the makers of the Tukon testers state that, with a load of 25 grams, the Knoop indentation would be 20 microns long. With the Vickers type, under the same load, also on hard steel, the length would be only 7 microns. For this type of work a double cone diamond indenter was suggested by P. Grodzinski in an article in 'Microtecnic'. The design of this followed similar reasoning to that which evolved the Knoop, but the diamond shape is very much more difficult to produce accurately. Once produced it has the advantage of being capable of use on any part of the edge formed between the two cones. So far it has not been generally adopted.

TRACER POINTS FOR SURFACE MEASURING INSTRUMENTS

Practical methods of measuring surface finish were developed only long after other dimensions could be accurately and easily established. Several of the instruments finally developed to fill this need employ a diamond tipped tracer that is drawn across the workpiece under controlled conditions. The rise and fall motions of the diamond tip in relation to the traverse provide the measure of surface roughness.

Such diamonds normally take the form of 90° cones with radii of 0·01 to 0·025 mm. (0·0004 to 0·001 in.) or square based pyramids with maximum tip dimensions of the order of 0·0025 to 0·0127 mm. (0·0001 to 0·0005 in.). The methods employed in their production follow the same lines as hardness testing indenters but, because of the smaller included angles and tip dimensions, they are the subject of considerable additional care in the final operation.

The main machine or instrument used in the field of surface measurement is the Talysurf by the Metrology Division of The Rank Organisation, Leicester, which employs pyramid diamonds, whilst the Profilometer by Physicists Research Company, of Ann Arbor, U.S.A., and the Brush Surface Analyser both use cones.

Whereas hardness testing instruments rely on the compressive strength of diamond for their proper function, surface measuring instruments rely on diamond's resistance to abrasion.

The only specification drawn up by a national standards institute in this field, known to the author, is that of the U.S.S.R. under GOST 9017–59. This specifies a cone angle of 90° (plus or minus 5°) and alternative radii at the tip of 0·002 mm. for reference 1 tools and 0·010 mm. for reference 2 tools. This is mounted in a 1·5 mm. diameter by 2 mm. long head with an optional threaded shank for attachment to the instrument.

The abrasion resistant quality of diamond surfaces is utilised to the full in size control devices fitted to automatic cycle precision grinding machines. The anti-friction bearing industry is one example of the wide use of this practice.

The calliper component of the system senses the size of the cylindrical component or the bore in the case of internal grinders. Contact with the work is maintained at three points of which two are fixed spherical diamond contacts and the third diamond, of the same form, is adjustable and follows the work diameter in the course of grinding. This movement of the third diamond is either transmitted to a dial gauge for visual guidance of the operator or to an automatic cycle control which stops the operation when the grinding has been completed to the pre-set size. The constant presence of the grinding slurry results in any material other than diamond being worn very rapidly with resulting inaccuracies in the control system.

In the case of complex forms, such as gears and threads, a flat diamond anvil is used to contact the working surface of the grinding wheel at predetermined intervals. The exact position of this working surface is then transmitted through the automatic control system of the machine and compensation is made for intervening wheel wear. Probably the best known example of this application is on the gear grinding machine made by S.A. des Engrenages Maag, of Zürich.

The 'compensator' diamond consists of a flat polished surface of an area specified to suit the application and orientated to provide maximum wear resistance.

Diamond tipped tools are also used to form various scale graduations and diffraction gratings. Another method, sometimes used for cutting graticule lines in glass, utilises lapping compound. An aluminium bronze disc of about 100 mm. (4 in.) diameter is turned to a vee form on the periphery. The 'knife edge' land is coated with Dialap 25/5 and the disc revolved at 1,000 r.p.m. When passed across this diamond loaded edge, clear cut lines were ground in the glass to a width of 0·063–0·076 mm. (·0025–·003 in.). The previous method had been to use a razor blade and emery which produced a rather ragged line of the order of 0·203 mm. (·008 in.) wide.

REFERENCES

Early Historical Uses of Diamond Tools—Prof. S. Tolansky, Royal Holloway College.
Fundamental Principles of Powder Metallurgy—W. D. Jones, M.ENG., PH.D., F.I.M.
The Tribological Aspects of Metal Bonded Diamond Grinding Wheels—J. R. Chalkley, B.A.(OXON), A.R.I.C. and D. M. Thomas, A.I.M.
Industrial Applications of the Diamond—N. R. Smith, A.M.I.P.E.
Coolant Additives and Diamond Wheel Efficiency—F. Hughes, De Beers Research.
The Use of Grinding Fluids with Diamond Wheels—J. R. Chalkley, B.A.(OXON), A.R.I.C.
Diamond Lapping Cuts Time and Cost—Warren W. West, Research Eng. Eastern Lab., Explosives Dept., E. I. Du Pont & Nemours.
'Versatility in Carbide'—*Tooling*—August 1971—Paul Daniel.
'Pantograph Diamond Dressers'—E. N. Hallewell and D. S. Classey, A.S.T.E./ I.D.A. Symposium, Chicago, 1969.
Diamonds in Metalworking—De Beers.
'A Rotary Diamond Dressing Operation'—*Toolmaking*—August 1971.
Diamond Facts Bulletin 2—Du Pont, Wilmington, Delaware, U.S.A.
British Patents: 1,044,784, 1,082,418, 1,163,811, 1,258,751,
                 1,081,449, 1,044,784,
                 1,279,413.
U.S. Patent: 3,683,560.
'Surface Grinding Carbide and Steel Combination with Diamond Wheels'— Herr Willi Rose, West Germany.

4

The transport industry

IT is in this field that diamond finds its widest scope of application and probably accounts for about 25–30% by value of the world's diamond bearing products. Among the major uses are the truing of abrasive wheels used in precision grinding mechanical components, the direct machining of non-ferrous metal parts, the honing of cylinder liners and other ferrous bores, the sharpening of hard metal cutting tools, the drilling, grinding and cutting of glass components and various operations in gauging and testing.

Behind these direct applications in the production of components, there also lies the part which diamond plays in the preparation of jigs, fixtures and tooling for the production of other parts, the drawing of wire for auto-electrics and the production of machine tools which are dealt with in separate chapters.

The following tables specify some of the main components in which diamonds are utilised:

Area	Component	Operation	Diamond
Motor assembly	Piston	Turn outside diameter	Turning tool
	Piston	Bore wrist-pin holes	Boring tool
	Con-rod	Bore bearings	Boring tool
	Main Bearings	Finish bore	Boring Tool
	Cylinder casing bores for liners	Finish bore	Boring tool
	Cylinder bores/ liners	Hone	Impregnated hone
	Diesel injector	Form grind needle	Chisel truer
	Crankshaft	Form grind	Rotary truer
	Crankshaft	Burnish thrust faces	Burnishing tool

Area	Component	Operation	Diamond
	Camshaft	Finish grind	Truing tool
	Valve	Form grind	Rotary truer
	Rocker arm	Form grind	Rotary truer
	Turbine blade roots	Form grind	Rotary truer
		Rough grind	Block truer/chisel
	Cowlings	Rough grind	Block truer/chisel
	Stepped shafts	Rough grind	Block truer/chisel
	Turbine blade periphery	Form grind	Truing tool
	Low pressure compressor casing	Machine Rokide lining	Machining tool
	Wankel combustion chambers	Grind silicon carbide electro-deposited lining	Grinding wheel
	Wankel Grey Iron pistons	Finish working surfaces	Hones
	Formed bolts	Form grind	Blade type truers
Automobile gear box	Gears	Form grind	Various truers
	Gears	Hobbing	Chisel truers
	Splines	Form grind	Various truers
	Shafts	Grind grooves	Rotary truers
	Bushes	Finish bore	Boring tool
Transmission and suspension	Universal spiders	Form grind	Rotary truer
	Shafts	Groove grind	Rotary truer
	Shafts	Spline grind	Various truers
	Differential gears	Grind	Various truers
	Anti-friction bearings	Grind components	Various truers
	Spiral springs	Centreless grind	Rotary truers
	Seals	Mould	Lapping compound
	Rear axle components	Form grind	Rotary truers
	Ball screw units for landing gear	Form grind	Chisel truers
Steering and brakes	Ball pins	Form grind	Rotary truers
	Racks	Form grind	Chisel truers
	Power assist unit	Form grind	Chisel truers
	Collapsible steering column	Pressing	Chisel truers
	Recirculating ball screws	Form grind	Rotary truers
	Brake drums and discs	Hone	Impregnated hone
Electrics (See also Chapter 5)	Dynamos Alternators Starter motors	Form grind shafts	Blade truers and rotary truers
	Screen wipers	Turn commutators	Turning tools
	Screen wipers	Press laminations	Chisel truers and profile wheels
	Screen wipers	Bore bearings	Boring tools

Area	Component	Operation	Diamond
	Spark plug Insulators	Form grind	Chisel truers
	Wiring	Draw wire	Drawing die
Coachwork	Heaters	Press outlet tubes	Chisel truers
and	Bumpers	Rolling	Chisel truers
fuselage (See also Chapter 3)	Grills, lamp surrounds and control panels	Mould to fine finish	Lapping compound to finish dies
	Fibre-glass components	Trim	Electro-deposited saws and routing tools
Glass	Windows	Pencil edge	Grooved wheel
(See also	Windows	Drill	Tube drill
Chapter 6)	Windows	Cut to shape	Vitrier cutting
	Mirrors	Cut to shape	Vitrier cutting
	Instrument covers	Cut to shape	Vitrier cutting
	Navigational instruments	Grind lens & prism	Impregnated cutters
Quality control	Hardness	Quantify	Conical or pyramid indenter
	Sizing	Gauge in production	Gauge anvils
	Sizing	Final inspection gauge	Lapping compound
	Surface finish	Measure	Stylus point
	Metallographic checks	Preparation of surfaces	Lapping compound

ENGINE COMPONENTS

In addition to these examples, where diamond plays a more direct part in producing the component, there is also the very wide field of tungsten carbide and ceramic tooling which, in turn, depends on diamond grinding tools for its ultimate efficiency. These are dealt with in more detail in Chapter 3 on Toolmaking.

Piston turning

As compared to the alternative of grinding, the diamond turning of aluminium pistons is more common in Europe. It is thought that the introduction of more sophisticated piston shapes and surface finishes has led in the same direction. Against this background several manufacturers have developed modified lathe designs to suit

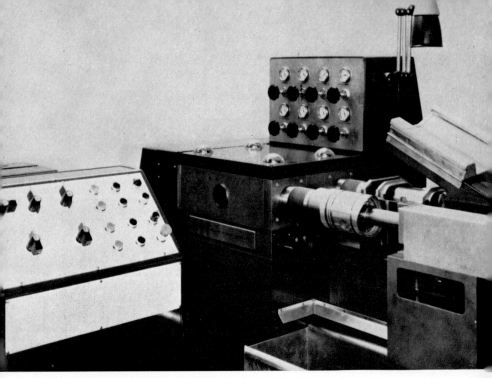

Special diamond turning set-up for automobile pistons (Bryant Symons & Co. Ltd.)

this market. Examples are Bryant Symons of England, Boley of Germany, Petrazzini of Italy and SIM of Switzerland.

The most advanced of these is probably the Bryant Symons machine. This double spindle lathe was designed specifically for copy turning pistons at high speed. 93–2,600 r.p.m. are available in 24 steps for turning diameters from 75–150 mm. (3 in.–6 in.). The maximum mainslide stroke is 300 mm. (12 in.). Feeds from 0·075 mm. (·003 in.) to 0·25 mm. (·010 in.) per revolution are available in 0·025 mm. (·C01 in.) or 0·05 mm. (·C02 in.) steps. The power is supplied by a 4-speed constant torque motor of $7\frac{1}{2}$ h.p. The two spindles are synchronised by a timing belt from the upper countershaft. Selection of dual speed operation, depending on the area of the component being machined, allows for optimum turning conditions, including a cast iron insert. Component positioning, in relation to the cam, is facilitated by a spindle positioning mechanism. There are two copying mechanisms—one being for the diamond turning of the piston skirt and the other for carbide turning the piston land which

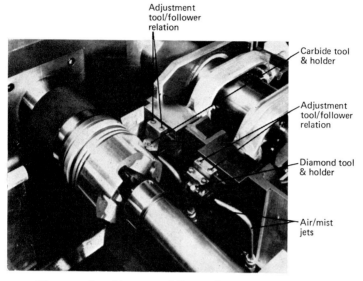

Close-up of working area of Bryant Symons piston turning lathe

includes the ferrous insert. The headstock has forced lubrication and is cooled. The Nitralloy steel spindle is carried in 75 mm. (3 in.) plain white metal bearings.

The details of an actual operation on this set-up were:

Example of piston turning on Bryant Symons lathe

Component	Diesel Piston Alum W52
Dimension	125 mm. (5 in.)
Finish	Controlled profile
Spindle speed	2,600 r.p.m. (93 for the land)
Tool traverse	0·25 mm. (·010 in.) per rev.
Depth of cut	0·58 mm. (·023 in.)
Coolant	Air blast
Diamond profile	3 facet (0·75 mm. [·030 in.] × 15°)
Diamond clearance	7°

In order to ensure that the lightly loaded follower mechanism did not depart from its true path at high speed, the tool holding device was reduced to a minimum weight compatible with the strength required and the need for accurate adjustment. It is claimed that this set-up reduced the floor-to-floor time from some 4 minutes to 65 seconds.

A further step in encouraging this development is the VM3 relapper which was originally designed for the critical jewellery and watch case industries (see Chapter 10). It is now being used by larger consumers of suitable diamond tools to deal with their own servicing. Apart from direct savings in handling and actual repairing, this procedure can be used to materially reduce diamond tool inventories—a very much reduced stock needs to be held in order to cover tools returned to the supplier for servicing. The

The VM3 diamond tool relapper developed for radius and flat grinding under optical control (L. M. Van Moppes & Sons S.A.)

illustration shows the multi-speed and reversing diamond charged lap to which the tool edge is applied. The latter is positioned in the universal fixture which can accommodate a wide range of tool holders. It also permits the diamond to be orientated through 360° to arrive at the correct grain to lap relationship. A crank device provides automatic traverse across the lap face and is a factor in producing the high standard of tool edge required.

Diamond tool life between relaps for normal silicon content pistons, as used in private cars, is generally of the order of 10–12,000 pistons, but it may be as low as 10% of this when machining high silicon pistons as used in air cooled motors.

Boring aluminium cylinder casings

In the case of V8 aluminium cylinder blocks, a greater degree of geometric and surface finish consistency is sometimes sought in the bores before fitting the steel liners. Both tungsten carbide and ceramic tools were tried, but maximum improvement in both qualities desired was obtained with diamond tools; this despite the less than ideal conditions in respect of the machine speeds and the purity of the castings. The operating conditions are shown in this table:

Example of cylinder block boring	
Machine	8 spindle Archdale borer
Dimension of bores	95 mm. dia. × 138 mm. L. (3¾ in. × 5½ in.)
Finish	Approx. 80 micro inches
Spindle speed	650 r.p.m.
Tool traverse	0·05 mm. (·002 in.) per rev.
Depth of cut	0·125 mm. (·005 in.)
Coolant	Soluble oil in water
Diamond profile	80° × 0·5 mm. (·02 in.)
Diamond clearance	7°

The diamond tools are mounted in Microbore adjustable inserts set in the boring bars. The inserts set at an angle or at 90° to bar-centres. It is interesting to note that, in addition to attaining the qualities required in the product, reports show a potential tool life improvement from 50 to 4,000 bores.

I

Con-rod bores

A Swedish case-history relates to an interesting combination of diamond applications. The forged steel housing is diamond honed before the small-end bronze bush is fitted. The operation is carried out on a Gehring (W. Germany) honing machine employing a spindle speed of 400 r.p.m. and a reciprocating speed of 250 per min. for a length of approximately 25 mm. (1in.). Mesh 170/220 diamond powder is metal bonded in four shoes of 25 mm. length and 3 mm. × 3 mm. section ($1 \times \frac{1}{8} \times \frac{1}{8}$in.) to provide a finish of 4–5 micron. A good fit for the bronze bush is thus assured, and the latter are diamond bored under the following conditions:

	Fine boring
Component	Bronze bushes for diesel and petrol motor con-rods
Dimensions	Bores 19–52 mm. ($\frac{3}{4}$–2 in.)
Finish	1·5–2 micron
Spindle speeds	2,400–4,000 r.p.m.
Tool traverse	0·022 mm. per rev. (·00086 in.)
Depth of cut	0·02–0·03 mm. (·00079–·0011 in.)
Diamond profile	90° × 0·5–0·8 mm. radius (·02–·03 in.)
Diamond clearance	8–17°

The operations are carried out on a 4-spindle vertical borer.

Another example of the diamond honing of con-rods is taken from Italian practice, utilising a Gehring honer:

	Workpiece
Dimensions	48·63 mm. dia. × 25 mm. (2 × 1 in.)
Material	Steel (80–90 kg./mm.²)
Stock Removal	0·03–0·06 mm. on dia. (·0011–·0024 in.)
Tolerance	H7
Surface finish before honing	4–5 micron Ra
Surface finish after honing	0·9–1 micron Ra
No. of ops. and time	1 op. × 20–30 sec.

For this operation a Gehring P3–150 3-spindle machine provides the conditions shown in this table:

Working details	
Speed	150–750 r.p.m.
Reciprocation	0–18 metres min. (59 ft.)
Pressure	36 kg./cm.^{2} (512 lb./sq. in.)
Head expansion range	46–55 mm.
Coolant	Paraffin and spindle oil
Work holding	Floating
Diamond hones (6 per spindle)	20 × 6 mm./D70 mesh/metal

An example from British practice was reported by the Perkins Company, of Peterborough, in the manufacture of connecting rods for their 4·235 diesel engine. The Nagel 2-spindle fully automatic honing machine is equipped with 80/100 mesh steel bonded diamond hones of 100 concentration. The rotational speed is 250 ft./min. (1·26 metres per second) and a stroke of 60 reciprocations per minute. The surface finish is 60/70 micro inches.

Honing with diamond impregnated inserts also plays an important part in the finishing of many small bore components used in diesel motors now used in many European commercial vehicles, taxis and even private cars used on a high mileage basis.

To mate with the injector nozzle bore, the corresponding multi-diameter pin must be extremely accurate and have a good surface finish. Some are ground on centreless grinders utilising chisel truers on 1 : 1 hydraulic copying devices to form and true the wheel. In order to improve standards, some makers are now employing the Model 8/1 Diaform which utilises a magnified template and a radius chisel diamond corresponding to the stylus diameter. The set-up is on a Fortuna grinder.

Cylinder bores are a critical area both in respect of geometry and surface finish. The latter is considered not only from the point of view of metered roughness, but also the pattern of the finish. Honing is generally accepted as the best finishing method and, in Europe, diamond hones predominate in this field. This is equally true of internal combustion and diesel engines for automobile, locomotive and ship engines. Details of two typical cases, taken from U.K. and West German practice, are shown in the tables which follow. Both

Honing machine equipped with diamond hones for finishing cast-iron bores
(Maschinenfabrik Gehring K.G.)

operations are carried out on 6-spindle units built by Gehring. The
first table compares the two workpieces:

Workpiece—6-cylinder block	*A*	*B*
Dimensions	103·2 × 200 mm.	90 × 130 mm.
Material	Cast iron	Cast iron
Stock removal (dia.)	0·05–0·07 mm.	0·05 mm.
Tolerance	H7	0·02 mm.
Surface finish before honing	120 micro inch RMS	12–15 micron Rt
Surface finish after honing	25–28 micro inch RMS	3 micron Rt
No. of ops. and time	2—rough 65 sec. finish 21 sec.	2—45 sec. total

The comparative working conditions are:

Working details		A	B
Speed	r.p.m.	25–375	50–300
Reciprocation	m/min.	0–20	0–23
Pressure	kg./cm.^{2}	36·5 (Fin 27)	34 (Fin 30)
Head expansion range	m/m	95–113	85–98
Coolant		Swift H–Castrol	Swift H–Castrol
Work hold		Floating	Floating
Diamond hones (6 per head)		100 × 6 mm.	75 × 5 mm.
		D100 (Fin D50)	D180 (Fin D105)

In addition to the greater consistency of finish provided by diamond hones, their longer life which reduces 'down-time' and closer dimensional tolerances, it has been pointed out that they are also an overall economy as compared to silicon carbide honing sticks. In his very comprehensive article on 'Diamond Honing in Mass Production', Dr. Kirmse, of Daimler-Benz A.G., quotes from some experiments carried out in Stuttgart. These showed that, on cast iron crankcase bores, the total cost of diamond honing was less than 50% of the cost of honing with silicon carbide sticks. This conclusion took into account the tool purchase costs, the tool maintenance cost and the operating costs. The biggest saving was in the latter element.

The Wankel engine of NSU depends on diamond hones for the finish and concentricity between the three diameters and lengths of the grey iron pistons. The surface finishes are reported as reducing the machined finish of 180 micro inches to 60 on rough honing and to 30 at the finishing operations. At a time of 3 minutes per component, a saving of time of 30% is claimed as compared to the previous grinding time. It has also been reported that diamond wheels are being used to finish grind the special electro-deposited silicon carbide grit impregnated lining of the combustion chambers of these engines. This method was introduced when conventional aluminium oxide and silicon carbide wheels had proved inadequate.

As ever greater stresses are borne by crankshafts, they have received considerable attention in the last few years. Particularly in the field of diesel motors, the importance of avoiding blemishes on the working surfaces and providing accurate radii have been emphasised. Fortunately, this demand coincided with the availability of diamond rotary truers which helped to solve the related problems.

Diamond set rotary truer for crankshaft grinding (A.-B. Industridiamanter)

Rough turning operations on crankshafts are also carried out with form ground turning tools for which the grinding wheel profiles are diamond chisel trued on Diaform pantograph truers.

The automation of crankshaft grinding has been extensively developed by the Newall Engineering Co. Ltd., of Peterborough,

Rigid belt driven drive unit for rotary dressers with superimposed diamond dresser (The Newall Engineering Co. Ltd.)

and one typical example is the Fiat project in the U.S.S.R. This consists of four multi-wheel grinders for the main bearings, six pin grinders and two end grinders, together with a central conveyor, an autoloader and a post process gauge unit with feed back for correction. The final resultant dimensional accuracy and surface finish depend very much on the consistency of the wheel truing arrangements. The whole assembly has a total of ten diamond rotary truers and two chisel truer units.

In the writer's opinion, the performance of diamond rotary truers is vitally affected by the design of the drive units, and continued co-operation in this development is essential as between machine and diamond tool makers. The abrasive wheel maker's contribution is also of importance, of course, and in this case consists of A463N5VE 1100 mm. (43 in.) diameter wheels used at 61 metres per second (12,000 surface feet per minute).

Another diamond application in crankshaft production is mentioned in a report on Vauxhall practice on their automated crankshaft line. The thrust faces of the shafts are diamond burnished

Form ground drive pinion. The next illustration shows the rotary truer profile

on a purpose built Weisser/Sundstrand lathe. The two tools employed have contact radii of 1·75 mm. (·070 in.).

In addition to the bearing and pin areas of the crankshaft, the terminal areas are also form ground on machines equipped with diamond rotary truers.

In another case from Peugeot, a formed rotary truer is used on a Constructions de Clichy grinder to form grind essential areas of a drive pinion fitted to the camshaft. The heat treated steel component is finish ground in the relevant areas to 23–28 micro inches. Super-finishing to 16 micro inches is then undertaken.

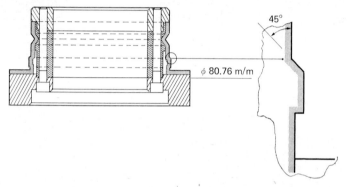

Rotary truer profile for drive pinion shown in previous illustration

The groove grinding of valve stems with the aid of diamond rotary truers is now quite commonplace, but an interesting rotary truer application in the grinding of the working face of the associated rocker arm has been reported. Precidia S.A., of France, co-operated with Peugeot, of Sochaux, in modifying a Scrivener centreless grinder. It was adapted to carry a belt driven rotary truer for forming two grooves of 8 mm. radius in the wheel. This was then used to grind two components simultaneously. The rotary truers replaced the previous hydraulic copying system employing a stationary single point tool. An aluminium oxide, vitrified, 60K wheel is used, of 500 mm. × 32 mm. to remove 0·3–0·4 mm., and produces a finish of 10 micro inches. The results are very much more consistent than before. At least part of the reason for this greater consistency is related to the area of contact between rotary truer and grinding wheel. It will be appreciated that only a line contact occurs between

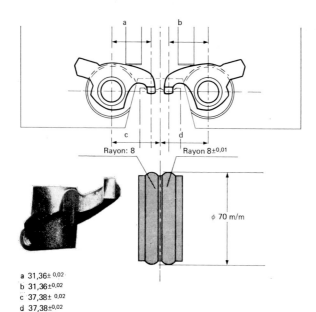

a 31,36± 0,02
b 31,36±0,02
c 37,38± 0,02
d 37,38±0,02

Rotary truer to form centreless grinder work wheel grinding the working faces of rocker arms

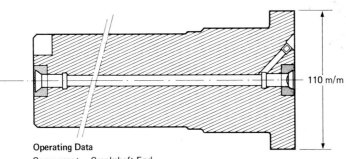

Operating Data

Component — Crankshaft End
Material — XC42 Forged Steel
Machine — c.c. Special Angle Head
Wheel — 38A60I8VBE/760 m/m x 65 m/m
Wheel Speed — 32 m/sec
Workpiece Finish — 24 micro inches
Stock Removal — 0.515 m/m on Diameter

Profile of rotary dresser used for wheels grinding crankshaft terminals
(Precidia S.A.)

the grinding wheel and the rotary truer throughout the life of the latter. Conversely, a single point truer has a fluctuating contact area. Consistency is further preserved by the very much greater overall diamond area available to keep wear rate to a minimum when using the rotary truer.

The rotary truer consists of small whole stones in a sintered matrix, or of diamond grit in an electro-deposited bond. Because of the smaller grain size, the usable layer thickness of the latter is less than in the sintered product.

In the production of the fir tree root of jet blades, the diamond application is in the form of a chisel truer or an electro-formed rotary truer. The chisel is used to form the required profile in a grinding wheel with the aid of a pantograph mechanism, such as the Diaform. The abrasive wheel thus formed is used to grind steel cutters which are mounted on 'broaching' machines to cut the required form in the nimonic blades. The rotary truers, however, are used to profile grinding wheels to the required form in a plunge

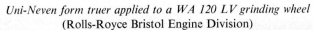

Uni-Neven form truer applied to a WA 120 LV grinding wheel
(Rolls-Royce Bristol Engine Division)

operation. The grinding wheel then transfers the form to the blades.

Nimonic seal segments for low pressure turbines are also ground in a similar way on special Excello grinders. Diamond tooling is generally associated with great precision and high finish, but, in this case, the diamond trued grinding process is applied to an operation with relatively open tolerances ± 0.025 mm. (± 0.001 in.) and a finish comparable to single point machining (125 micro inches). The benefits accrue entirely from simplification and overall economy.

Another typical diamond application arose in the manufacture of the Concorde's Olympus 593 engines, jointly by the Bristol Engines Division of Rolls-Royce Ltd. and the French S.N.E.C.M.A. organisation. This was in the low pressure compressor area. The 1·22 m. (4 ft.) diameter casing flexes at the normal operating speeds so that the revolving compressor blades contact the inner surface.

A single diamond machines an abrasive ceramic coating inside the compressor casing of the Concorde's Olympus 593 engine. The casing will tend to flex under the stresses of supersonic flight, but should the rotating compressor blades contact the casing, their tips will be ground off by the abrasive ceramic, preventing serious damage

To avoid loss of efficiency by fitting shorter blades, the casing was coated with Rokide, which is an abrasive ceramic material.

The surface adjacent to the blades was machined with a shaped diamond tool. The blade tips are worn away if they contact the abrasive lining. The component is machined on a Webster and Bennett vertical borer and is rotated at 20 r.p.m. to give a cutting speed of 1·24 metres per second (244 feet per min.). The depth of cut is 0·1 mm. (0·004 in.) and the infeed 0·178 mm. (0·007 in.) per pass. A soluble oil base coolant is used.

Many more normal operations, comparable to those carried out on the high volume automobile components, are to be found in aero engine production and where the same techniques are employed.

GEAR BOX COMPONENTS

Equally, in the production of various speed change gear boxes, the use of diamond products is similar in the automobile and aero industries. Truing operations on such gear grinding machines as the Orcutt and Reishauer are common to both.

As indicated in the summary tables, there is a wide use of diamond tooling in gear box production, and, among the grinding machines

Rotary truer adaption for Reishauer gear grinding machine (Precidia S.A.)

used in this field, the Reishauer is well known. A development in this connection is the introduction of rotary truers for roughing out the form on new wheels. The modification illustrated was designed and manufactured by Precidia S.A., of France. It provides the usual benefits of rotary truing as compared to crush dressing and makes it possible for the user to reduce his grinding wheel inventory.

Diamond rotary trued abrasive wheels are also used as a matter of course to replace earlier methods of grooving gear box main shafts to take circlips. One example of this operation is the Newall 'MU' unit grinder using 26 in. diameter (660 mm.) A60RB wheels for operation at 10,000–12,000 surface feet per minute (51–61 metres per second). The multiple rotary truers are housed in a rigid belt driven unit.

Diamond chisel truers are also widely used on the Diaform pantograph equipment fitted to special hob grinders which produce the cutters for the alternative means of gear shaping.

TRANSMISSION, SUSPENSION AND LANDING GEAR

The next examples are taken from the production of transmission components, and the first concerns the front wheel drive 'tripods' for the 'Peugeot 204'. The grinding of the main diameters, as well as the circlip and clearance grooves, is carried out on a multi-wheel Constructions de Clichy grinder on which truing occurs after each component and whilst the next is being loaded. Some 120,000 components are produced per rotary truer. The 60 grit, aluminium oxide, vitrified wheels run at 32 metres per second.

For back axle shafts the same grinding machine maker has developed a twin head angle approach grinder utilising diamond rotary truers. This still complex set-up would have been almost impossible without the simplified truing possibilities offered by rotary truers.

On another machine from this maker, the Gorki (U.S.S.R.) plant is grinding multiple diameter rear axle casings. The actual grinding conditions are similar to the previous example as regards wheel specification and speed. The finish required is 45 micro inches and 0·7–1 mm. (·03–·04 in.) has to be removed from diameter. The machine cycle allows for truing after each seven components.

Each of the two sintered rotary truer assemblies consists of three diamond elements and four spacers all mounted on a common

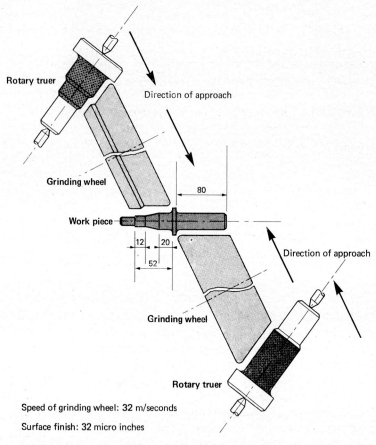

Rotary truer

Direction of approach

Grinding wheel

Work piece

80

12 20

52

Direction of approach

Grinding wheel

Rotary truer

Speed of grinding wheel: 32 m/seconds

Surface finish: 32 micro inches

Rotary truer set-up for truing twin head angle approach grinding auto back axle shafts (Precidia S.A.)

spindle. The diamond elements in operation contact three conventional abrasive wheels spaced out on a common spindle and which in turn grind the registers and faces on the back axle component. By having the two angle heads each with its own rotary truer unit and grinding wheel assembly, the operating time is, of course, only 50% of that which would be required on a single head machine.

Another example in this area is the form grinding of universal joint components. The finish-machining of universal joint spiders has been done by the centreless grinding method for many years. However, wheel dressing operation by conventional single stone or blade type diamond tools for form grinding left much to be desired. This was occasioned by the fact that opposing ends of the component were to be ground simultaneously. Consequently, two separate wheel dressing operations, involving opposing radii, were required. Further, these problems were intensified by dissimilar diamond wear and thus dressing times became a major factor in component costing. The rotary truing method has now overcome these variable factors. A B.S.A. No. 8 Centreless Grinding Machine was suitably modified and equipped with a rotary truer. Two pre-formed diamond impregnated truers, with diamonds suitably spaced and orientated and having a nominal 76·2 mm. (3 in.) diameter, were mounted in a drive unit. The whole assembly was built into a special dovetail slide that replaces the standard diamond quill. The infeed of the rotary truer to the wheels is imparted by a lead screw and nut operated by a graduated hand-wheel, while rotation of the truer is from an electric motor through a flexible drive; the motor is mounted at the rear of the truing slide.

One of the main uses of ball and roller bearings is, of course, in the transport field. Trains, ships, aircraft, automobiles, motor

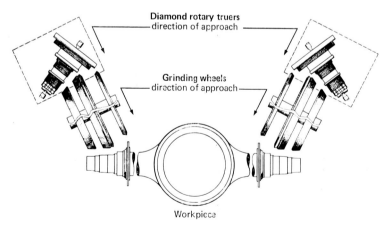

Diamond rotary truers
direction of approach

Grinding wheels
direction of approach

Workpiece

Rotary truers, grinding wheels and component layout for back axle case grinding (Precidia S.A.)

cycles, even the humble pedal cycle, all depend on these for their smooth running to a greater or lesser degree.

All of the main components, the outer and inner rings, the balls and the rollers are finish ground on diamond trued wheels. The external surfaces are ground on centreless grinders, such as Cincinnati, Lidkoping or Malcus, often equipped with rotary truers in the case of ball tracks. These form the critical grooves in which the balls run. Bores are ground on internal grinders, such as those offered by UVA of Sweden or Excello of the U.S.A. In many cases, the sizing control also depends on a spherical diamond gauge anvil in contact with the work surface being ground. This indicates when the correct size has been achieved and the component is ejected from the work station. The wear on the diamond face is almost negligible and this characteristic ensures repeatability over long periods.

In the aircraft field, the ball screw units made by Rotax Precision Products are fitted in pairs to the Lockheed C5A Galaxy airbus to raise and lower the nose landing gear. The formed grinding wheels, used to finish grind these ball screws, are profiled with the aid of very accurate chisel form truers. A similar mechanism is used for the wing-slot actuation system.

Hydraulic cylinders, used in landing gear and other actuating mechanisms, are diamond honed using similar techniques to those used in the honing of automobile engine cylinders.

STEERING AND BRAKES

In the area of steering and brakes, the biggest single contribution of the diamond industry has almost certainly been the introduction of rotary truers for centreless form grinding ball-pins. Jaguar rack and power steering components are, however, form ground by another method. Accurate chisel form diamond truers are essential components of Diaform Pantograph Truing Units as mentioned elsewhere. They, in turn, are mounted, in this case on a Thule surface grinder, to true the tooth form of the rack.

The tough and abrasive materials used as brake linings are cut to size with electrometallic diamond saws. To avoid any subsequent drying operation of the absorbent material, the operation is carried out dry. Six to twelve saws are mounted on a common spindle for use at a recommended cutting speed of 38 metres per second (7,500 ft.

per minute). Power is supplied at approximately 1½ h.p. per disc in the smaller sizes, up to 4 h.p. in the larger. The workpieces are mounted on a revolving drum and fed into the saws at 0·15 metres per second (30 ft. per minute). Workpiece thickness up to 19 mm. (¾ in.) is cut in one pass. To achieve final dimensional accuracy, segmental diamond wheels are also used in subsequent sizing operations.

Groove details in the power steering component are ground in a similar manner on a Jones & Shipman 1011 grinder employing a model BT Diaform.

A less direct application of diamond chisel truers is in the production of 'collapsible' or energy-absorbing steering columns. The press tools needed to produce the main component rely for their efficiency on accurate form grinding of the components. This is ensured by the use of accurate diamond chisels controlled by a 10:1

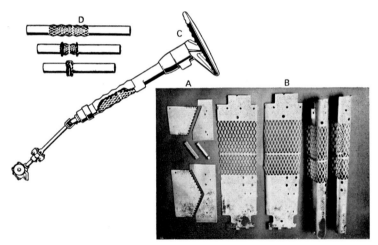

Components for the manufacture of energy absorbing steering columns are produced from form ground press tools:

a. Templates (10 × actual size) used to control the path of a diamond chisel
b. Pressed steel components made from the Diaform ground press tools in various stages of development
c. The component mounted in the steering column
d. In various stages of collapse

K

pantograph on the alternative type of Diaform (Model 5) mounted on a Jones & Shipman 1400 surface grinder.

Brake drums are internally ground and, to ensure smooth operation and long life, they are finally honed. One example is taken from the Volkswagen plant in Germany. The honing of the blind bore is carried out on a 2-spindle Gehring machine, and the details are shown in the next two tables:

Workpiece	
Dimensions	230 mm. dia. × 44 mm.
Material	Grey cast iron (HB 210 approx.)
Stock removal	0·03–0·05 mm. from diameter
Tolerance	0·2 mm.
Surface finish before honing	Approx. 25 micron Rt.
Surface finish after honing	12–14 micron Rt.
No. of ops. and time	1 × 27 seconds

and the operating conditions:

Working details	
Speed	60–300 r.p.m.
Reciprocation	0–20 m./min.
Pressure	46 kg./cm.^{2}
Head expansion range	220–240 mm. dia.
Coolant	Paraffin oil
Work holding	Floating
Diamond hones (7 per set)	25 × 6 D100 metal

COACHWORK AND FUSELAGE

Turning now to the actual body shell and details, again diamond plays its part not only in the tooling, but also in a more direct way in the case of the fibre-glass bodies made for short run or individual automobile types such as the Marcos. The diamond tools and associated equipment used in this work are shown in the illustrations. They show a range of electro-deposited diamond routers employing about 60 grit natural diamond in a single layer.

They are operated in the air driven hand held unit, also shown. This operates at 50,000 r.p.m. from a 6/7 kg. per sq. cm. (80/100 lb

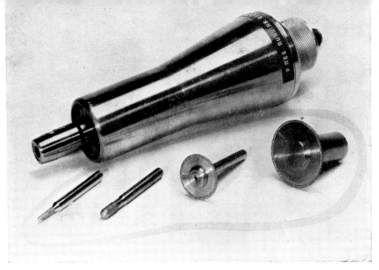

Electro-deposited diamond routers used for trimming fibre-glass components. The 50,000 r.p.m. air driven power unit is shown in the background (Diagrit Electrometallics Ltd.)

per sq. inch) supply, and is rated to consume 0·34 cubic metres per minute (12 cubic ft. per minute). Weighing less than a kilogram (32 ozs.) and being only 22 cm. (8¾ in.) long, it is easily hand held and supplies ample power for the very free cutting diamond tools. The trimming can be carried out without templates or fixtures. For straight line work, the saw shown in the second illustration is used. It will be seen that this also incorporates a dust extracting hood. The saw operates from an air supply of the same pressure as the router unit and is rated to consume C·42 cubic metres per minute (15 cubic feet per minute). It is designed to take an electro-deposited

Electro-deposited diamond saw complete with 20,000 r.p.m. air driven unit and dust extraction hood (Diagrit Electrometallics Ltd.)

diamond saw up to 65 mm. ($2\frac{1}{2}$ in.) in diameter, and employing the same diamond grit as the routing cutters. The weight in this case is 1·25 kg. ($2\frac{3}{4}$ lb.). The operating speed is 20,000 r.p.m.

In addition to the economies of longer life as compared to tungsten carbide, on the highly abrasive glass fibre the higher speeds utilised provide greater productivity per manhour, and complete freedom from chipping on the job. Tool life is reported to be in excess of 6 months in many cases.

Coming now to the use of plastics in mass produced automobiles, there are, of course, many detail items, such as grills, lamp surrounds and dashboards, which are made with exposed surfaces moulded to a very high degree of finish. The mould surfaces reproduced on many such components are finished with diamond lapping compound.

GLASS COMPONENTS

The windscreens, rear windows and side windows, whether of laminated or toughened glass, are 'pencil edged' with grooved periphery metal bonded diamond grinding wheels which have a useful life of hundreds of thousands of metres. Where necessary, they are also drilled with diamond impregnated hollow drills in order to attach winding mechanisms or locking devices. Automatic circle cutting machines, utilising traditional 'vitrier' diamonds, are used to cut circles of glass for mirrors and instrument covers. For glass shapes, other than rectangles or circles, template controlled machines, either power or hand operated, such as the SN.50C and SN.50D, are available. They are designed to accommodate shapes up to a circle of 250 mm. (10 in.) diameter and between 300 mm. × 250 mm. (12 × 10 in.) and 900 mm. × 750 mm. (36 × 30 in.) respectively.

More details of the use of diamonds in glass are given in Chapter 6.

QUALITY CONTROL

The hardness testing of metals would be less accurate and reliable without the use of diamond penetrators. To the well established single operation hardness tester has now been added semi-automatic equipment, such as the Maier set-up shown overleaf in use on the testing of rocker arms on the Rockwell A scale. In one test, ten

Semi-automatic hardness testers using diamond cones for Rockwell scales
(Maier & Co.)

rocker arms are classified at two opposing positions at the rate of 720 rockers per hour.

Diamond anvils are also used as work contacts on auto-sizing devices fitted to precision grinders, and thus contribute to the accuracy of the component.

Measuring crankshaft surface finish with diamond tracer point on Talysurf equipment (Rank Precision Industries Ltd.)

In the constant search for metal fatigue, surface cracks and similar defects, diamond lapping compounds are used to prepare the specimen surfaces, and diamond tipped microtome knives to cut sample slices for examination on electron microscopes.

The specification and measurement of surface roughness often also depends on an accurately lapped diamond stylus point, as is the case with the Talysurf instrument.

REFERENCES

Dr. Ing. A. Scholz—Maschinenfabrik Gehring K.G., Stuttgart—Honing data.
Dipl-Ing. W. Kirmse—Daimler-Benz A.G., Stuttgart—'Diamond honing in mass production'—*Industrial Diamond Review*, April 1968.
M. P. Fricou—Precidia S.A., Lisieux—'Nouveaux Developpements de la Molette Diamantée', Paris, 23.4.68.
Mr. G. Garratt, Assistant Editor, *Machinery*—'Vauxhall automated crankshaft line', 21.5.69.
'Honing bores in Wankel pistons'—*Machinery*, 21st May, 1969.
Mr. K. W. Hards—'Robot Inspectors that Guide the Machine'—*New Scientist*, 20.4.67.
U.S.S.R. Gost 16014 – 70 Diamond rollers for abrasive wheels.
16606 – 71 Diamond honing sticks.
10110 – 71 Diamond saws.
17368 – 71 Diamond tools for profile of abrasive hobbing wheels (Reishauer).

5

Electrical and electronics production

DIAMOND dies are widely used for drawing the wire utilised in this field. In the production of these dies and those made of tungsten carbide accurately graded diamond powder plays an important part. This material is also bonded in grinding wheels employed to sharpen the tungsten carbide tools so widely used in turning the many millions of small metal parts utilised in the industry. The diamond lapped tungsten carbide edges of these cutting tools materially increase the number of parts that can be produced on the automatic lathes without readjustment of the tool setting.

Most copper commutators of electric motors and dynamos are finish turned with diamond tipped tools. The steel shafts on which they are mounted are precision ground on centreless grinders. The wheel form and cutting properties are preserved with diamond tooling. The laminations of which the rotor is composed are stamped out on progression dies. These dies made to very exacting limits are finish form ground on wheels of which the profiles are generated with diamond chisel truers controlled by the 10:1 pantograph linkage of a Diaform attachment.

Ceramic insulators are ground in the green state on abrasive wheels profiled by similar means and can be milled after heat treatment with diamond faced cutters.

Diamond slitting saws and 'chisel' like tools are indispensable in the cutting of germanium and silicon used in transistors. The jewel bearings in many meters are formed and their bearing surfaces highly polished with diamond powder charged tools.

Vacuum cleaners, floor polishers, washing machines, spin driers, hair driers, radios, televisions, film projectors, cameras and most of the other complex equipment found in a modern household have a diamond cost content.

The needle on the record player is either sapphire which has been cut, ground and polished with diamond powder charged tools or is itself a minute diamond ground to the same conical form as the sapphire and again utilises diamond powder charged tools.

WIRE DRAWING

A wire drawing die is a tool with a specially tapered hole through which wire is pulled to reduce its diameter. It is manufactured in tungsten carbide for the larger sizes and diamond for smaller sizes. The two types of dies are complementary. The rolled rod of metal is first drawn as heavy gauge wire through tungsten carbide dies, the economic sizes for changing over to diamond dies being about 2 mm. (0·080 in.) diameter for copper wire and about 1 mm. (0·040 in.) diameter for the harder wires. Below these size limits, the diamond, on account of its great mechanical hardness and resistance

Twenty-one die wire drawing machine (W. H. A. Robertson & Co. Ltd.)

to wear, holds an unassailable position among materials for wire drawing dies; in fact there is no substitute for diamond dies for the continuous drawing of unbroken miles of wire accurately sized within close tolerances and which on fine diameter wire can be as close as 1 or 2 microns.

Diamond dies are made with holes having a purely circular cross-section and, apart from a few cases of 'single-holing' for special purposes, are used in a multiple machine. Since wire drawing is a process of plastic deformation induced by the circumferential pressure of the wire against the taper in the die, there is a limit to the reduction in diameter which can be made at one die, according to the amount of pull the wire can withstand without breaking. Multiple die wire drawing machines are designed to suit the class of wire and sizes to be drawn, but, as an example, copper wire of 1·8 mm. (0·072 in.) diameter can be reduced to 0·21 mm. (0·0084 in.) diameter through a series of 21 successively smaller diamond dies, each giving the wire 23% elongation. The speed of progression of the drawing cones takes care of the 23% elongation at each die, so that, whereas the inlet wire is drawn through the first die at approximately 0·67 metres per second (134 ft./min.), the wire is being drawn through the finishing die at 40 metres per second (8,000 ft./min.).

The basic requirements in a diamond die are:

1. A good quality diamond.
2. Adequate reinforcement of the diamond.
3. A bearing or drawing cylinder of exact diameter.
4. A reduction cone of the correct shape for the particular metal to be drawn.
5. An exit relief of correct shape.
6. A mirror polish over the whole surface.

A diamond die is processed on the following lines:

The selection of the diamond from the point of view of size, shape, colour and purity.

Flatting or grinding two parallel surfaces from which to locate subsequent operations. The orientation is sometimes determined by X-ray.

Drilling performed with a revolving and reciprocating needle fed with a fine diamond powder slurry, by electrolytic and ultrasonic methods or, more recently, with the aid of laser beams.

Counter piercing on the reverse side to provide the exit.

Polishing to blend the various angles of the working area and final sizing with a mirror finish. This is accomplished with successively finer grades of diamond powder slurry.

Mounting: With the exception of dies to draw tungsten wire, the very small diameter dies are mounted with a hard brazing alloy in brass cases, whereas the larger dies are reinforced in steel slugs and subsequently mounted in brass cases which are accurately turned so that the periphery is concentric with the axis of the die bore. As tungsten wire is drawn hot, steel cases are used instead of brass. The standard diameter of the die case is 25 mm. (1 in.) and the nominal thickness is shown in the following table:

| | Diameter of bore | Nominal thickness of case | |
mm.	in.	mm.	in.
Up to 0·024	Up to 0·0009	3·2	$\frac{1}{8}$
0·025 to 0·150	0·001 to 0·006	4·8	$\frac{3}{16}$
0·151 to 0·280	0·00601 to 0·011	6·4	$\frac{1}{4}$
0·281 to 0·480	0·01101 to 0·019	7·2	$\frac{9}{32}$
0·481 to 0·760	0·01901 to 0·030	8·0	$\frac{5}{16}$
0·761 to 1·120	0·03001 to 0·044	9·5	$\frac{3}{8}$
1·121 to 2·030	0·04401 to 0·080	11·1	$\frac{7}{16}$
2·031 and over	0·08001 and over	12·7	$\frac{1}{2}$

Reproduced from B.S.2946:1958

British Standards specification: Diamond dies are specified in B.S.2946:1958 which suggest the following methods for the appraisal of polish or surface finish:

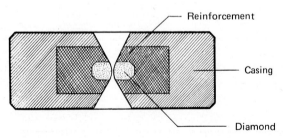

Mounting components of a diamond die

'For dies above 0·15 mm. (0·006 in.) diameter, a watchmaker's eyeglass or "loupe" giving a magnification of × 16 is sufficient. This should preferably be of the double lens type, and for illumination of the die, from the exit side, it is sufficient to use a 40W or 60W pearl lamp, in an opaque shade which is so adjusted that it prevents direct rays of light from reaching the operator.

'For medium bore dies, some form of binocular microscope is recommended. This should be arranged so that a direct source of light can be fixed below the stage, in line with the optical axis of the instrument, and a second source of light should be arranged so as to cast a beam of light obliquely downwards into the bore of the die when it is mounted on the microscope stage so as adequately to illuminate the surface of the die. It is a great advantage to use some form of die holder which permits the rotation of the die and also its being tilted at any angle relative to the axis of the microscope.

'It is recommended that an objective of not less than 32 mm. focal length be used in conjunction with suitable eyepieces to give a magnification of × 50 for the examination of dies between 0·05 mm. (0·002 in.) and 0·15 mm. (0·006 in.) bore and a magnification of × 100 for dies below 0·05 mm. (0·002 in.). For fine-bore dies, a monocular microscope equipped for magnifications of × 100 or greater is most convenient. The microscope should be fitted with a well-corrected substage condenser of an aplanatic type and diffuse illumination used, supplied either from a 40W or 60W pearl lamp or from light passed through a ground-glass filter.'

Diamond die maintenance: Despite its extreme hardness, diamond is very brittle and easily destroyed by ill use. Even when drawing exactly similar metals, die life in some wire mills is better than in others and it is certainly true that the life of a diamond die depends upon its treatment by the user.

Whilst in use, dies must be kept under close observation. If a die is left on the machine too long before receiving attention, it may either have to be scrapped or else a large amount of diamond has to be cut away which should be used for drawing wire. Not only is better quality production obtained by the correct method, but maintenance costs are thereby considerably reduced.

All the dies in the machine should be withdrawn after a predetermined period, according to the size and class of wire being drawn, and replaced by another set. The dies removed for inspection should be thoroughly washed in a degreasing agent before being cleaned with a wood point, although for the finest diameter dies an ultrasonic cleaner is recommended. Careful examination of each die must be made before deciding what treatment, if any, it requires. This examination will reveal whether the polish is sufficient or whether the reduction zone, bearing or exit relief is damaged.

The first indication of wear in a die (often before any alteration in size has occurred) is usually the appearance of a 'drawing ring' corresponding with the line of impact of the entering wire. If this is dealt with in good time, it can be removed by repolishing on a needle type polishing machine without affecting the size of the die.

When a die is worn out of tolerance, it is necessary to open it out to the next larger size required by the wire mill. The types of machines used for the different stages of repolishing depend upon the amount of work to be done. A die of 1·00 mm. (0·040 in.) used in continuous drawing may require increasing in size by as much as 0·125 mm. (0·005 in.), whereas a finishing die of 0·125 mm. (0·005 in.) may only need increasing 0·005 mm. (0·0002 in.). The needle type machines would be used extensively in the case of the larger die for reshaping and enlarging, with final polishing on the wire type machines. In the case of the small die, the work would be almost entirely done on the wire polishers.

The use of the different grades of diamond powder also depends on the amount of work to be done. Only by experience can the operator determine the coarsest grade that can be used for the commencement of any particular job, and subsequently all the intermediate grades must be used down to the finest grade. The table on the facing page is intended as a general guide. Gradings may be varied to suit alternative techniques and equipment.

Polishing must not be hurried. Even with the best technique it takes time to obtain a mirror finish. Polishing machines must be kept clean and correctly adjusted. Too much tension on the springs will cause ringing and scouring.

Diamond powder must be applied frequently and in very small

Die sizes	Diamond powder sizes for drilling (microns)	Diamond powder sizes for polishing or repolishing (microns)
Up to 0·05 mm.	20/40	4/8
Up to 0·002 in.	8/25	2/6
	6/12	$\frac{1}{2}$/3
	4/8	0/1
0·05–0·15 mm.	20/40	6/12
0·002–0·006 in.	8/25	4/8
	6/12	2/6
	4/8	$\frac{1}{2}$/3
		0/1
0·15–0·38 mm.	20/40	6/12
0·006–0·015 in.	8/25	4/8
	6/12	2/6
		$\frac{1}{2}$/3
		0/1
0·38–0·60 mm.	20/40	8/25
0·015–0·024 in.	8/25	6/12
	6/12	4/8
		2/6
		$\frac{1}{2}$/3
		0/1
0·60–0·91 mm.	Mesh 150/170	8/25
0·024–0·036 in.	20/40	6/12
	8/25	4/8
		2/6
		$\frac{1}{2}$/3
		0/1
0·91–1·11 mm.	Mesh 150/170	20/40
0·036–0·044 in.	20/40	8/25
		6/12
		4/8
		2/6
		$\frac{1}{2}$/3
		0/1
Over 1·11 mm.	Mesh 120/150	20/40
Over 0·044 in.	Mesh 150/170	8/25
		6/12
		4/8
		2/6
		$\frac{1}{2}$/3
		0/1

quantities. This is far more economical than applying larger amounts of powder at longer intervals.

The profile of the die must be maintained to ensure good life and trouble free drawing. Merely resizing a die is not sufficient.

Every die should have its own record card. On this card should be recorded the maker's number, the original size and the repolished sizes, together with the production of wire obtained at the original size and all the repolished sizes.

Wire production is, of course, an integral part of the electrical and electronics industries. Power, lighting and telephone cables and many other types of stranded and braided flexible conductors use up enormous quantities of copper wire. Cables often contain a great number of wires as, for instance the 1,818 pair unit type telephone cable which is made up of 3,636 wires of 0·40 mm. (0·0159 in.) diameter, so that one mile of this cable contains approximately 6,000 km. (approximately 3,700 miles) of wire.

Fine diameter copper wires are used for transformer windings, motor windings and coils for an infinite variety of industrial equipment, not to mention radio, television, domestic appliances and so forth.

A large quantity of copper wire goes into the manufacture of preformed wiring, i.e. made-to-measure 'harnesses' or 'cable assemblies' for aircraft, jet engines, automobiles, electronic equipment, etc. In motor car 'harnesses', the lengths of wire used (0·254–0·30 mm. diameter—0·010–0·012 in.) vary from approximately 1,200 metres (4,000 ft.) for a small car to approximately 3,000 metres (10,000 ft.) for a large car.

The amount of cable used on a modern airliner is from approximately 36,500 to 51,800 metres (120,000 ft. to 170,000 ft.), made up of multi-core cables in which the number of copper wires varies from 19 to 666, most of them being in the size range 0·152 to 0·30 mm. (0·006 to 0·012 in.) with a small proportion of 0·45 mm. (0·018 in.). It is calculated that at least 1,200 km. (750 miles) of single wires are used in the build-up of the various conductor cables and this does not include the internal wiring of the various instruments and flying aids, etc.

For industrial use there are approximately 350 alloys in the precious metal group consisting of gold, silver, platinum and palladium alloyed with iridium, rhodium, ruthenium and base metals. Some of these alloys are drawn down to extremely fine sizes for fuses, potentiometer windings, galvonometer suspensions, resistance windings, contact wires, etc. The finest wires produced are iridium/platinum and rhodium/platinum alloys down to 0·0063 mm. (0·00025 in.) (one tenth the diameter of a human hair), for use when space is an important feature such as in aircraft potentiometers; 1,740,000 metres (5,640,000 ft.) of this 0·0063 mm. (0·00025 in.) diameter wire weighs exactly 0·45 kg. (5½ lb.).

Nickel chromium alloy wires are used for resistances including high temperature heating elements in electric furnaces, domestic fires, cookers, water heaters, etc., whilst nickel copper alloys are used for low temperature resistances and for thermocouples.

Most of the tungsten wire produced is drawn down to fine diameters through diamond dies for electric lamp filaments.

ELECTRIC MOTORS AND GENERATORS

Many basic components are produced on presses. The tooling for the latter, whether they be in steel or carbide, depends on diamond in one form or another. These applications are described under Toolmaking in Chapter 3.

The commutators and windings are usually mounted on stepped steel shafts which are finish ground on the diamond trued abrasive wheels of centreless grinders. The spindles run in anti-friction bearings of which the load bearing surfaces are all ground on

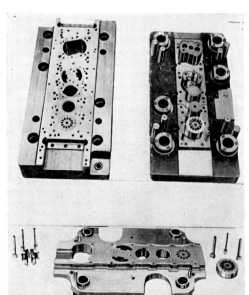

Diamond ground tungsten carbide lamination tool for electric motor component (Toolmasters [Manufacturing] Ltd.)

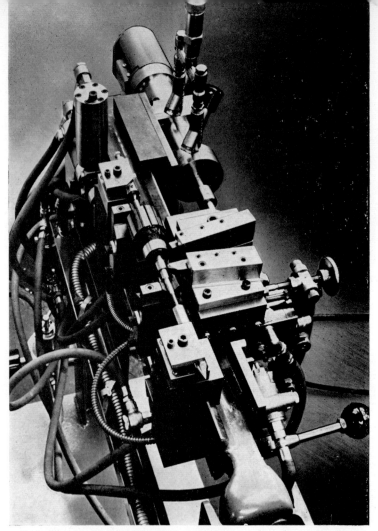

Example of special purpose diamond turning machine for commutators
(Small Electric Motors Ltd.)

diamond trued abrasive wheels. The copper commutators depend on
diamond turning to provide the finish required to minimise the
wear of the carbon brushes. This operation is not only applied to
fractional horse-power and other mass produced commutators, but
also to traction motors for locomotives and power station installations. In the latter case, the commutators are sometimes resurfaced
in the same way *in situ* after a period of service.

Close-up of commutator after partial diamond turning (Precidia S.A.)

The mass production work is often carried out on specially developed machines instead of standard diamond turning lathes such as those produced by Bryant Symons Ltd. (England) and Boley (Germany). The special purpose machines have been developed by Small Electric Motors of London, Spider Inc., of Sudbury, Mass., and Electrolux of Sweden. Such units will take workpieces from about 25 mm. (1 in.) to 200 mm. (8 in.) in length and have a swing over the bed of up to 200 mm. (8 in.). The linear speed of the driving belt

L

is 11·50 metres per second (2,260 ft. per minute). Production rates claimed are up to 10–15 pieces per minute depending upon length of cut, finish required and rate of feed. Prior undercutting of the laminations is recommended.

The carbon brushes which form the electrical connection with the commutators are cut to size with electrometallic diamond slitting saws such as a continuous rim blade 200 mm. (8 in.) diameter × 1·5 mm. ($\frac{1}{16}$ in.) thick in grit 36. They are also finish ground to size with electrometallic taper cup wheels with an angled leading edge. One example used in this field is 125 mm. (5 in.) diameter by 8 mm. ($\frac{5}{16}$ in.) face in grit 36.

The motors in the mass produced categories are not only used in general industry, but also form the power unit for refrigerators, vacuum cleaners, washing machines, spin driers, hair driers, food mixers and many other household appliances as well as in automobiles.

METERS

One area in which diamond plays an important part is in the grinding and polishing of jewel bearings for use in these instruments. Because they are even more widely used in watches, they are discussed in Chapter 10 on Jewellery.

Also employed in meter component production are, of course, form grinding techniques to produce punches and dies for stamping out gears and other movement parts and indicator hands. As in most profile grinding, diamond tooling plays an important part as the medium for truing and shaping the formed abrasive wheels for steel tools or providing the actual grinding tools for carbide press tools.

CERAMICS, QUARTZ AND FERRITES

Just as diamond grinding plays such an important role in producing jewel bearings for meters, it also finds a wide usage in producing the ceramic insulators, the quartz crystals and the ferrite components used elsewhere in the electrical industries.

Diamond plays its part in drilling, grinding and polishing ceramics, not only for insulators but also for crucible components, pyrometry, water-tight terminals and diode caps. The diamond grinding tools are used on cylindrical, internal, vertical spindle surface and centreless grinders. Generally bronze bond wheels are used, but, particularly for cutting off in the green state and for form grinding, electro-metallic bonds are advantageous. Diamond milling tools can also be used.

Special polishing machines utilise diamond lapping compound. Working conditions are similar to those employed for hard metals. One well known mass production item is the ceramic insulators for automobile sparking plugs on which an extensive form grinding operation is undertaken with Diaform pantograph equipment.

The sawing of quartz crystals and the subsequent grinding to the required form has long been common practice in producing components for solid-state electronic devices. One application of quartz resonators is the quartz clock of the type manufactured by Rohde and Schwarz, the Munich electronics company. The actual quartz crystal is produced by the specialists, Quarzkeramic G.m.b.H., who employ diamond tooling extensively in their production. The sequence of operations is:

1. Slice the orientated quartz crystal using a peripheral diamond saw 300 mm. (12 in.) diameter and 1·8 mm. (0·07 in.) thick at a peripheral speed of 20/25 metres per second (4,000–5,000 ft. per min.). The 80/100 grit is at 150 concentration in a bronze bond. A special thin oil is used to keep the temperature below the critical 570°C.

2. Trepan discs form the slices formed in the first operation. Diamond trepanning tools, to approximately the same formulation as the slitting discs and having inside diameters between 8 mm. ($\frac{5}{16}$ in.) and 30 mm. (1·2 in.), are used to perform this operation on a standard hand fed drilling machine. Oil or paraffin is used as a coolant.

3. The discs thus formed are then milled to a convex form on one or both faces, employing methods similar to those described for glass lens milling in Chapter 6. A 20 mm. (0·8 in.) diameter diamond milling tool is used at approximately 15,000 r.p.m. The operating rim is 80/120 grit diamond at 100 concentration in a bronze bond.

Permanent magnet materials include many grades of ferrite in common use in electronics. Metal bond diamond grinding wheels are extensively applied and, in some cases, high concentration resin bond wheels containing nickel-clad diamond grit are also used to provide improved surface finishes on these brittle materials. Where still further improvement is required in this respect, diamond lapping compounds are applied down to 0·25 micron grain size.

TRANSISTORS

Sintered diamond saws were originally used to slice the germanium and silicon materials used for this purpose, but resulted in an unacceptable loss of expensive material. The position was improved with the advent of electrometallic saws, and the present state of the art rests with the use of the annular saw also produced by the same manufacturing method. The Post Office Research Establishment, at Dollis Hill, London, was very active in this development, and the original machine was produced commercially by the Caplin Engineering Company, Ltd., in England.

Electrometallic peripheral and annular cutting discs for slicing germanium and silicon

As the name implies, the electrometallic diamond rim is deposited on the bore of the stainless steel ring and is attached by the outside diameter to a drum under tension. The precise method of providing the tension has been the subject of considerable discussion and a number of alternatives are still in use. In addition to the original horizontal spindle layout of the Capco Q35 and the Do-All 70ID equipment, vertical spindle machines are also available from Capco and from Hamco or Creuzet. The range of diamond saws, used in this field at present, has the following characteristics:

Outside diameter		I/D cutting diameter		Cutting rim thickness range		Steel core thickness	
mm.	in.	mm.	in.	mm.	in.	mm.	in.
216	8⅛	82·5	3¼	0·125–0·200	0·005/0·000/8	0·050–0·100	0·004/0·008
257	10⅛	101·6	4	0·150–0·200	0·006/0·008	0·075–0·100	0·003/0·008
305	12	101·6	4	0·200	0·008	0·100	0·004
422	16⅝	152·4	6	0·200	0·008	0·100	0·004

The fixing holes are provided to international standards to suit the various machines.

The smaller kerf widths are attractive from the point of view of material saving, but have to be balanced against shorter saw life. Techniques have been developed to extend the diamond bearing working edge and thus the working life, but the thinner blades are, of course, still more susceptible to damage in use. Discontinuous edges have also been tried on these I/D saws to improve the clearance of cuttings and are showing some promise under laboratory conditions. The slice thickness obtained with this equipment is generally of the order of 0·25 mm. (0·010 in.) to 0·35 mm. (0·014 in.), but can be down to 0·075 mm. (0·003 in.), and from 10 mm. (0·4 in.) to 80 mm. (3·2 in.) in diameter. The saws are used at speeds from 3,000–4,000 r.p.m. for the smaller bore range and 1,500–2,500 for the larger range. The workpiece is usually attached to the work holding bar with wax at the required orientation. Feed rates of the order of 25–50 mm. (1–2 in.) per minute are normal, but higher speeds are used. These very high feed rates sometimes result in premature disc failure due to fatigue in the steel core, slackening at the cutting edge and consequent tapering and bowing of the slice surfaces. Slower feeds also tend to give improved surface finish readings which may be as low as 0·3 micron.

Improvements in dimensional accuracy and surface finish are sought to reduce the subsequent grinding and polishing required before the unit is usable. One of the alternatives being tried is the use of diamond compound fed on to a battery of tungsten wires. The latter are of the order of 0·140 mm. (0·0055 in.) in diameter and have been tried at cutting speeds in excess of 1 metre per second (200 ft. per minute). The wires ride on spools and pass through a trough containing the micron size diamond slurry. It is claimed that a 25 mm. (1 in.) diameter silicon bar can be reduced to fine wafers in about 12 minutes, and that the fine diamond sizes practically eliminate subsequent lapping. The method is also being tried on subsequent dicing operations.

These subsequent grinding operations are carried out generally with metal bond diamond wheels, but resin bonds are used successfully to produce high finishes. Examples of machines used in this field are the Autoflow/Abwood Model SG4 (Glass) Mark II precision surface grinder and the Blanchard 11–16. The latter can be used to grind some 150 silicon slices at a single loading and give the following results:

Slice size:	25 mm. diameter × 0·2 mm. thick (1 in. × 0·008 in.).
Stock removal:	0·2 mm. total (0·008 in.).
Surfaces per hour:	1,800.
Surface finish:	Approx. 0·25 microns.

The resulting slices, having been completed, are usually diced or parted into even smaller rectangles for final utilisation. From a material conservation point of view, the best method has been found to make minute grooves in the surfaces and then break the brittle materials along these lines of weakness. These resulting 'chips' or 'dice' are of the order of 0·5 mm. to 1 mm. square (0·020 in. to 0·040 in.) and are parted along the scribed grid pattern by passing between rubber rollers.

In order to ensure a maximum consistency, specially lapped diamond tipped tools are used to cut these grooves and the 'dicing' is achieved without any of the loss of material which results from any form of sawing. The tools normally used are of orientated chisel, truncated pyramid or conical form, the latter being applied mainly to circular cutting. The work is normally carried out dry, but, where a coolant can be applied, there is a considerable economy in tool life. Whilst, originally, the machines on which dicing was undertaken were developed by the ultimate users themselves, a number of makers have made the equipment commercially available. Examples are those offered by Tempress and Kulicke & Soffa of America and Karl Suss of Germany.

OTHER DIAMOND MACHINING APPLICATIONS

In addition to the commutator turning and transistor dicing operations already described, there is a number of other applications where diamond machining is employed to produce components for the industry.

Vee form diamond cutters are used to cut the pattern of printed circuits in copper laminate surfaces. Such a tool will complete at least four times as many boards as a carbide tool. The diamond also cuts faster. An electronic copying device controls the tool path in relation to the drum which revolves at about 20 r.p.m. whilst the pattern is transferred to it.

Gold sliding contacts are used in miniature precision slip ring assemblies to minimise corrosion. The surfaces are diamond turned to a 3 micro-inch finish. Diamond tools are also used for shaping and grooving epoxy components, copper substrates and silver surfaces in similar equipment.

Diamond turning a copper surfaced computer memory drum
(Bryant Symons & Co. Ltd.)

The light alloy rollers on which dictating machine belts run are critical as to concentricity and surface finish if an acceptable sound level is to be maintained. To achieve these ends, diamond tooling is used to provide concentricity within 0·05 mm. (0·002 in.) and a surface finish of 16 micro inches.

The critical memory discs and drums used in computers rely increasingly on diamond turning to produce the precise accuracy and finish required.

For this very critical work, purpose-designed lathes have been developed by Bryant Symons & Co. Ltd., of London. The main characteristics of two turning jobs on copper surfaced computer memory drums are tabulated below:

Element	Example 1	Example 2
Lathe type	Bryant Symons Model 2148	
Capacity	525 mm. (21 in.) dia. × 1,200 mm. (48 in.) tool traverse	
Work size	525 mm. (21 in.) dia. × 1,175 mm. (47 in.) long	450 mm. (18 in.) dia. × 750 mm. (30 in.) long
Surface finish	1 micro inch CLA	1 micro inch CLA
Spindle speed	350 r.p.m.	500 r.p.m.
Tool traverse per revolution	0·125 mm. (0·005 in.)	0·125 mm. (0·005 in.)
Diamond tool type	Single facet	Single facet

For facing computer data storage discs, an even less conventional lathe is in use, and the details of two examples are:

Diamond turning an aluminium vacuum chuck on a special facing lathe for computer storage discs (Bryant Symons & Co. Ltd.)

Element	Example 3	Example 4
Lathe type	Bryant Symons 36F21	Bryant Symons 17F6
Capacity	900 mm. (36 in.) dia.	425 mm. (17 in.) dia.
Tool traverse	525 (21 in.)	150 mm. (6 in.)
Chuck	900 mm. (36 in.) vacuum	350 mm. (14 in.) vacuum
Spindle speed	350 r.p.m.	1,000 r.p.m.
Traverse per rev.	0·18 mm. (0·007 in.)	0·13 mm. (0·005 in.)
Workpiece	Brass	Aluminium
Diamond tool	Single facet	Single facet
Surface finish	2 micro inch CLA	0·5 micro inch CLA

STYLI FOR RECORD PLAYERS

Sapphire styli are produced by methods very similar to those used in the jewel bearing industry and as described in Chapter 10.

In the search for better quality reproduction, the diamond stylus has also been developed. Vacuum setting has been adopted to permit the use of smaller and more readily available diamonds, and the subsequent shaping and polishing of the working area follows the general principles of other diamond cone grinding techniques, except that they are applied on a mass production basis. Recently, methods have been devised to have an even smaller diamond content welded on to a sapphire shank. It is claimed that these can be produced down to a size of 0·2 mm. (0·008 in.) diameter and 0·7 mm. (0·028 in.) long, having a weight of only 0·09 mg.

REFERENCES

'From Quartz Crystal to Precision Electronics'—Ing. B. Machule, Rohde & Schwarz, Munich, West Germany.

'Philips Diamond Drawing Dies'—N.V. Philips, Gloeilampenfabrieken, Eindhoven, Holland, *The Wire Industry*—July 1965.

'Tiniest Diamond Drills'—*Financial Times*—October 7th, 1968.

'Precision Machining of Alumina Components and Cutting Tools'—Prof. E. Blanpain, University of Charleroi, Belgium.

'Dressing of a Metal Bonded Diamond Wheel in Grinding Ceramics for Circuit Components'—Yuzo Arai, Ichiroida and Mitsutoshi Fukuda, Bulletin of Japan Society of Grinding Engineers, Vol. 8—1968.

'Abrasive Cutoff Operations for Plastics and Semiconductive Materials'—Akira Kobayashi, Electrotechnical Laboratory, Ginza-Higashi, Tokyo, Japan.

'Mullard Adds an "A" to R. & D.'—Stan Herbert, *Industrial Diamond Review*—June, 1972.

'The Grinding of Alumina'—N. W. Thiel, b.sc.(eng.), London, 21.9.71.

'A New Concept in Diamond Styli'—*Industrial Diamond Review,* February, 1972.

Technical Reports of the Precision Engineering Research Centre of Toshiba, the Tokyo Shibaura Electric Co. Ltd., Kawasaki, Japan.

U.S.S.R. Gost 17006 and 17007—1971.

6

Glass working

EVEN 'the man in the street' associates diamonds with glass. The hand operated 'vitrier' diamond glass cutter is still widely used. In fact, much wider use is made of other types of diamond tools in the glass industry. In the course of manufacture, wide use of tough refractories is made in furnace linings and conduits to carry the molten glass. In shaping the refractory blocks, of which these heat resistant linings are made, diamond saw blades are extensively used. In the case of continuous glass processing, the lengths are then cut automatically with diamond cutters. From then on, most types of flat glass are cut to shape with conventional 'glazier' diamonds or similar tools adapted to operate under mechanical control. Diamond grinding tools are then used for edging, bevelling and drilling not only conventional household glass and mirrors but also toughened and laminated automobile glass, ships' portholes, armour plate glass and vitrolite.

Diamond grinding, however, finds one of its greatest glass applications in the ophthalmic and scientific lens production fields. To form the lens' surfaces and grind the edges, to shape prisms and other optical forms, diamond grinding and smoothing tools are indispensable. Diamond cutting tools are also used to machine plastic contact lenses and the metal mounts of composite units such as microscope and zoom lens.

Glass components are extensively diamond machined for other industrial applications. Gas-tight joints for bottles and scientific glassware are formed with taper reamers, tube is cut to length with vitrier diamonds and many other sawing, drilling and grinding operations are carried out on a wide range of components.

Diamond grinding and etching tools are now also indispensable

in the finishing and decorating of glass tableware and glass orna-
ments.

MACHINING REFRACTORIES FOR GLASS PRODUCTION

The sawing of refractories, such as Zac or Monofrax, is usually
accomplished with segmental diamond saws under conditions very
similar to those employed for stone sawing except that the actual
formula used for the segments must be suitable for the material.
Where necessary, the materials can also be milled with diamond
impregnated cutters or drilled with diamond tube drills. The latter
is applied in some cases even whilst the furnace is in operation. The
water coolant fed through the drill centre solidifies the glass
temporarily and thus allows for the introduction of an element, for
instance, without shutting down the furnace. Refractories containing
a very high proportion of corundum result in shorter tool life than
normal refractories. This applies to sawing, milling and drilling. In
order to avoid contact with coolant, it is sometimes necessary to
machine these refractories dry, and this puts a further strain not
only on the diamond itself but also the bond and special measures
have to be taken in manufacture.

FLAT GLASS

Historically speaking, probably the oldest application for diamond
is for engraving and etching on glass. The Venetian glass makers
in the early 16th century were using a diamond point for this
purpose and it was probably not until much later that the diamond
was used for the actual cutting of glass to rectangular or circular
shapes. Certainly the clockmakers of the 17th century had round
and square glass covers for their dials. Perhaps the first example of a
writing diamond in this country was over 400 years ago when
Sir Walter Raleigh, in a moment of indecision, etched on a window
the line:

'Fain would I climb yet fear I to fall'

to which later Queen Elizabeth I added her censure:

'If thy heart fail thee climb not at all.'

Times have not changed.

The cutting operation

The glaziers' diamond industry can be traced back for nearly 200 years and has been for most of this time one of continuous expansion. The expertise of manufacture and the design of tool have developed from the simplest form, not unlike a pencil in appearance, to quite sophisticated automatic machinery having a diamond tipped inter-changeable insert.

Originally, the diamond used for cutting glass was what is known as a 'cutting spark'. This was a prerequisite to the manufacturer in the days before the art of polishing a diamond suitably had become established. A 'cutting spark' is a perfectly formed dodecahedron, not too sharp but rounded and will cut glass very well provided it has been accurately set. As some, but not all, of the few manufacturers discovered how to polish, a wider range of diamond became acceptable to the industry which grew rapidly.

The design of the conventional English pattern hand tools has not changed significantly since the introduction of the swivel block over 100 years ago. To be used properly, four basic rules must be obeyed. These are:

The correct manipulation of an English pattern glass cutter:
A. The cut   *B. The break*

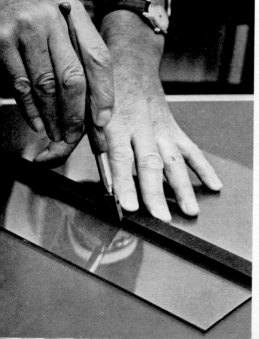

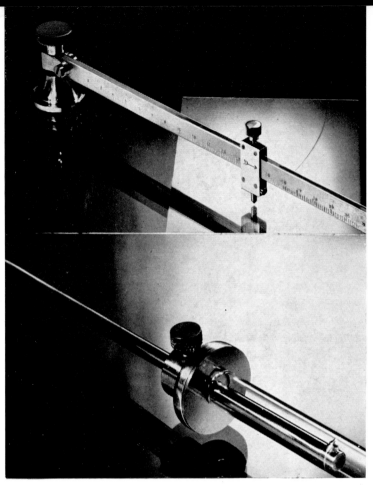

Glass circle and tube cutters for hand use

1. The cutting edge of the diamond is used parallel to the direction of the cut being made. The error in this is very small and should not exceed 1°. The swivel block is designed to facilitate this.
2. The diamond, which has a rounded silhouette when looked at from the side, must be held at such an angle for the whole length of the cut that the part in contact with the glass is just behind the actual point.
3. The tool should not lean over to either side of the cutting lath.
4. Just enough pressure is used to make the diamond 'sing'.

With these four rules satisfied, a diamond will cut miles of glass, frequently lasting its owner years between resets and a lifetime before it is worn out. This English pattern is sold all over the world with the exception of the Continent of Europe where the Continental pattern is more popular. This pattern is a polished metal drop forging or a polished metal head having a wooden handle. They are held vertically, not at the slope of the English pattern, and have no swivel head, but, because of the width of head, are easily held flat against the lath when in use.

Glass is made in a great variety of thicknesses ranging from 0·3 mm. (·012 in.), which is used in microscope work, to plate glass 25 mm. (1 in.) thick or more. Plate glass normally covers large areas and has all surface irregularities polished out. This will cure all visual distortion and has the effect of removing the hard skin and making the surface to be cut comparatively soft. Window glass, that is not polished, has a harder skin which becomes progressively harder as the substance is made thinner. Thus, a diamond designed to cut thin glass will be polished to a different geometry than the diamond for plate glass, and the diamond used for cutting tubes and those used for micro glass each have an individual geometry of their own. More and more glass today is being made on the new 'float' principle. This obviates the polishing process and takes out much of the surface tension inherent in glass drawn vertically from a molten tank and cooling as it rises. The accurate and correct setting of a diamond and its subsequent polishing for the purpose for which it is designed is what the industry is all about.

The 'Glass Age' truly arrived after the 1939–45 war and the consumption of glass since then has risen dramatically. Glass is so much taken for granted that its presence passes unnoticed.

There is a silvered mirror circle in every lady's powder compact and the consumption amounts to several million a year. Virtually every torch is provided with a glass circle at its end and once again the consumption runs into millions. Most motor cars have at least three dials and three mirrors apart from the glass windows and screens, and on to all this must be added the glass which forms the major part of any modern factory, office block or flat. This enormous consumption of glass has led to the design of automatic and semi-automatic glass cutting machinery.

Circles can now be cut in thin glass and in diameters ranging

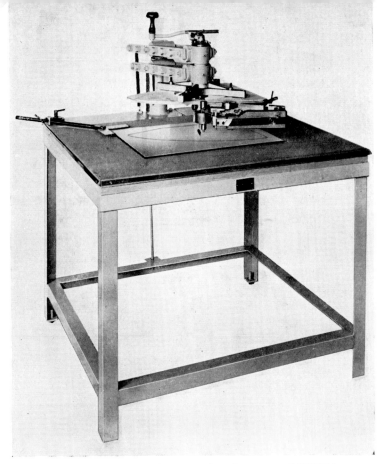

A hand operated template type glass form cutter (SN50D)
(Sharratt & Newth)

An automatic glass circle cutter (the SN61) (Sharratt & Newth)

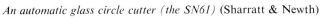

from 30 mm. (1·2 in.) to 150 mm. (6 in.) at the rate of 3,000 per hour on an automatic circle cutting machine. A similar machine, having a belt feed, can reduce 1,000 square metres (10,000 sq. ft.) of glass per hour to squares or rectangles of any size from approximately 30 mm. (1·2 in.) square upwards. These machines using diamond cutters have the great advantage that the diamonds do not produce a sliver of detritus material when cutting, thus making the problem of packaging, particularly silvered glass, much easier. There is a number of smaller hand operated machines which have been designed for cutting circles of larger diameters in small quantities and for cutting shaped glasses. The shape glass trade lies largely in shaped mirrors either for the motor car industry or for dressing table sets. There are also many dial covers that are kidney shaped.

Accurately set and with polishing geometry suitable for the purpose for which the tool is designed, there is nothing to touch the diamond for most glass cutting purposes.

Hand cutting needs skill and practice to be really effective, but no more than average knowledge is required when putting diamond inserts into well designed machinery. The glass writing diamond is used extensively throughout the medical and scientific professions for decorating, inscribing formulae and other data on to glass slides and bottles, etc.

Sawing and grinding operations on flat glass

In addition to the glass cutting operations carried out by these single diamond tools, there is a number of cases where, due to

An auto-straight line cutter (the SN59) (Sharratt & Newth)

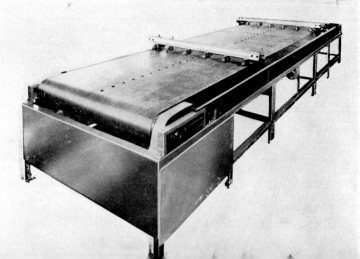

*Matching pair of mid-eighteenth century goblets presented to Messrs. L. E.
and E. M. Van Moppes on their retirement. The decoration was carried out
entirely with diamond tipped tools by Miss Honoria Marsh, the artist*
(Miss Honoria Marsh)

glass thickness, wire reinforcement or other factors, diamond saws
are used. Generally, these are of the sintered metal bond continuous
rim type, but, for depths of cut over about 125 mm. (5 in.), may be
of the segmental type as used on stone, concrete and refractories.
Delicate operations, where finish and absence of 'chipping' or
'breakout' are essential, are best accomplished with resin bond
continuous rim saws. A grain size of about mesh 120 and concentration 50 would be a normal specification.

For medium duty work a range of continuous rim saws is utilised
in diameters from about 75–350 mm. (3–14 in.) with thicknesses
varying from 0·8 mm. (0·03 in.) in the smaller diameters and up to
2·5 mm. (0·1 in.) in the larger sizes. Grain sizes in the thinner saws
are of the order of 100/150 mesh—concentrations of 50–75 are
usual. For the larger sizes, say over 125 mm. (5 in.) diameter and
0·8 mm. (0·03 in.) thick, coarser grain sizes in the 60/120 range with
25 or 50 concentration are preferred. The heavy duty segmental

M

saws are generally of the range of 400–600 mm. (16–24 in.) diameter and have segments of the order of 60 mesh and 25 concentration.

In the continuous rim range, the thinner blades are usually chosen on the ground of economy. Where any form of side pressure is anticipated or other conditions are suspect, the thicker blades should, however, be employed. It is important that maximum diameter flanges be employed; the flange diameter should be at least a third of the saw diameter; they should be accurate and clean for optimum saw life realisation. As in all glass working operations with diamond, coolants are essential. To the same end, wherever possible, machinery of rigid construction, adequate power and massive spindles should be employed. Peripheral speeds of about 30 m.p.s. (5,500 ft. per min.) are normally employed.

Generally electro-metallic saws are not economic on glass sawing, but some cases have been quoted of the use of band saws made in this way. In the U.S.A. a 125 mm. (5 in.) Pyrex glass disc had to be cut to an accurate ellipse. This was done on a conventional band saw machine at a rate of 750 mm. (30 in.) per hour.

Having shaped the panel of glass to the required dimensions, the resulting edges are sharp and unacceptable whether produced with the conventional glass cutter or the diamond saw. This was previously corrected by a laborious sequence of operations with conventional abrasive wheels or belts. Now, diamond grinding wheels serve most of the industry's needs although other abrasives are used to supplement the fast cutting diamond where a particularly high polish is required.

Typical metal bond diamond impregnated tools used in the glass industry

The basic operation used to make the glass edge condition acceptable is known as 'pencil-edging'. The metal bond diamond wheel has a grooved periphery whose dimensions vary according to the machine employed and the glass thickness and configuration required. In smaller plants, and even larger ones, where the runs are short, hand operated machines are used. The equipment consists of a motorised spindle providing a wheel peripheral speed of about 30 m.p.s. (5,500 ft. per min.) and heavy enough to carry up to four diamond wheels. A copious coolant supply is included and a built-in dressing arrangement is to be preferred. A typical example of such a machine is the Autoflow Model HPE/6/MR11. The 38 mm. ($1\frac{1}{2}$ in.) spindle is driven by a 1 h.p. motor and is of sufficient length to take up to four wheels according to width. Included in these may be a split vee diamond wheel for 'double arrising'. The dressing unit is easily attached and is driven by a $\frac{1}{6}$ h.p. motor and adequate coolant arrangements are provided. It carries 150 mm. (6 in.) diameter wheels. Other machines for this operation are made by Cutrock, Cortesi, Habit, Sun Tool and Sommer Maca.

Heavy duty universal automatic straight line edger
(Autoflow Engineering Ltd.)

The range of diamond wheels used in this type of operation is generally:

Diameters:	100–250 mm. (4–10 in.) according to machine.
Width range:	4·5–12·5 mm. (0·18–0·49 in.) according to glass thickness.
Grain sizes:	120 or 170 for roughing.
	240 or 300 for finishing.
Bond:	Metal.
Concentrations:	35-50.
Groove sizes:	Radii according to glass and wheel widths

The normal working conditions would employ a glass movement over the wheel of the order of 4–8 metres per minute (12–25 ft.) and a coolant volume of about 10 litres (2 gallons) per minute. On horizontal spindle machines, the glass is normally passed downward at a firm pressure over the roughing wheel, leaving small unground areas (known as 'brights') in the middle of the edge as control that minimum glass has been removed. This helps to maximise wheel life. No 'firing' should take place during this operation. Such a phenomenon indicates excessive wheel wear and possible damage to the glass. To eliminate this, the following should be checked:

1. Adequacy and direction of coolant supply. This must reach the bottom of the groove on pencil edging wheels.
2. Working pressure and speed is not excessive.
3. Poor cutting is not leaving 'flanges'.
4. That the diamond wheel is not glazed or out of true.

For the subsequent smoothing operation, a lighter pressure should be used and the glass passed very steadily upward. This should remove the unground witness areas (brights), improve the overall surface finish and edge 'shelling' in one operation. Work speeds and pressures should be modified so that one pass only is used for each operation. The exception to this might be 10 mm. thick glass—the thickest normally hand edged.

On vertical spindle machines, either the glass or the wheel may move, but the same principles apply if maximum efficiency and economy are to be attained. The glass must always be square with the wheel.

The cutting properties of the diamond wheel deteriorate under the influence of the glass being ground and eventually become 'glazed' and cease to cut. Before this point is reached a 'cleaning stick' should be applied briefly to the working area at about 25 p.s.i. The normal abrasive block used for this purpose is about grade 0–80–IV and 150 mm.×100 mm.×6 mm. (6×4×¼ in.). A fully glazed wheel needs to be returned to the manufacturer for works reconditioning. To restore concentricity, the wheel dressing unit is used. This may be power driven or of the brake-controlled type. An abrasive wheel of WA–150 or 6–80–KV is used. By removing the high spots on the diamond wheel, work finish is improved and better wheel life obtained. This operation should be carried out on mounting a new wheel and before the used wheel becomes too eccentric. Before being used again, the cleaning stick should once more be applied. Some 'firing' may take place immediately after these maintenance operations, but should not be allowed to persist.

In addition to the general rounding and smoothing operations covered by 'pencil edging', the final junction between the curved edge and the glass face is chamfered off in a subsequent operation known as 'arrising'. The operation may in some cases be carried out on an edge which has not been previously 'pencil edged'. The vee form wheel is usually mounted on the same spindle as the pencil edging wheel and has the following range of characteristics:

Form:	90° included angle formed by two 45° bevel units 3 or 4 mm. wide in each case and separated by a spacer which can be readily replaced with alternative thickness to prolong wheel life.
Range of diameter:	150–250 mm. (6–10 in.).
Grit size:	200 mesh.
Bond:	Metal.
Concentration:	50.

The operating conditions are similar to those for hand pencil edging.

For the larger producer and the more sophisticated plant, automatic equipment has been developed to mechanise these operations and has been extended to cover automobile glass. The range of operations has also been extended to cover automatic bevelling of mirrors and plate glass shop front components. Machines have been developed for these automatic operations in the U.K., U.S.A. and Germany by Autoflow, Bielerfelder, Union, Corvesa, Sun Tool and Sommer Maca. They usually have from 2–4 diamond edging and arrising spindles, each driven by a 3–7 h.p. motor for the edging and lower horsepower for the arrising. Supplementary spindles of intermediate horsepower are provided for polishing. The cut rectangles of glass are located on a conveyor which is an integral part of the machine. As the operating cycle starts, the glass is gripped between spring-loaded resilient pads. The lower glass edge passes over a series of diamond wheels and emerges on another conveyor, located beyond the working area of the machine, for unloading and relocation for subsequent edges. The supplementary polishing spindles carry conventional abrasive wheels of about 300 mm. (12 in.) × 12·5 mm. ($\frac{1}{2}$ in.) and about specification WA 220–300–400 FR 10. It is this operation which sometimes limits the throughput of the diamond wheels. Generally, output is between 0·5 m. (20 in.) and 4 m. (150 in.) per minute depending on the polishing operation as mentioned and:

1. The number of wheels.
2. Glass thickness.
3. Size of plate. In theory this has no effect, but, in practice, large panes must be traversed more slowly for optimum results.

The range of diamond wheels usually employed is:

Diameters:	200–250 mm. (8–10 in.) according to machine.
Edge details:	As for hand operating.
Grain sizes:	85–100 Roughing.
	170 Semi-finishing.
	280 Smoothing.
Bond:	Metal.
Concentration:	35–50.

There are two alternative diamond applications for arrising on these automatic edgers, that employing one cup wheel and, the other, a pair of bevelled arrising wheels. The single cup type is considered more economical because of its self-dressing action, but the vee configuration gives a better finish. In both cases metal bonds are used with 200 grit 50 concentration diamond.

The automatic edgers discussed so far have processed only one straight edge at a time. Mass producers of standard size rectangular mirrors, table tops and doors, however, now utilise 'double edgers' which process two opposing edges simultaneously. The Autoflow GP model is an example. The specification for this machine claims:

Output speeds:	Up to 13 metres per minute.
Range of edge form:	Rounded pencil edge only.
	Rounded pencil edge with double arris.
	Flat with double arris.
	Double arris only (unpolished).
Glass thickness range:	2–10 mm. ($\frac{3}{32}-\frac{3}{8}$ in.).
Glass sizes:	178 mm. (7 in.) to 1,525 mm. (60 in.)—normal.
	76 mm. (3 in.) to 253 mm. (10 in.)—with one track removed.
Motor:	Grinding/polishing spindles 2 h.p. Conveyor 2 h.p. Reset drive 1 h.p. (geared).

The wheels normally utilised are of the following order:

Diameter: 200 mm. (8 in.).

Glass thickness, width and radius relation:

Glass mm.	Impregnation width	Radius
4	6 mm. ($\frac{1}{4}$ in.)	4·5 mm. ($\frac{3}{16}$ in.)
5	7·5 mm. ($\frac{5}{16}$ in.)	
6	9 mm. ($\frac{3}{8}$ in.)	7·5 mm. ($\frac{5}{16}$ in.)
6	7·5 mm. ($\frac{5}{16}$ in.)	Flat
10	12·5 mm. ($\frac{1}{2}$ in.)	Flat
Any	3 mm. ($\frac{1}{8}$ in.)	Vee used in pairs

In addition to these straight line edging machines, others have been developed specifically to deal with the irregular shapes required in the automobile industry. The glass is cut as accurately as possible and located in the work holding fixture.

The diamond wheel or wheels then follow a template corres-

ponding to the glass shape and the grooved diamond wheel trans-
forms the flat cut edge to a smooth rounded form. The wheels used
on the Sun Tool range of machines designed for automobile glass
are generally 244 mm. (9¾ in.) diameter and 6 mm. (¼ in.) or 7 mm.
(0·276 in.) wide for 4 mm. and 5 mm. glass thickness respectively.
The grit sizes vary according to the operation: between 120 mesh
for roughing, 170 or 200 for single wheel working and 240 mesh for
finishing.

The glass traverses across the diamond wheel face at a speed of
about 1·5 metres (5 ft.) per minute and some 'firing' on acute corners
has to be tolerated. In Europe, some preference is shown for flat
ground edges with arrised corners and in such cases a flat peripheral
diamond replaces the grooved 'pencil edger'.

*Flexible shaft driven equipment for the finishing of plate glass edges. A
100 mm. (4 in.) cup type metal bonded diamond grinding wheel is used,
180 mesh. The wheel r.p.m. is 3,500 and water is used as a coolant. Concave
periphery wheels are used for 'pencil-edging' and 120° external 'V' wheel for
'brilliant cutting'* (Flextol Engineering Co. Ltd.)

For work which lies between purely hand operation and fully automatic, machines have been developed which clamp the glass in place and provide guide rails or other systems for the diamond wheel spindle, but on which the traverse is by hand. The wheels are generally of 100 mm. (4 in.), 175 mm. (7 in.) or 200 mm. (8 in.) diameter, but, otherwise, as for operations on the machines described earlier. The spindle is driven through a flexible shaft driven by a ¾ h.p. motor. A water supply is provided as coolant.

Whilst these semi-automatic machines are also used for mirror and other bevelling work, if this is being done on a production basis fully automatic machines, such as the Autoflow automatic mirror beveller, are used. The latter is available in three models carrying respectively 6, 9 or 12 spindles. It can accommodate up to 6 mm. (¼ in.) thick glass in sizes from 20 cm. (8 in.) square up to 2 m. (80 in.) square.

The glass can be processed as a continuous sequence:

Diamond grinding bevels.
Diamond pencil edging.
Smoothing of bevels.
Felt polishing of bevels.

The output of the machine is governed by the quality of polish required and the diamond tools used, but the makers quote the following as a guide to the outputs per minute to be expected from each machine:

Machine type	Width of bevel					
	6 mm. ¼ in.	9 mm. ⅜ in.	13 mm. ½ in.	16 mm. ⅝ in.	19 mm. ¾ in.	25 mm. 1 in.
6-spindle model	91·5 cm. 36 in.	63·5 cm. 25 in.	46 cm. 18 in.	46 cm. 18 in.		
9-spindle model	1·14 m. 45 in.	1·02 m. 40 in.	91·5 cm. 36 in.	63·5 cm. 25 in.	46 cm. 18 in.	30·5 cm. 12 in.
12-spindle model	1·22 m. 48 in.	1·14 m. 45 in.	1·02 m. 40 in.	89 cm. 35 in.	61 cm. 24 in.	46 cm. 18 in.

Up to four diamond grinding wheels are fitted for bevelling. They are cup wheels having a diameter of 250 mm. (10 in.) and cutting face 3 mm. (⅛ in.) wide. With a concentration of 40, grit 44 and 60

Twelve spindle 'double edger' diamond grinding machine for thicker plate and laminated glass. Six spindles grind flat, two seam arris and four have automatic actuation (Autoflow Engineering Ltd.)

are used for roughing or 85 and 100 for smoothing. The glass then passes over up to two pencil edging wheels to smooth and profile the edge, and then up to three abrasive smoothing cup wheels such as WA 280 and 320 PB. The bevels are finally polished by three or more felt buffs fed with recirculated cerium oxide compounds.

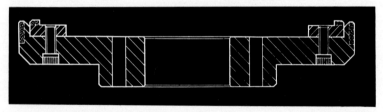

Combination diamond wheel used on plate glass edge and bevel grinding on Autoflow Jobber. The outer ring is for roughing, whereas the inner has a finer diamond grit, stands proud of the outer and removes only a small amount of glass to produce a smooth finish (Autoflow Engineering Ltd.)

A similar operation is carried out on plate glass sheets for shop windows. Two such sheets can be used adjacent to one another at right angles or some other angle without the use of a frame. They may be butt-jointed or mitre bevelled to provide a concealed joint. The Autoflow Automatic Jobber was developed for these and similar operations. A combination diamond wheel can be used to produce accurate bevels up to 18·75 mm. ($\frac{3}{4}$ in.) wide with a smooth finish. These wheels are generally from the following range of characteristics:

Diameters:	Outer 150, 175, 200 mm. (6, 7 or 8 in.). Inner 140, 165, 190 mm.
Ring width:	Outer 3 mm. ($\frac{1}{8}$ in.). Inner 6 mm. ($\frac{1}{4}$ in.).
Grain size:	Outer 60 mesh. Inner 170 mesh.
Concentration:	Outer 40. Inner 50.

For lighter equipment used in these operations, such as the Flextol GW90, smaller single metal bond wheels are used:

Decorative grooving on glass. Vee diamond wheel mounted on flexible drive equipment (Flextol Engineering Co. Ltd.)

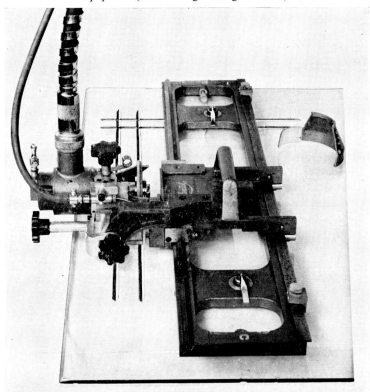

Diameter: 100 mm. (4 in.).
Ring width: 10 mm. (0·4 in.) light duty.
                   15 mm. (0·6 in.) heavy duty.
Grit size: 120 mesh.
Concentration: 50.

Lying, perhaps, a little between optical glass and the flat glass discussed so far is the special laminated product used in aircraft windows. High purity optical crown glass is used to avoid distortion and interference with the pilot's vision. After heat treatment, the glass is rolled and annealed and at this stage the surfaces are corrugated. In order to withstand the aircraft pressurisation, several sheets have to be laminated to form the window. To ensure successful adhesion between the layers, the mating surfaces must be almost perfectly flat. The corrugations are removed to provide sheet thicknesses of 4·5 mm. ($\frac{3}{16}$ in.) up to 18 mm. ($\frac{3}{4}$ in.) This is done on a Blanchard 42–84 vertical spindle grinder carrying segmental diamond wheels of about 80 grit at 50 concentration in a metal bond. Both sides of each sheet are ground and finally smoothed and polished before assembly. The grinding operation with the diamond wheel is carried out with the machine table revolving at about 6 r.p.m. and the diamond tools at 300 r.p.m.

Drilling, trepanning and counterboring flat glass

The combination of diamond tube drill and high speed machine has revolutionised glass drilling. This can be said of even a single head machine, but even more so if one refers to the more recent 'double-driller' that cuts from both sides of the glass. This not only halves the actual cutting time, but avoids the alternatives of turning over the glass or risking a ragged hole. A coolant supply, preferably through the drill-centre, is essential.

Diamond drills are now almost universally used in flat glass drilling for fixing holes in mirrors, doors, shop front components, windows, shelves, table tops and bathroom fittings. Where this has to be done *in situ* or on a wide variety of glass sizes, the 'Wall Arm' type drill set-up is used. Where the operation is to be carried out on smaller size sheets on a mass production basis, the double head machine is used. In the case of the latter, the two drills should

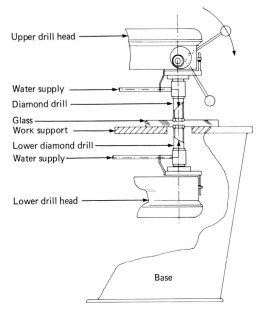

Upper drill head
Water supply
Diamond drill
Glass
Work support
Lower diamond drill
Water supply
Lower drill head
Base

Schematic layout of double diamond drilling machine

be used as a pair, as the lower one is normally about 0·2 mm. (0·008 in.) larger in diameter than the top one. The spindle speed and water pressure range normally recommended by the suppliers are:

Speeds:

Drill diameter		R.P.M.
mm.	in.	approx.
6–11	$\frac{1}{4}-\frac{7}{16}$	3,500
12–23	$\frac{1}{2}-\frac{7}{8}$	2,000
25–48	$1-1\frac{7}{8}$	1,000
50–75	2–3	500

Water:

Glass thickness		Water pressure	
mm.	in.	kg./cm.^{2}	p.s.i.
–6	$-\frac{1}{4}$	0·35–0·7	5–10
9–12	$\frac{3}{8}-\frac{1}{2}$	0·7–1·75	10–25
15–38	$\frac{5}{8}-1\frac{1}{2}$	1·75–2·1	25–30
+38	$+1\frac{1}{2}$	Maximum	

If a double head machine is not available for a particular operation and it is necessary to drill only from one side, some chipping or 'shelling' may result on the underside edge. If this is undesirable, it will be necessary to drill only half the depth in the first operation. The glass should then be turned over and the drill relocated over the half drilled hole. Care should be taken to drill only till the two halves meet otherwise chipping may result on the first side. The alignment of the two halves is important as inaccuracy in this respect may result in damage to the diamond tube drill. On repetition work, a suitable drill jig is recommended. In the case of very thin glass it may be necessary to drill into a solid support. The core should be cleared from the tube drill after each hole. Should a drill cease to cut, its cutting properties may be restored by circular rubbing on the side of a wet abrasive wheel of about 100/120 grit. The abrasive should not be applied to the rotating drill nor the latter drilled into even a soft abrasive wheel.

Diamond tube drills for this type of operation may be in electro-metallic or sintered metal bond. The former generally have a thinner wall, but the latter are more robust. The diameter range of electro-metallic drills is generally in 1 mm. steps from 3–22 mm., then in 2–3 mm. steps up to 45 mm. and then 50 mm. The German Standard DIN 58744 (hollow drills used in optics), however, lists many more alternatives and quotes the following characteristics:

Diameter range	Grit size	Concentration	Depth of impregnation
3–6.5 mm.	D150	50	5 mm.
12.5–26 mm.	D100	75	5 mm.

Unless a special shank is required for a specific machine, drills up to 12 mm. ($\frac{1}{2}$ in.) are supplied with 6 mm. ($\frac{1}{4}$ in.) diameter shanks, 37 mm. ($1\frac{1}{2}$ in.) long, and larger ones 12·5 mm. ($\frac{1}{2}$ in.).

One manufacturer of double head drilling machines claims that over 240 holes of 6 mm. ($\frac{1}{4}$ in.) diameter can be drilled per hour in 6 mm. ($\frac{1}{4}$ in.) plate glass.

Where necessary the drilled holes are countersunk, for which operation conical or spherical diamond tools are made—generally in 10 mm. and 12 mm. diameters. For general application in hand operated power tools, an electrometallic spherical tool is recommended. In order to distribute wear, it should be applied with an oscillating movement. Coolant must be applied, but, if the operation follows immediately after diamond drilling, the glass is usually sufficiently wet. The normal centre flow of water cannot be applied.

Where glass discs have to be cut from plate or sheet glass, larger tube drills are used as trepanning tools. They are generally in the 50–100 mm. diameter range (2–4 in.) for such items as instrument covers. Another example is the cutting of 32 mm. ($1\frac{1}{4}$ in.) discs from lead glass plate to provide windows for X-ray equipment. They are cut from 8 mm. ($\frac{5}{16}$ in.) plate on a standard Meddings Pacera precision drill to an accuracy of 0·25–0·40 mm. (0·010–0·015 in.) with the spindle running at 900 r.p.m. A small percentage of rust inhibiter is used in the coolant water.

Where ultrasonics are applied to glass drilling, diamond probes are also used as on the Dawe Universal Ultrasonic Machine. This provides a means for drilling small diameter accurate holes to depths of several inches.

The scientific optical trade

This industry probably uses the widest range of impregnated diamond tools. The specific needs of the ophthalmic optical trade is in addition and is dealt with later in the chapter. The range produced may vary from microscope lens of 1 mm. diameter up to windows for Radioactive Closed Areas 200 mm. (8 in.) thick and 1,000 mm. (40 in.) square. The lenses produced in quantities, however, are the key components in cameras, projectors, field-glasses, telescopes, microscopes and other industrial magnifiers. The materials vary from soft, high lead content glass to hard natural and fused quartz. It is this wide range of workpiece specification that gives rise to the extensive scope of the diamond milling, grinding and smoothing equipment.

Previously, all grinding operations were carried out on cast-iron laps fed with abrasive powder slurry. Smaller lenses are still frequently batched by fixing to a spherical metal base to make a 'block'. The metal base is called a 'mushroom'.

With the advent of diamond tooling, the normal procedure for surfacing a lens can now be summarised:

Op. 1: One or more diamond milling operations to generate the approximate radius required and remove excess material from one side of the lens. This is then reversed and a similar operation carried out on the second side.

Op. 2: One or more 'diamond pellet' smoothing operations to correct the curve and improve the surface finish.

Op. 3: The final polishing operation not yet within the range of diamond applications.

The machines used for Operation 1 are known as Curve Generators

Lens curve generator RF1A employing diamond grinding wheel
(Wilhelm Loh K.G.)

and, for workpieces up to 100 mm. (4 in.) machines such as the
Autoflow 124/158, the CMV60, the Dama MFS40 and FS3, the
Loh RF1 and the Optibel MDM are examples. For larger work-
pieces up to 550 mm. (22 in.) some of the machines in general use
are the Adcock & Shipley OVS and 2VS, the Autoflow 159, the
Dama FSK150 and 300, the Loh RF2 and the Optibel GDM.
Although these two ranges of machines include both vertical and
horizontal layouts, the principle of operation is similar throughout.
The lens is held in the work fixture and rotated at about 5–25 r.p.m.

$$\text{Sin } \phi = \frac{D}{2(R+r)}$$
Convex curves

$$\text{Sin } \phi = \frac{D}{2(R-r)}$$
Concave curves

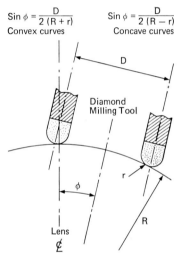

Diamond
Milling Tool

Lens
℄

D must be greater than one half
of the Chordal Diameter of Lens

*Basis of calculation for
machine head setting when
applying diamond impregnated
milling tools*

The edge of a round nosed diamond milling tool is presented to the
lens centre and rotated at 2,000 to 16,000 r.p.m. The approach
angle of this milling tool is variable by adjustment of the machine
head. The angle chosen is a function of the radius of curvature
required on the lens and the radius on the edge of the milling tool.
The 'pitch circle diameter' of the latter is generally about 75% of
the chordal diameter of the lens workpiece. Where the radius of the
lens is particularly steep, as, for example, in hyper-hemisphere work,
the P.C.D. of the milling tool is critical. If the radius is shallow or for
plane surfaces, the diameter over half the chordal diameter is
relatively unimportant. To compensate for the movement of the

N

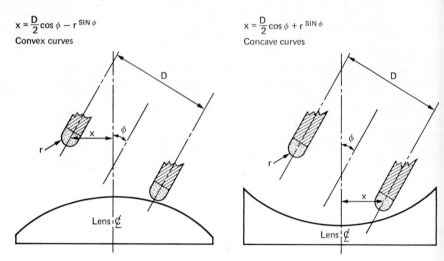

$$x = \frac{D}{2} \cos \phi - r \sin \phi$$

Convex curves

$$x = \frac{D}{2} \cos \phi + r \sin \phi$$

Concave curves

Calculations to determine the workpiece centreline position (x) when applying diamond impregnated milling tools

point of contact between milling tool and lens, as the head angle varies, a further calculation is required to set the lateral displacement of the workpiece.

Transfer and magazine loading equipment has been developed to carry lenses through the various grinding processes where they are being produced on a mass production basis, and examples of such machines are the Dama SM80 Transfer, which includes smoothing and polishing as well as curve generation, and the Loh RF1(A) Magazine Loading Curve Generator. In such cases the diamond application remains unchanged.

Where aspherical curves have to be generated, machines such as the Dama ASG120 and 600 have been developed. These employ peripheral diamond wheels controlled by a copying mechanism.

The basic range of milling tools required varies from a pitch diameter of about 5 mm. ($\frac{3}{16}$ in.) to 100 mm. (4 in.), but the German Standard DIN 58741 includes diameters up to 250 mm. (10 in.). Wall thicknesses range from 1·5 mm. ($\frac{1}{16}$ in.) up to 6 mm. ($\frac{1}{4}$ in.) or 10 mm. in the larger German sizes. The depth of impregnation is usually either 4 or 6 mm. For heavy duty and use on interrupted cuts, as for surfacing large 'blocks' of large lenses, special 'bull-nosed' milling tools have been developed. These are usually supplied in a range of sizes from about 115 mm. (4·5 in.) to 340 mm. (13·4 in.). The 10 mm. (0·4 in.) wall thickness is tapered towards the cutting face and terminates in a 3 mm. ($\frac{1}{8}$ in.) radius. This is designed to provide maximum strength and stock removal properties.

The diamond grain sizes specified depend on the user's stock removal and surface finish requirements, and generally the grit size to finish relationship is of the following order:

Grit size	Approx. finish Rt–microns
60	5–6
85	2–3
100	1·5–2
120	1–1·5

The coarsest grades provide a stock removal rate of up to 10 cubic centimetres per minute, reducing to about 4 for the 120 grit. The results are, of course, dependent on the type of glass, the machine condition and the coolant. The latter can be particularly significant and has been the subject of considerable research in recent years. The German Standard DIN 58741 mentions 100 concentration, but concentrations down to 50 are often specified for use on machines with lower spindle speeds.

Using these milling methods, Sir Howard Grubb Parsons & Company, Ltd. removed almost 907 kgs. (2,000 lb.) of glass from a slab of low-expansion Pyrex glass to produce a 2·5 metres (98 in.) diameter mirror for the Isaac Newton telescope recently commissioned at the Royal Observatory in Herstmonceux, Sussex.

Another unusual application in the glass milling field occurred in the preparation of observation windows for the working area of the type of wind tunnel used in the development of the shape of the Concorde. The window is used to observe changes in air density in high speed operation. Diamond tools were used in all the primary operations in shaping the 450 mm. diameter by 100 mm. thick (18 by 4 in.) slab. To mill the bevel, a metal bond segmental wheel of 60/80 mesh diamond was applied at 1,000 r.p.m., whilst the top grade crown glass workpiece rotated at $\frac{1}{3}$ r.p.m.

In addition to its use in these primary operations, diamond is beginning to encroach on the smoothing operations previously

Examples of diamond impregnated pellet assemblies for lens semi-finishing (Precidia S.A.)

carried out entirely with cast-iron laps fed with abrasive slurry. A significant advance in recent years has been the development of diamond pellets which are attached to spherical metal preforms. Originally, tools were made with a complete diamond layer, but the pellet system improves the clearance of the debris and facilitates manufacture of the tool. The lens is rotated and oscillated in contact with this interrupted surface spherical form tool. The working area of the preform is normally covered to the extent of between 25 and 50%. The improvements claimed for this new method are in the following areas:

1. Higher outputs—up to 1,000% improvement.
2. Greater accuracy—with less operator skill.
3. Greater consistency—reduced wear rates on the tool give dimensional stability with less time spent on correction.
4. Fixed abrasive—resulting in less scratching and cleaner operating conditions.
5. Reduction in subsequent polishing times.

The machines designed to utilise the advantages of the diamond pellet incorporate the following basic features:

1. A vertical spindle carrying the diamond pelleted lap at from 200 r.p.m., for say a 500 mm. lap (20 in.), up to 4,000 r.p.m. for a 10 mm. (0·4 in.) lap.
2. An upper spindle on which the lens rotates freely and which oscillates from 20/60 cycles (per minute) carrying the lens holder on a ball joint.
3. A pressure of the order of 1·5 to 6 atmospheres between tool and workpieces.
4. Coolant feed through the tool spindle.
5. In some cases, interchangeability between lap and lens position.

Examples of such machines are the Autoflow Pellgrinder, the Bothner, the CMV 'ICMF', and the LP50/100 and PLM 200/400 from Loh. They provide stock removal of the order of 0·1 mm. (0·004 in.) for cycle times of from 10 seconds to 5 minutes.

The diamond pellets are covered by German standard DIN 58745 in the following dimensions:

Diameter mm.	Thickness alternative in each diameter mm.
4	
5	2
6	3
8	or 4
10	

In practice, however, for inventory purposes, a list such as the following is determined from experience:

Diameter	Thickness	Grain sizes available in each Ø		Approx. finish attainable
mm.	mm.	DIN	micron range	micron Rt
4	2	D30	20/40	
5	2	D22	15/30	0·65
6	2	D15	10/20	0·55
8	2	D9	6/12	0·50
10	3	D6	4/8	0·47
		D4	2/6	0·45
		D3	1/5	

The successful application of diamond pellets depends very much on the accuracy of the diamond grading. This factor has been sometimes confused by the existence of different methods of measuring diamond particles. British Standard 1987 specifies the projected area method of measurement, as does American Standard CS 261–63; another method is to measure the longest dimension of a particle and the maximum dimension on a line at right angles to this longest dimension. The mean of these two measurements is then quoted as the size of the particle. These methods and their many variations depend on a microscopic examination and measurement of the particles, but other methods depend on the sedimentation behaviour of particles in a fluid, e.g. Andreasen pipette and sedimentation balance methods, and there are very many variations on these basic methods. The question has been the subject of extensive investigation by F.E.P.A. and it is anticipated that a finally agreed basis will clarify this factor in the near future. Meanwhile, some manufacturers have devised their own safeguards to ensure their product is acceptable to the user of this type of tool.

The 'working surfaces' of the lens having been completed, the outside diameter has to be finished and prepared for mounting. This is generally referred to as 'centering'. This is done to achieve the following results:

1. To grind the lens edge so that the optical and geometric centres coincide.
2. Reduce the diameter to the exact dimension required.
3. Improve the finish on the edge of the lens, and

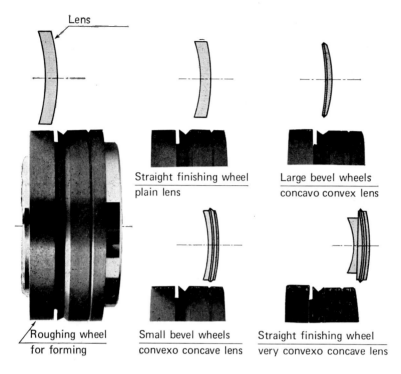

Straight finishing wheel	Large bevel wheels
plain lens	concavo convex lens

Small bevel wheels	Straight finishing wheel
convexo concave lens	very convexo concave lens

Roughing wheel
for forming

Examples of diamond grinding operations on lens edging (Precidia S.A.)

4. Chamfer the edges so that any small chips are removed. These chips may otherwise result in undesirable effects inside the lens system.

The operation is, of course, basically a cylindrical grinding operation and can be carried out quite successfully on standard metal grinding machines, but purpose made machines have been developed such as the Bothner centering machine; the Dama type FOM2; the Loh types WG, LZ25 and 80. The normal characteristics are:

Lens diameter accommodated: 1–150 mm. (0·040–6 in.).
Work spindle speed: 30–90 r.p.m.
Cycle time: 0·5–12 minutes.

Grinding spindle speed: 3,000–5,000 r.p.m.
Grinding wheel diameter: 100–160 mm. (4–6½ in.).
Coolant: Recirculated.

In addition to the peripheral wheels used for grinding the plain diameters, chamfering wheels are often used simultaneously. They have a root diameter corresponding to the appropriate plain wheel and project 0·5 mm. (0·020 in.), 1 mm. (0·040 in.) or 2 mm. (0·080 in.) beyond the peripheral wheel. Both the latter and the chamfering wheels are normally supplied with centres to German Standard DIN 58742 and this specifies alternative projections of 0·5, 1, 1·6, 2·5 and 4 mm., with alternative angles of 30°, 45°, 60° and at right angles to the peripheral wheel with 15° and 75° as further possibilities. In practice, the following range of wheels appears to cover most requirements:

Peripheral wheel			Chamfering components		
Diameter mm.	Width mm.	Bore mm.	Diameter mm.	Width mm.	Bore mm.
100	5 ⎤ 8 ⎬ 10 ⎦	25	⎡101 ⎨102 ⎣104	1·0 1·5 2·5	
150	5 ⎤ 8 ⎮ 10 ⎬ 12 ⎮ 15 ⎦	30	⎡151 ⎨152 ⎣154	1·0 1·5 2·5	to suit peripheral wheels
160	5 ⎤ 8 ⎮ 10 ⎬ 12 ⎮ 15 ⎦	30	⎡161 ⎨162 ⎣164	1·0 1·5 2·5	
250 ⎤ 300 ⎬ 350 ⎦	25	127			

In practice, grain sizes of between D50 (240 mesh) and D30 (320 mesh) are used with concentrations from 50–100 in the plain and 100–150 in the chamfering tools. The angle of the latter is generally fixed at 45°.

Although in theory there is a great degree of interchangeability between pairs of peripheral and chamfering wheels, in practice the possibilities are limited. The minor diameter of the chamfering component must correspond with the working diameter of the peripheral component. Unless both are at the same stage of wear, matching is uncertain. The higher concentration in the chamfering units is designed to balance the wear rate as far as possible.

In addition to the foregoing widely used applications of diamond in the scientific optical industry, use is also made of operations which, in essence, are described under flat glass applications. Where necessary, the optical glass is sawn to size with diamond saws. Large blocks and prisms may be sawn with segmental saws which are indispensable for cuts of 120 mm. (4½ in.) or more. For this a typical example would be the cutting of tank periscope prisms. A 300 mm. (12 in.) diameter segmental saw, 2·5 mm. wide (0·10 in.), containing 60 mesh grit at 25 concentration, is used on a Clipper sawbench, and the time for cutting 40 sq./cms. is 20 seconds. The blade life is of the order of 240,000 sq./cms.

Alternative equipment from Autoflow is available for sawing operations on glass and ceramics:

Machine type	Minor	Standard and 'laboratory'
Motor HP/r.p.m.	1½/2880	3/1420 (Spindle 1,600 or 3,100 r.p.m.)
Saw diameter	150/200 mm. (6/8 in.)	250 mm. (10 in.)
Max. cut length	300 mm. (12 in.)	500 mm. (20 in.)
Max. cut depth	150 mm. Saw 32 mm. (1¼ in.) 200 mm. Saw 44 mm. (1¾ in.)	63·5 mm. (2½ in.)
Table	350 × 300 mm. (14 × 12 in.)	600 × 500 mm. (24 × 20 in.)

Lighter duty on smaller components utilises metal bond continuous rim saws of which the following are typical alternatives:

Diameter mm.	in.	Width mm.	in.	Grain size and concentration	Notes
150	6	1 or 1·5	0·04/0·06	Grains	The finer
200	8	1 or 1·5	0·04/0·06	85–120	grits are
250	10	1·5 or 2	0·06/0·08	Concentration	for minimum
300	12	1·5 or 2	0·06 or 0·10	15–25	chipping

Trepanning is another method of preparing lens blanks and

generally employs the methods of diamond tube drilling under flat glass except that the diameters are generally larger. In order to minimise chipping where double head drilling machines are not available, the rough plates are waxed together in stacks with a scrap piece at the bottom and are trepanned as a 'stack'.

In some cases an intermediate or alternative operation of surface grinding flat faces is introduced. Blanchard make a range of machines suitable for this purpose and which have the following main characteristics. The diamond wheel features have been included in the three alternatives:

Machine type:	11–16	11–16	40
Workpieces:	Blocks up to 340 mm. diameter load	Prisms to fill table	Block 1 metre square
Table r.p.m.	24	24	N/A
Downfeed:	0·3 mm. per min.	0·35 mm. per min.	0·25 mm. per min.
Wheel sizes:	Cup 250 × 20 mm.	30 Pellets 12 × 10 mm.	340 Pellets 12 × 10 mm.
Wheel grit:	100	120	72
Wheel conc.:	50	50	50
Finish attainable:	1·8 Micron RT	2 Micron RT	4·5 Micron RT

For simultaneous grinding of two parallel faces, the following Loh machines can be used for the work ranges shown:

Loh universal milling machine	Maximum workpiece length mm.	in.
UFM	150	6
UFMS 500	500	20
UFMS 1,000	1,500	60

The latter machines can be adapted for vertical milling of plane surfaces or grooving with milling tools and peripheral wheels. Also included in their range of diamond applications are rounding off glass squares into lens blanks using radius edge peripheral wheels, cutting or grooving with diamond discs and angle milling for prism manufacture. Two angled faces can be milled simultaneously.

The Autoflow-Abwood model SG4 (Glass) Mark II surface grinder is also used for grinding flat glass surfaces. The 5 h.p. motor drives a vertical spindle carrying 150 mm. (6 in.) or 200 mm. (8 in.) diamond wheels and having a work table area of 500×203 mm. (20×8 in.).

In addition to these operations on the lens itself, diamond tools are also used to provide the accuracy and high finish demanded for the metal mounts of such assemblies as zoom lenses for television and other cameras. They also play an extensive part in optical components used in the space programmes; one example is in the manufacture of high accuracy diffraction gratings in the U.S. programme. Diamond saws are used to cut the blank from a block of optical glass—this is then ground flat and smooth; subsequently, a single polished diamond cutter is used to scribe 250,000 lines to the linear inch and the work is accomplished at a rate of 10 grooves per minute and each is exactly identical and parallel.

The ophthalmic optical industry

Much of what has been said under scientific optics can be broadly applied to this industry. The components are varied in the working surface dimensions and shapes, but more consistent in material, overall size and application.

Apart from spectacle frame makers, the industry divides into three main producer categories:

Mass production establishments: they purchase moulded lenses and surface them. The lenses may be finished or semi-finished. The latter are surfaced on one side only for use mainly as 'bifocals' or high power single vision lenses.

Wholesale and/or RX (prescription) producers: they buy from the mass producers. They usually have surfacing plant for further processing of semi-finished items. The lenses' surfaces having been finished, the edges are ground and fitted into frames to the prescription of the Dispensing Optician.

Dispensing opticians: who also sometimes have a small workshop. Grouped together, such outlets often have their own 'RX' establishment.

The lenses' surfaces to be processed fall into the following main types:

1. Single Vision
   1.1 True meniscus with one concave and one convex surface.
   1.2 The toric lens—which is a form of meniscus, with a toroidal surface on one side. The latter has base and cylinder curves at right angles.
2. Multifocal Lenses
   2.1 Fused bifocal where a 'button' of glass of a different refractive index from the main lens is fused into the lower portion.
   This protrudes above the lens blank and must be ground down to the same curve as the rest of the surface. This is normally done on a diamond spherical generator.
   2.2 Solid bifocals have a different curve generated into the lower section of a homogeneous lens surface. This is very much specialists' work using special equipment and skills such as are not found in the normal Wholesale House. Special diamond tools are purpose made for such applications.

Spherical curve generators, using standard milling tools of about 40 mm. (1·6 in.) Pitch Circle Diameter, are less complicated in construction than their counterparts in the scientific optical industry. The fixed milling tool diameter obviates the need for lateral head adjustment or base movements. A simple formula using the angle of the head about the contact point of the milling tool and the pitch diameter/edge radius of the latter is all that is necessary. The lens rotates in its holder and is roughed to the required curve. On the second side, excess material, including fused bifocal inserts, can be removed. Examples of machines for this operation are the Autoflow 200, C.M.V.60, Dama FS2 and Optibel MDM.

Single lens machines for toroidal curve generation are usually of a horizontal spindle configuration with provision for passing the stationary lens moulding across a milling tool of about 80 mm. (3·1 in.) Pitch Diameter. The compound curve is a function of the tool diameter and edge radius for base power, and the radius from the pivot point of the swing which determines the cylinder curve. For this work, machine examples are the Autoflow 122, Radmaster, Cyclomatic and Supermatic; Coburn Manumatic; Optibel M.T.A. and Shuron Continental. Using this equipment, surface finishes of

'Supermatic' advanced automated toric generator
(Autoflow Engineering Ltd.)

about 5 micron Rt., at stock removal rates of up to 40 cm.[3] per min. are attainable and typical diamond equipment is listed below:

Machine type	Pitch dia. mm.	Pitch dia. in.	Wall thickness mm.	Wall thickness in.	Edge radius mm.	Edge radius in.	Diamond grit/ conc.
Autoflow Toric 122	75	3	6	$\frac{1}{4}$	3	$\frac{1}{8}$	85/50
Autoflow Sphere 124 Mark III	38	$1\frac{1}{2}$	6	$\frac{1}{4}$	4	0·16	85/50
Autoflow Sphere 200	38	$1\frac{1}{2}$	6	$\frac{1}{4}$	4	0·16	85/50
Autoflow Radmaster Toric Mark I	76	3	5	0·20	2·5	0·10	60/40
Autoflow Supermatic	86	$3\frac{1}{2}$	6	0·25	3	$\frac{1}{8}$	60/15
C.M.V. Sphere	41	1·61	2	0·08	Square edge		85/50
Coburn Toric	81	3·19	6	$\frac{1}{4}$	3	$\frac{1}{8}$	85/40
Dama Sphere	40	1·57	3	$\frac{1}{8}$	1·5	$\frac{1}{16}$	120/50
I.D.P. GF. 4 Sphere	36·5	1·43	9	$\frac{3}{8}$	6	$\frac{1}{4}$	60/50
Optibel Sphere	37	1·46	2	0·08	Square edge		85/50
Optibel Torric	80	3·15	6	$\frac{1}{4}$	3	$\frac{1}{8}$	85/40
Shuron Torric	68	2·68	6	$\frac{1}{4}$	3	$\frac{1}{8}$	85/40

Mass production of 'Plus' toric surfaces is carried out on 'drum' machines using either an 80 mm. milling tool as above or a peripheral wheel. The latter type is used, for instance, on the Adcock & Shipley and Dama Torri-Ring types FT1 and FT3. The wheel is 100 mm. (4 in.) × 10 mm. (0·4 in.), and has a diamond content of grit 120 and concentration 35.

The three dimensional copying method using peripheral wheels is the subject of considerable development on the lines of the copymiller used in metal working. It is thought that, if fully successful, this approach will eliminate considerable corrective lapping in future.

Diamond 'pellet' smoothing, as described earlier in this chapter, has revolutionised the relevant operations in the plants of the mass producers of spectacle lenses, but has not made much impact elsewhere in the industry.

When the lens has been finally polished on both surfaces, it must be edged to fit the spectacle frame. This lens edging or glazing is now generally performed on Automatic V Edgers. These machines have horizontal spindles and utilise a copying cam system to produce the required perimeter form. The lens is clamped in a chuck and rotated against a peripheral type roughing wheel to remove excess material. The average time is of the order of 35 seconds for this operation. For the second operation the lens is lifted away from this wheel and applied for one 15 second revolution to a V wheel which forms the 125° or 135° included angle bevel to secure the lens in the frame channel. Examples of the machines developed to perform these operations are: the Raphael 'Silwing'; the Rodway 'Double Diamond' and 'Super D'; the Autoflow 'Glazomatic'; the Wernicke 'Weco 88' and 'D 111'; the Essel 'MDM'; the Coburn 'Rocket' and the Lemay 'Dimoline'. Some examples of the diamond wheels used in these applications are shown below:

Machine type	Wheel dia. mm.	in.	Wheel width mm.	in.	Bore	Angle	Diamond grit/ conc.
Double	100	4	12	0·47	1 in.	Square	100/25
Diamond	100	4	12	0·47	1 in.	120° (2·5 mm.)	280/50
	106	4·1	10	0·39	1 in.	120°	280/35
Electro-V-Matic	150	6	9·5	⅜	1½ in.	Square	100/25

Machine type	Wheel dia. mm.	in.	Wheel width mm.	in.	Bore	Angle	Diamond grit/ conc.
F.M.D.	158	6·2	9	0·35	25 mm.	45°	100/25
Glazomatic	150	6	9	3/8	2½ in.	Square	100/25
	150	6	9	3/8	2½ in.	125°	280/35
88	110	4·3	15	0·59	20 mm.	Square	100/25
	110	4·3	7	0·27	20 mm.	120°	280/35
	110	4·3	10	0·39	20 mm.	120°	280/35
	110	4·3	18	0·70	20 mm.	120° (2·7 mm.)	280/40
Silwing	150	6	9	3/8	1 in.	Square	100/25
	150	6	12·5	½	1 in.	Square	100/25
	150	6	9	3/8	1 in.	125°	280/35
	150	6	12·5	½	1 in.	125°	280/35
	150	6	12·5	½	1 in.	120° (2·5 mm.)	280/50
	150	6	15·9	5/8	1 in.	135°	280/35

'Angled spindle' edgers have been introduced to improve the uniformity of the V edge of the lens. Three examples are the Autoflow 'Anglomatic', the AO 'Dualamatic' and the Weco 'F.M.D.'. This development calls for wheels basically as listed above but with working faces at other angles.

In order to improve the appearance of thick edge lenses when mounted, the 'Mini' or 'Hide-a-Bevel' facility has been introduced; this employs a fully formed vee wheel.

Although largely superseded by efficient auto edgers, for the abnormal job most glazing shops are still equipped with hand edgers such as the I.D.P. 'GF8', the Raphael, Rodway, Pad Specs. or Weco machines. These utilise standard peripheral wheels 150 mm. (6 in.) diameter in widths from 12·5 mm. (½ in.) to 25 mm. (1 in.), and are generally in diamond grit 170 at 50 concentration or 200 at 35 concentration.

Some lenses are held in the upper part of the frame by a length of nylon thread about 0·5 mm. diameter (0·020 in.). The groove to take this thread is cut with a 20 mm. diameter electrometallic cutting disc 0·5 mm. wide.

Plastic lenses can be surfaced with the normal tooling described earlier, especially if mixed with glass production. However, if volume permits some machines to be put aside for this work it is sometimes found to be more economical to use electrometallic bond equivalents to the usual sintered metal tools.

In the case of acrylic contact lenses, methods are being developed to machine the surface to the required prescription with single point polished diamond tools. This operation was first carried out soon after the last war on an experimental basis, but is now being developed on a commercial basis. High speed steel and tungsten carbide tools wear too quickly to be satisfactory on this soft but abrasive material.

Industrial glass applications

Some of the uses which might be considered as within this heading have been referred to under 'Flat Glass', but, in addition, there is a considerable number of other industrial glass uses.

Probably the best known is the use of single point 'glaziers'' tool

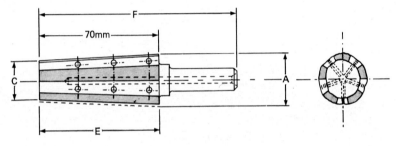

Joint size No.	Dia. A mm.	Dia. C mm.	Length E mm.	Length F mm.
B10	11	5	60	98·5
B12	13·5	7·5	60	98·5
B14	15·5	9·5	60	98·5
B16	17	10·5	65	111
B19	19·8	13·2	65	111
B24	25	18	70	114
B29	30	23	70	114
B34	35·5	28·1	74	118

Taper to BS.572:1950

Electrometallic conical laps for ground glass joints

inserts mounted in rods to cut off glass tube. Equipment such as the 'Rolacut' has been developed to facilitate this operation. The glass rests on two light alloy rollers which will accommodate from 19 mm. ($\frac{3}{4}$ in.) to 125 mm. (5 in.) inside diameter tubing. The break is induced with a gas flame. This may also be done, of course, with a diamond saw.

Holes required in industrial glass components and circles to be cut depend on the 'glaziers'' diamond too or on the impregnated tube drill. The choice depends mainly on the size, with drills being used up to 100 mm.

Taper reamers are used to provide interchangeable joints in scientific glassware and other glass containers. Electrometallic diamond tools are made to B.S.572:1950 dimensions. Prior to reaming, the hole may be parallel and no subsequent lapping is required. The operation can be carried out on a conventional drill but coolant is essential.

The tube cutting technique, referred to a little earlier, is also applied to the finishing of glass tableware except that the diamond is applied from the outside. The surplus glass after blowing a wine goblet, for instance, is removed in this way. It leaves a sharp edge, however, quite unacceptable to the user. The surface is smoothed on a diamond wheel which is then also used to bevel the outer edge. A smaller diamond wheel is also used to bevel the inner edge.

Diamond grinding a tumbler edge after parting-off surplus glass

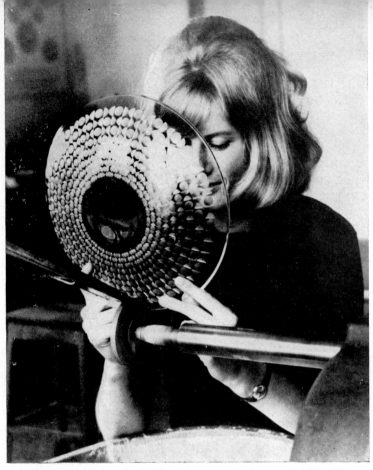

Diamond brilliant cutting wheel used to decorate a glass bowl
(Mrs. Benita Miram-Tillipaul)

The wheels used are normally 100 or 150 mm. (4 or 6 in.) diameter in grit 240 and 100 concentration. The method has been further developed in the Biebuyck edge grinder which uses 200 mm. (8 in.) flexible diamond discs as cup wheels. Production of up to 1,800 pieces per hour is claimed. Alternatively, some makers have combined the cut-off and face grinding operations by using a fine diamond saw to part off the surplus.

Decorating glassware

Better quality glass drinking vessels and their accompanying decanters use diamond grinding extensively for this purpose.

They are well established for the decorative pattern grinding of lead glass (crystal) tableware. Machines such as the Biebuyck are used for hand applications and the Kutscher for automatic production. The latter mounts eight 'brilliant cutting wheels' and can produce some 120 tumblers per hour depending on size and pattern. Metal bond diamond wheels hold their form much longer than the corresponding conventional abrasive wheel and can rough and finish in one operation.

The wheels utilised are generally in the 50–250 mm. (2–10 in.) diameter range, with a V periphery, an included angle ranging from 90–145° and widths from 6–20 mm. ($\frac{1}{4}$–$\frac{3}{4}$ in.). The grain size selected is about 240 mesh for hand use and some hard glass and 280 on automatic working. Concentrations of 35, 50 or 80 are normally utilised.

The hand techniques are also used for purely free-hand decoration of other items of glassware such as fruit bowls, dishes and, for the most intricate, diamond 'pencils' are used to trace fine lines in the pattern.

REFERENCES

'Diamond—A Prescription for Accuracy'—Stan Herbert, *Industrial Diamond Review*, June 1971.

'Diamonds as a Basis for Rationalising Glass Processing in the Optical Industry' —E. Loh, of Wilhelm Loh KG., Wetzlar, June 1969.

'Use of Diamond Tools in the Schott Glass Works'—Ing. F. Neukater, Jenaer Glaswerk Schott & Gen, Mainz, June 1969.

'The Influence of the Cooling Agent in the Milling of Glass'—Prof. Dr. Ing. G. Pahlitzsch and Dipl-Ing. D. Kern, Institute for Machine Tools and Manufacturing Techniques, Technical University, Braunschweig, June 1969.

'The Italian Optical Industry'—Dr. Claudio Morpurgo, *Manufacturing Optics International*, June 1972.

'The Diamond Drilling of Glass'—A. N. Reznikov and L. F. Boitsova, U.S.S.R., September 1969.

'Influence of Out-of-Roundness and Eccentricity of the Diamond Saw Blade on its Behaviour when Sawing Glass'—Prof. Dr. Ing. G. Pahlitzsch and Dipl-Ing. W. Karsten, Engineering College of Braunschweig, June 1969.

'Diamonds and New Techniques in the Italian Optical Industry'—T. C. Trancu, *Industrial Diamond Review*, March 1968.

German Standards Organisation: DIN 69110, DIN 848, DIN 58741/2/3/4/5.

'Ostsee Perle'—16th June, 1967—'Glas-Studio 66' in *Timmendorfer Strand*.

'Hampshire'—February 1970—'More Hampshire Houses in Glass'—Honoria D. Marsh.

'Optical Production Technology'—D. F. Horne. Published by Adam Hilger Ltd. (Rank Precision Industries Ltd.), October 1972.

7

Stone industry

THE stone industry is the largest consumer of diamond by weight. Although some surface set tools are made containing whole diamonds, by far the greatest consumption is in the form of coarse grit. Diamond plays a part in the industry's activities throughout the whole processing phase from establishing the extent and quality of the quarry site by way of sample core cutting and finally to drill holes for the attachment of the cut and polished slab.

There are many variations with the broad types of stone that are encountered in the various diamond applications. The main classifications are marble, granite, travertine, slate, limestone and sandstone. The whole range covers great variation in cutting properties attributable to factors such as abrasive hardness, crushing-strength, porosity and specific gravity.

Broadly the operations carried out on these materials and involving the use of diamonds are:

1. Core cutting to establish the quarry value.
2. Blast hole drilling to remove blocks from the quarry face.
3. Wire sawing blocks from the quarry.
4. Primary sawing with large circular frame saws or wire saws.
5. Secondary sawing with smaller circular saws.
6. Surface preparation of sawn slabs (often undertaken between operations 4 and 5).
7. Drilling, trepanning and milling architectural and other forms such as window sills, jambs and coping stones, curling stones, ash trays, lamp bases, memorial vases, fireplace surrounds, and for fixing to base structures.

Most countries have an indigenous stone industry but the major ones are Italy, America and Greece.

CORE CUTTING

This application is generally carried out in the same manner, by the same equipment and very often the same contractors as when prospecting for minerals and is dealt with in Chapter 9. Analysis and evaluation of the cores follow and which in some cases involves the cutting of core sections with diamond blades.

BLAST HOLE AND SEAM DRILLING

This is also accomplished by very similar methods except that:

1. Solid bits can be used as no core is required.
2. The drilling pattern is different from that used to recover mineral bearing ores from mines as blocks of massive rock are required instead of controlled fragmentation.
3. The holes are not so deep, seldom exceeding 20 m. (60 ft.).
4. In softer rocks tungsten carbide or even steel drills can be used.

WIRE SAWING IN QUARRIES

Diamond wire saws are in course of development but generally a slurry of silicon carbide grit is used as the cutting medium in this operation.

PRIMARY SAWING

Whilst large circular diamond saws up to 3 m. (10 ft.) in diameter are still used on blocks which cannot be economically cut otherwise, they are generally being replaced with multi blade frame saws. One example of the size of such large circular saws is quoted from Belgium where a 2·5 m. (8 ft.) saw is used to cut hard limestone. The saw is used with a peripheral speed of 40 metres per sec. (8,000 ft. per min.). Another is the cutting of Welsh slate with an approx. 2 m. (85 in.) saw. This saw cuts the slate at nearly 800 square centimetres per minute (120 square inches). Yet another example from Belgium concerns the cutting of Belgian Blue Stone. This is a blue and not particularly abrasive limestone but which is considerably harder than white Carrara marble. The 2·5 m. diameter (8 ft.) saw has a normal blade life of 6,000 m.² (64,583 sq. ft.).

Stone cutting diamond frame saw (B.R.A.)

Although of relatively high capital cost, the adoption of frame
sawing machines specially designed to use diamond blades has
progressed with increasing momentum particularly in the main
marble working areas of Italy and Greece. In addition to the very
relevant time saving, this method improves the accuracy and surface
quality of the sawn stone as well as saving material. The very much
thinner high tensile steel blades and their diamond segments result
in less material being wasted in the operation. The multiple blades
are located in the machine under tension, usually applied by means of
an hydraulic device. The load on each blade is of the order of 8–10
tons. Unlike the swinging motion of the old machines using chilled
steel shot as the cutting medium, the new diamond frame saws operate
in parallel strokes. The distance between blades can be varied to
accommodate the slab thickness required. Units employing some
30/70 blades are quite normal and, for example, marble cladding
slabs may vary from say 20–30 mm. thick ($\frac{2}{4}$–1$\frac{1}{4}$ in.). It is claimed

that hard sandstone can be cut at rates approaching 10 times that of the production methods employed earlier. A cutting speed of up to 140 mm. per hour ($5\frac{1}{2}$ inches per hour) is claimed for this method on a 15 blade frame saw, made by the Anderson-Grice Company and designed especially for granite.

On the softer stones ultimate economies of up to 75% of total cost are claimed over other methods. The dimensions of the blades are determined by the design of the machine but the Fédération Européenne des Fabricants de Produits Abrasifs have suggested the following workpiece to blade dimension:

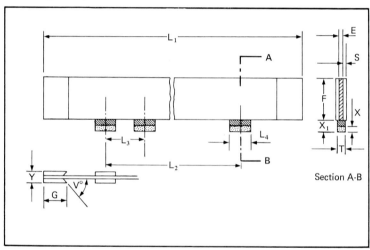

The main elements of a diamond frame saw blade are indicated by the following code:
E.   Thickness of steel blade
F.   Depth of steel blade
G.   Length of end plates
L_1.   Blade length
L_2.   Segmented length
L_3.   Segment spacing
L_4.   Length of segment
S.   Side clearance
T.   Width of diamond segment
V.   Angle of end plates
X.   Depth of diamond section
X_1.   Overall depth of segment
Y.   Overall thickness at end plates

(Fédération Européenne
des Fabricants de
Produits Abrasifs)

(dimensions in millimetres)

Length of block of material to be sawn	Segmented length	Total length	Cross-section	Recommended tension in mp.
2,000 (78·8 in.)	2,000 (78·8 in.)	2,900 (114·2 in.)	180 × 3·0 (7·1 × ·12 in.) 180 × 3·0	
2,500 (98·4 in.)	2,500 (98·4 in.)	3,400 (133·9 in.)	(7·1 × ·12 in.) 180 × 3·5 (7·1 × ·14 in.) 180 × 3·0	
3,000 (118·1 in.)	3,000 (118·1 in.)	3,900 (153·5 in.)	(7·1 × ·12 in.) 180 × 3·5 (7·1 × ·14 in.)	8–11
3,250 (127·9 in.)	3,250 (127·9 in.)	4,150 (163·4 in.)	180 × 3·5 (7·1 × ·14 in.)	
3,500 (137·8 in.)	3,500 (137·8 in.)	4,400 (173·2 in.)	180 × 3·5 (7·1 × ·14 in.)	
3,750 (147·6 in.)	3,750 (147·6 in.)	4,650 (183·1 in.)	180 × 3·5 (7·1 × ·14 in.)	
4,000 (157·5 in.)	4,000 (157·5 in.)	4,900 (173·0 in.)	180 × 3·5 (7·1 × ·14 in.)	

It is in this field that surface set diamond segments are sometimes used. The diamond and matrix specifications are based on knowledge gained in rock drilling operations. The individual diamonds are set to a pre-determined pattern in a carbon mould which is then filled with the matrix powder. The assembly is pressed and heat treated. The resulting segment is then brazed to the steel blade in the same way as a conventional impregnated segment.

Assuming a normal quarried block of say $3 \times 2 \times 1$ metre ($9 \times 6 \times 3$ feet) diamond frame saws will cut at a down feed of approximately 300 to 500 mm. per hour (12–20 in. per hour) in soft sandstone or limestone, 200 to 300 mm. per hour (8–12 in.) in travertine and 100–200 mm. per hour (4–8 in.) in harder stones. To sustain the forces needed to achieve these cutting rates the construction of the machines has to be extremely robust. The crank and flywheel action generally provide for about 100–120 strokes per minute over a length of movement of some 400–600 mm. (16–24 in.). The relative speed of saw and stone of course varies from zero at the end of each stroke to some 2·79 m.p.s. (550 ft. per min.) at the centre.

Although the actual materials used in the diamond impregnated segments are the same as in circular saws, the actual proportions and final characteristics often are quite different to provide optimum results under such different working conditions. The steel blade must also be of a specification that provides high yield strength and resistance to fatigue. The tensioning operation before mounting on the machine is achieved by passing the blade through rollers under pressure. This decreases the assembly's tendency to deviate in cut direction under the influence of varying stone hardness. The riveted terminal cleats on the blades provide a vee form for attachment to the machine arms and which in turn provide the hydraulic tensioning devices that, when applied to the blade, resist the tendency for the blade to bend upward in the centre under the applied load.

The fixing of the stone block on the machine bed is important to avoid any movement during sawing. Parallelism and blade movement in the direction of feed should be regularly checked to avoid distortion and uneven wear.

Most machines provide for a copious water supply distributed evenly over the whole cutting area. A water supply of the order of 8 litres per min. (1½ gal. per min.) per blade is considered normal when the saws are in full operation but a little less might be satisfactory at the beginning of a cut. In some cases various additives have been found to improve results. The nature and quantity of these additives of course depend on the analysis of the local water supply.

An alternative to the frame saw in this multi-slab cutting is the wire saw which still at present generally uses Silicon Carbide Grit Slurry as the cutting medium. Bonded diamond should show considerable advantage in this field when a suitable formulation has been developed.

SECONDARY SAWING

It is in this field that diamond saws are most widely used. The sizing operations on the pre-sawn slabs are generally carried out with circular saws mounted on one of two basic machines:

1. Where the blade moves through the stone.
2. Where the stone is passed across the saw.

Until recently most equipment was of the latter type but with the application of more conventional machine tool design principles

Circular segmental diamond stone saws in operation (Breton)

the first has become widely used in repetitive secondary sawing. Important factors in the design of diamond sawing machines are adequate motor horsepower, some effective means of ensuring that the carriage does not lift and sufficient rigidity to avoid deflection in other directions when under load. The traverse mechanism may be mechanical, hydraulic, electro-mechanical or even manual but not pneumatic. Constant load conditions are most favourable to the diamond blade and an ammeter wired into the wheel head motor assists in achieving this end.

The steel saw centres on which the diamond impregnated segments are mounted fall into two basic categories. These are described as 'Wide Slot' or 'Narrow Slot'. The latter may be elaborated by the narrow slot being converted to a keyhole form. The Fédération Européenne des Fabricants de Produits Abrasifs has recently published standard dimensions for these blades which will greatly assist in interchangeability from both the users' and the suppliers' points of view.

The diamond bearing segments for both straight and circular

saws are the same except of course that those for the straight blades are rectangular and those for the circular saws are curved to fit the periphery of the steel centre. As in the case of other diamond impregnated products, the diamond content is described as to grit, size by their mesh (B.S.410:1962), and concentration by the weight of diamond per cubic centimetre with 'concentration 100' being representative of a diamond content of 4·4 cts. per cubic centimetre. Thus concentration 50 would be 2·2 cts. per cubic centimetre and 25 would be 1·1 cts. per cubic centimetre. The depth of impregnation is half the linear difference between the saw O/D over the segments and the diameter where the diamond impregnation ceases. The metal matrix or bond is varied to suit the conditions under which the saw is to be used.

The segments are brazed on to the steel centre and the whole assembly planished and tensioned. The former corrects any deformation in the blade caused by the brazing. The latter is an induced stress pattern when the saw is static and is designed to resist deflection at the saw's working speed.

Next to the type of stone to be cut, the conditions under which a diamond saw blade is used is of course the decisive factor in the economics of production. Some of the salient points are outlined:

Storage

Wherever possible saws should be stored in their original packing boxes and replaced in them if temporarily taken out of use. If this is found to be impractical they should be located in a vertical position from their centre hole. This can be done by attaching a dummy spindle to a wall or other structure. They can also be laid on a flat surface but this is uneconomic in space and involves the risk of the blade being deformed by having other articles put on top of it. Diamond saws should never be stacked horizontally on the floor or leaned against a wall.

Mounting the saw

Normally blades are marked with an arrow to indicate recommended direction of rotation. This should be observed when fitting the saw to the spindle. Clearance between spindle and centre hole of blade should not exceed 0·1 mm. (0·004 in.). As the blade centre hole is normally held to tolerance H7 failure to hold to this clearance can

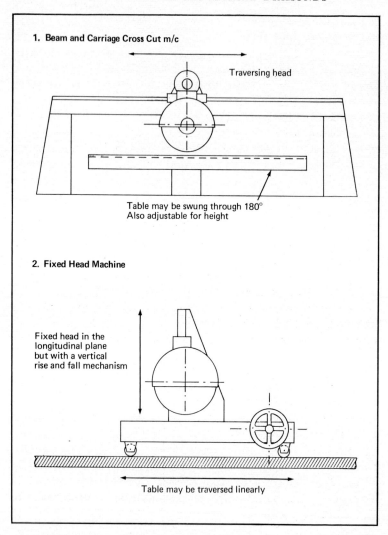

1. Beam and Carriage Cross Cut m/c

Traversing head

Table may be swung through 180°
Also adjustable for height

2. Fixed Head Machine

Fixed head in the
longitudinal plane
but with a vertical
rise and fall mechanism

Table may be traversed linearly

Alternative machine types using segmental diamond saws in stone cutting

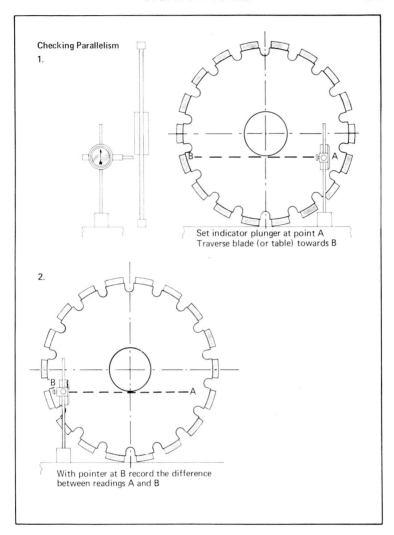

Checking Parallelism
1.

Set indicator plunger at point A
Traverse blade (or table) towards B

2.

With pointer at B record the difference
between readings A and B

Checking parallelism before using a diamond saw

generally be traced to a worn spindle or an incorrect bore being specified. Whilst it is permissible to use a 'slip bush' to change the bore size, multiple bushing may lead to eccentricity and should be avoided.

Flanges

Flanges should be clean and free of burrs. They should be square to the spindle to a high degree of accuracy. They should be recessed and ground on their mating faces. The flange diameter should be at least almost thirty per cent of the saw diameter and thus a typical recommendation would be according to the following table which also shows the resulting maximum cutting depth.

Saw diameter		Min. flange diameter		Max. cutting depth	
mm.	approx. in.	mm.	approx. in.	mm.	approx. in.
200	8	70	2·8	65	2·6
300	12	100	3·9	100	3·9
400	16	130	· 5·1	135	5·3
600	24	200	7·9	200	7·9
800	32	250	9·8	275	10·8
1,000	40	300	11·8	350	13·8
1,500	60	400	15·7	550	21·7
2,000	80	500	19·7	750	29·5
2,500	100	700	27·6	900	35·4
3,000	120	800	31·5	1,100	43·3

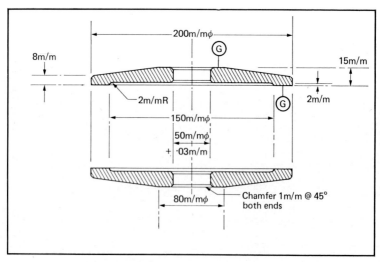

Typical flanges for a 600 mm. diamond saw blade

It is recommended that on removal the blade, flanges and spindle be suitably marked so that they can be reassembled in the same relative positions. Paper washers as used with conventional abrasive blades should never be applied between diamond blades and flanges.

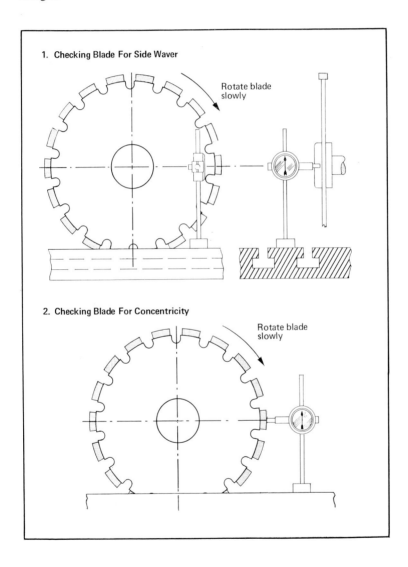

1. Checking Blade For Side Waver

Rotate blade slowly

2. Checking Blade For Concentricity

Rotate blade slowly

Running truth

Both as regards concentricity and any sideways movement or waver, running truth should be checked with a dial gauge. The base of the indicator should be placed on the machine table or other firm support and contact made with the steel centre just within the gullets. The blade should then be rotated one revolution by hand and the lowest reading positions established. The indicator dial is then adjusted to zero at that point. The blade is then again rotated by hand and the maximum movement recorded on the dial will indicate the full degree of side waver. The permissible readings are proportional to saw diameter.

To check concentricity, the dial gauge contact should first be positioned on the centre of a segment. The dial should be returned to zero and the segment marked. A reading should then be taken on each segment and the maximum difference between any two readings will be the measure of eccentricity. Because of the very abrasive nature of the diamond segment surfaces, the indicator plunger should be manually withdrawn between each reading. Typical recommendation for maximum tolerance of eccentricity and side waver are shown in the following table.

Saw diameter		Max. side waver		Max. eccentricity	
mm.	approx. in.	mm.	approx. in.	mm.	approx. in.
200	8	0·2	·008	0·2	·008
300	12	0·2	·008	0·2	·008
400	16	0·3	·012	0·2	·008
600	24	0·4	·016	0·3	·012
800	32	0·6	·024	0·6	·024
1,000	40	0·6	·024	0·6	·024
1,500	60	0·7	·028	0·6	·024
2,000	80	1·0	·039	0·8	·032
2,500	100	1·3	·051	1·0	·039
3,000	120	1·8	·071	1·5	·059

Spindles and slides

The debris resulting from stone working is of course extremely abrasive and results in relatively rapid deterioration in machine conditions. The efficiency of the diamond saw depends not only on its own built-in accuracy but also on its movements in relation to the stone being cut. The movements provided by the machine must remain accurate if the full potential of the diamond blade is to be realised. Machines should therefore be checked regularly and maintained in good repair. One of the main items to be watched is of course the spindle on which the saw runs. This should be free of radial or axial movement. The next most important is the table or head slides and runners. The parallelism of the movements of these factors should be periodically checked with a dial gauge. The base of the gauge should be located on the table and the saw blade contacted just below the flange. The table should then be traversed so that the gauge contact passes across the diamond blade and the maximum and minimum readings recorded. This should then be repeated for two table positions and two saw positions. If allowance for the saw side waver readings is then made, a good indication of the table to blade parallelity will be provided. Under normal circumstances the readings should not indicate more than 0·1 mm. (0·004 in.) out of parallel per 300 mm. (12 in.) of table or head movement. Out of parallelism may be caused by worn table or head bogies, wear in table or head bearings or slides. In some cases it may also result from the sawing head being incorrectly set or aligned.

Cutting fluid

A copious and well directed water supply is of paramount importance if diamond blades are to function satisfactorily. The fluid must flush away the cutting debris to prevent unnecessary abrasion of the diamond bonding material and the steel blade. It must also act as a coolant and control the increase in temperature occasioned by the actual cutting operation. To be effective the supply must not only be copious but must be under sufficient pressure to break through the air layer carried round by the saw and thus make contact with the diamond and its bonding. This is particularly important when cutting harder stones to avoid 'glazing'. This state in the saw surface results in bad finish, chipping, run-off and eventual deformation of the whole blade due to resulting higher cutting pressures. Assuming the volume and pressure are adequate is however not sufficient to ensure good results. The flow must be well directed.

P

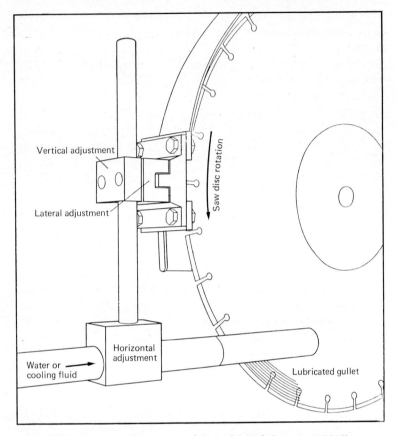

The R.G.S. saw lubricant applicator (British Patent: 115614)

(Robertson Geotechnical Services Ltd.)

Suitable forked supply tubes, perforated nozzles and fishtails are supplied with machines or are available as specialised accessories.

Typical cutting fluid supply conditions for circular diamond saws are:

Saw diameter		Cutting fluid			
mm.	approx. in.	Flow lit./min.	gal./min.	Pressure atmos.	lb./in.²
200	8	8	1·8	4 ⎫	
300	12	10	2·2	4 ⎬	60
400	16	15	3·3	4 ⎭	
600	24	25	5·5	5 ⎫	
800	32	30	6·6	5 ⎪	
1,000	40	35	7·7	5 ⎪	
1,500	60	50	11·0	5 ⎬	75
2,000	80	60	13·2	5 ⎪	
2,500	100	70	15·4	5 ⎭	
3,000	120	80	17·6	6	90

Water is generally considered adequate but as in the case of frame saws additives have been found beneficial particularly with harder denser stones and are worth investigating under specialist advice.

Power and speed requirements

The positive cutting power of the very hard diamond content can only be fully utilised if sufficient power is available to drive the saw

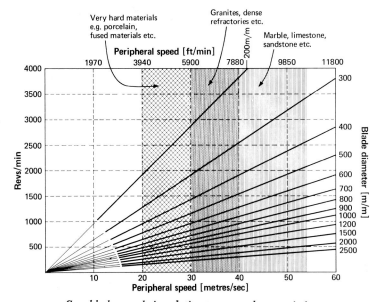

Saw blade speeds in relation to stone characteristics

at the recommended peripheral speed. The latter, however, must be tempered by the fact that the faster a blade is run the harder will the bond appear in any given material. In general therefore it will be seen that harder materials will tend to require lower speeds than softer stones when other factors are equal. The actual speed used is also influenced by a number of other factors so that the following table must be taken as only a broad generalisation.

Typical peripheral speeds for diamond stone saws

Material	Peripheral speed metres/sec.	ft./min.
Granites, quartzite, etc.	20–30	4,000–6,000
Hard marbles and dense sandstones	30–40	6,000–8,000
Soft marbles, limestones, soft standstones	45–55	9,000–11,000
Travertine	35–45	7,000–9,000
Semi precious stone (may be with continuous rim saws)	25–35	5,000–6,000

In order to achieve these speeds, to keep the saw cutting freely and to obtain an economic life for the diamond content, horsepowers of the following order are considered necessary. Experienced operators can form a good judgement of the cutting efficiency of a diamond blade by the sound whilst in use. A useful check is provided, however, if an ammeter is wired into the motor circuit and provides for a greater degree of consistency.

Horsepower requirements related to saw diameters

Saw diameter		
mm.	approx. in.	horsepower
200	8	2
300	12	3
400	16	7
600	24	15–20
800	32	25–30
1,000	40	30
1,500	60	40
2,000	80	50
2,500	100	75
3,000	120	100

An under-loaded blade can become glazed and lose its cutting ability due to insufficient debris being produced to break down the bond. Conversely, overload can result in shortened life through accelerated bond attrition and sometimes deformation of the steel centre.

Saw blade performance

The very large number of variables involved in the use of diamond saws has precluded a precise definition of the parameters within which this can be forecast. Local knowledge of all the factors involved in a specific application is still the best guide and takes into account the following interrelated factors:

1. Saw diameter and specification.
2. Machine power, rigidity and general condition.
3. Depth of cut.
4. Finish requirements.
5. The actual materials to be cut and in which some of the relative variables are shown in the following table.

Some properties of natural stones

Stone types	Relative abrasive hardness	Crushing strength PSI	Transverse strength PSI	% Porosity	Relative specific gravity	Weight ft.³ lb.
Granite	35–90	17–37,000	1,400–5,600	0·4–4·0	2·6–3·0	160–200
Limestone	1–25	2,500–2,800	500–2,000	1·0–30·0	1·87–2·69	140–175
Marble	8–40	8–27,000	600–4,000	0·4–2·0	2·7–2·9	168–180
Quartzite	N/A	16–4,5000	N/A	1·5–3·0	N/A	160–165
Sandstone	2–27	5–20,000	700–2,300	2·0–30·0	2·2–2·7	130–165
Serpentine	12–110	11–28,000	1,300–11,000	N/A	2·5–2·7	N/A
Slate	5–12	N/A	6,000–15,000	0·1–1·8	2·6–2·8	165–180
Travertine	1–16	N/A	N/A	N/A	N/A	N/A

Taking all of these factors into account and as a general guide the anticipated cutting performance to be expected is shown in the adjacent graph.

Factors involved in circular saw specification

1. The blade dimensions are generally determined by the machine requirements but may also be influenced by the work in hand.

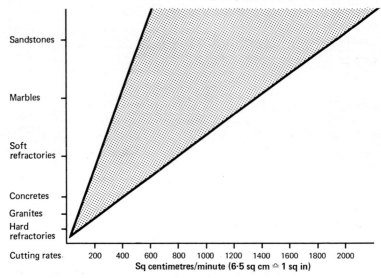

Guide to cutting rates (Circular segmental saws)

- Sandstones
- Marbles
- Soft refractories
- Concretes
- Granites
- Hard refractories

Cutting rates 200 400 600 800 1000 1200 1400 1600 1800 2000

Sq centimetres/minute (6·5 sq cm $\simeq$ 1 sq in)

2. Slot width is influenced by the balance between the finish required and optimum cutting speed. Generally, narrow slot saws provide better finish and less edge chipping. Wide slot blades are used for deep cutting operations where finish is less vital.

3. Physical properties of the stone—some of the variables are shown in the table mentioned under Saw Blade Performance.

4. Diamond grit size is influenced by the hardness of the material and the finish required. Generally harder materials call for smaller grits, as do finer finishes.

5. Type of grit. The harder the stone the greater the impact which the diamond has to sustain. Generally the appropriate synthetic grit is tougher and of better shape than natural diamond in this field.

6. Diamond concentration is generally between 20 and 35 but sometimes up to 50. Selection within these limits will depend on stone hardness, abrasive properties, the peripheral speed of the blade and the required finish.

7. Depth of diamond impregnation will normally be between 5 mm. (0·2 in.) and 7·5 mm. (0·3 in.).

By applying these broad principles a manufacturer would probably offer for normal granite cutting a relatively fine grit synthetic diamond of the order of 50 mesh to cover the hard abrasive nature of the material, a concentration of 30 and a tough wear resistant bond with an impregnation depth of 5 mm. (0·2 in.). If for reasons of high labour cost or to reduce subsequent polishing costs or lack of power or high spindle speed a faster cutting blade is required, the specification would probably be changed to 36 mesh, the concentration to 20 and the depth of impregnation to 7·5 mm. (0·3 in.). Other factors would be unaltered. Conversely, however, in work done on two South African granites and on rock known as Norite by Messrs. R. D. Walker and M. G. Wood of the De Beers Research Laboratory, Johannesburg, it was concluded that 45 concentration was the optimum at 21 metres per second (4,134 ft. per min.).

The softer types of abrasive sandstone, where deep cutting is being undertaken and finish is less important, would call for a wide slot blade, a coarser grit, say mesh 18, a higher concentration such as 40 and a very durable bond to a depth of 5 mm. (0·2 in.) or 7·5 mm. (0·3 in.) if it was thought that the full blade potential could be realised in practice.

The harder abrasive sandstones would call for a modification in the form of the concentration being lowered to say 30.

The term marble is taken to cover a wide range of metamorphic limestone but is generally regarded as one of the softer natural materials not having great abrasive properties. When cut in the polished state a good finish is required and narrow gap saws are specified. A finer grit size is quoted, such as 44 mesh synthetic, and a lower concentration such as 20 and a bond of lower wear resistance to a depth of 5 mm. (0·2 in.).

Some notes on the solution of problems that arise from time to time may be appropriate here.

If the cutting speed of the blade is reducing and the power consumption increasing it may be due to one of several causes.

1. The peripheral speed of the blade may be too high. It should be borne in mind that the harder the material the lower the required speed.
2. The working load may be too low. If this is established the blade should be 'dressed' or its free cutting properties restored

by cutting through some more abrasive material, e.g. soft sandstone. Work should be resumed under increased feed rate.
3. If insufficient cutting fluid is being used the working surface may have become 'glazed'. The blade should be dressed and more fluid applied.
4. The blade may be buckled or 'dished'. The checks described earlier should be applied. If the blade has been deformed it should be returned to the manufacturer for repair.
5. Check that the saw is being used on the material for which it was designed. A blade provided for soft abrasive materials will glaze very quickly on hard granite or less abrasive marble.

If the diamond segments appear to be wearing with abnormal rapidity it may be due to:

1. The peripheral speed being too low. This should be checked against the speed chart.
2. The feed rate/work load may be too high.
3. Insufficient cutting fluid. If cutting debris is not being efficiently carried away it will cause rapid bond attrition and release of diamond particles before they have been fully utilised.
4. Check the saw specification against the actual job of the moment. A narrow gullet granite or marble saw will wear rapidly if used on soft abrasive stone.

If surface finish is unacceptable and arris chipping is apparent it may result from:

1. A deformed blade. The checks described earlier should be applied and suitable corrections made. If necessary the blade will need to be returned to the manufacturer.
2. Excessive vibration due to a worn machine and suitable maintenance should be undertaken on spindle bearings, tables bogies, etc.
3. In the case of arris chipping, improvement can be made by cutting into a bed of marble or slate. If this is not possible the blade projection through the cut should be increased. If step cutting, the final step should be taken in an 'upcutting' direction.

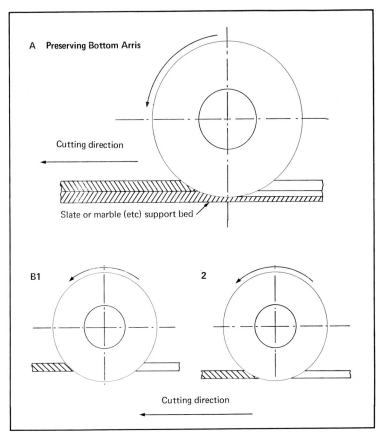

A. Best edges can be obtained by, if possible, cutting into a firm bed of marble, slate, or other suitable alternative

B. If it is not possible to cut into a supporting bed, the results can be improved by increasing blade projection through the cut

If the blade is deviating or 'running off' from the line of cut examine:

1. The machine for misalignment in table movement.
2. The blade for dishing or buckling and for running truth.
3. The feed rate—it may be too high.

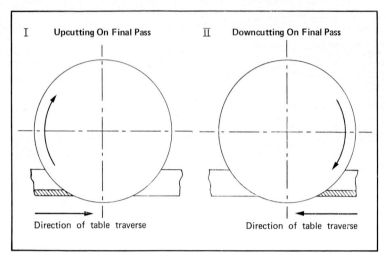

I Upcutting On Final Pass   II Downcutting On Final Pass

Direction of table traverse   Direction of table traverse

Example I will give better bottom edges than II. If step cutting, the final step should be taken in an upcutting direction, i.e. as example I

4. As a result of 3 or some other cause the diamond segments are 'glazing'. Dress as described earlier and resume operation.

SURFACE PREPARATION OF SAWN SLABS

As mentioned in the introduction to this chapter these operations are generally carried out between the primary and secondary sawing,

Alternative types of diamond stone surfacing tools

but because of the common factors of the two sawing phases they have been dealt with consecutively.

The diamond tools used in these operations are often referred to as 'Polishing heads' or stone 'Rubbers'. The former is really a misnomer as they are generally used after sawing to provide rapid surface improvement before final polishing by other methods.

The conventional preparation of granite and marble surfaces utilises 3–5 stages of abrasive segmented heads followed by absorbent felt pads with polishing powders such as tin oxide. Diamond impregnated heads are made in several forms and are used to reduce labour costs by replacing the coarser abrasive stages. They may be used on fully automatic polishers, Jenny Lind type or even manually guided flexible shaft driven units.

In addition to being used on solid stone these surfacing methods are also used on such materials as reconstructed granite tiles which are very much cheaper than solid stone.

The diamond grain size is the main factor in determining the rate of surface stock removed and the resulting finish. For example a coarse mesh such as 18 will give rapid removal rates but the finish imparted will require more work from the ensuing abrasive stages. A finer mesh diamond such as 60 will be slower in stock removal but leaves less work to be done in the succeeding abrasive stages. In some cases two diamond and two abrasive stages are found to be best. Typical grain sizes for marble or granite are 25 mesh for roughing and 100 for smoothing but grades as fine as 200 have been quoted in the U.S.A. on marble. Intermediate grades of 60/80 mesh are quoted for Portland Stone, utilising cup type tools on flexible shaft driven heads. Medium concentration of the order of 45–50 are normally adequate but in the case of abrasive sandstones where similar tools are used to eliminate saw marks about 18 mesh is used with a concentration as high as 90.

For hand surfacing with the aid of flexible shaft or portable electric tools smaller diamond heads are being introduced. They are generally available in 100 mm. (4 in.) and 125 mm. (5 in.) diameters for use at speeds between 1,500 and 2,500 r.p.m. They are used on granite, marble and composites or reconstructed materials and are of the following order of specification:

Material	Operation	Grit	Concentration
Marble and Composites	Roughing	60 or 80	25 or 30
Marble and Composites	Semi-finishing	170	20
Granite	Roughing	50 or 80	30 or 40
Granite	Semi-finishing	170	20

In some of the more progressive stonemasons' yards automatic smoothing, sawing equipment and edge polishers are all inter-connected by a conveyor system employing diamond tooling at each stage. This has resulted in major savings in labour.

Very much improved results are obtained from machinery specifically designed for diamond tooling. These machines employ the same principles that are applied to the use of diamond abrasives in grinding other hard materials such as carbides and ceramics. Table traverse rates of 1–1·3 m. per min. (3–4 ft.) and depths of cut up to 3 mm. ($\frac{1}{8}$ in.) are claimed. The machines must be rigid and of adequate horsepower.

At the opposite end of the scale hand rubbing blocks are also used for smoothing and chamfering edges of granite or marble slabs that require polishing. These are generally in the form of a rectangular diamond impregnated block fitted to holders with the two long edges chamfered. They are of the order of 150 mm. × 12 mm. × 10 mm. (6 in. × $\frac{1}{2}$ in. × $\frac{3}{8}$ in.) in 50 concentration with mesh 170 for roughing, 320 for smoothing and 600 for finishing.

DRILLING, TREPANNING AND MILLING

The basic principle involved and the plant and tools employed in drilling and trepanning are very similar to those used in the construction industry. A classical example of the use of diamond impregnated tube drills in the stone working field is the drilling of the container section in memorial vases for graves. They are also used to provide accurate clean holes through stone cladding and flooring when services have to pass through or fixings are required. The same type of tool is used to trepan the original blanks from which curling stones are made. Granite from the island of Ailsa Craig is trepanned to 280 mm. (11⅛ in.) cylinders with diamond impregnated tools containing 18 mesh grit at a concentration of 100. This is one case where additives introduced into the coolant proved beneficial. With Castrol Miracol 80 added to the water (about 75:1) it was claimed that the rate of penetration was 17 min. per 30·48 cm. (per foot) and the total bit life 1,297·4 metres (4,250 ft.). These cores are then cut into the required lengths with twin mounted segmented 600 mm. (24 in.) diameter saw blades containing 50/60 mesh grit at 60 concentration. These primary operations greatly facilitate the final shaping and polishing of the curling stones.

The blanks for stone table lamp bases can be produced by the same techniques from various stones and the centre holes drilled to take the wire and fix the lamp holder.

For profiling stone sections three types of diamond tooling are available. For use under similar cutting conditions to saws impregnated segmented cutters are made, particularly for relatively simple forms. A typical tool would be 250/350 mm. (10/14 in.) diameter and 25/50 mm. (1/2 in.) wide. For use on granite the mesh size would be about 45 and the concentration 35. For more complicated shapes and for the flat planing of less abrasive materials such as slate, marble and limestone, electrometallic cutters are available. The steel base can be readily machined to the required profile for copings, dados and similar components. The diamond and metal coating is then deposited on the blank in the areas required. Such tools would be used at speeds of 2,000/2,500 r.p.m. on limestone to cut in 3–5 mm. (0·125–0·20 in.) steps.

The third type of profiling tool follows the manufacturing technology of surface set drill bits as used in the mining, oil well and construction industries and as referred to under 'Primary Sawing'. These are designed to operate at much lower peripheral speeds and can be likened to milling practice as opposed to grinding which is the basis for most stone working. They are in fact often used in converted conventional metal working milling machines. However, specially designed machines are also available. These have been designed for such operations as milling granite slabs to a total width of 1·2 m. (47 in.) with a depth of cut up to 2 mm. (0·08 in.) and a feed rate of 40–100 cm. per min. (16–40 in. per min.). The final operating data is dependent on the type of granite.

Another typical example of the use of these surface set cutters is in the profile milling of window sills from limestone.

Ash trays and soap dishes of stone are also machined with diamond tooling. A machine specifically designed for these operations has been produced in Italy. This has a 5 horsepower drive motor and employs diamond cutters up to 150 mm. (6 in.) with a face of 20 mm. (0·8 in.).

The 'rock-hound' hobby so popular in America and increasingly so elsewhere also utilises diamond tooling on semi-precious stones but this is referred to in Chapter 10 on Jewellery.

REFERENCES

Charles Simpson—'Shaping Stone to Size in the '70s'—*Engineering*, 15th August, 1969.

De Beers—*Diamonds in the Stone Industry*.

G. Finnigan, M.ENG., A.M.I.MECH.E.—*Machining Stone with Diamond Tools*.

British Patent Specification 115,614—Robertson Geotechnical Services Ltd.

R. Copeman, M.COM., F.G.S., F.S.S., Lecturer in Investment Analysis at Birmingham University and I. Ford, B.SC., F.G.S., Senior Lecturer in Geology at Bristol University—'Geotechnical Aspects of the Machining of Natural Stones with Diamond'. Industrial Diamond Conference Papers, 25.3.69, London.

Ing. Ermanno Pacini and Dr. Lando Panizzari—published papers of L'Enapi and L'Assodiam, Convention on Diamond in the Stone Industry, Italy, September 1971. (Reported in *Borsa Marmi*.)

FEPA Standard of Diamond Saws.

U.S.S.R. Gost 16115–70—Diamond segment cut-off wheels with standard intersegment slots. Construction and sizes.

U.S.S.R. Gost 16116–70—Diamond segment cut-off wheels with narrow slots.

U.S.S.R. Gost 16117–70—Diamond segment cut-off wheels. Technical requirements.

8

The role of diamond in the construction, building and civil engineering fields

ALTHOUGH a considerable consumer of industrial diamonds, this field of activity generally makes use of only two basic tool types: the segmental saw and the diamond drill bit. The stone working operations described in the last chapter could, of course, be considered, and indeed are, a part of the construction industry, but its impact on the diamond industry is so extensive that it was thought appropriate to deal with it separately.

TUNNELLING

One of the first uses for diamond in rock drilling was in the digging of the Mount Cenis tunnel in 1863. Much of this early diamond drilling was accomplished with hand set diamond bits utilising large Brazilian Carbonado and were driven by steam powered rigs. The fundamental drilling method, however, has not changed. Thrust is applied at one end of a hollow rotating shaft with the result that the diamonds set in the other end of the tube groove the rock. A fluid is passed through the shaft to float out the cuttings. In these tunnel digging operations, because of their greater affinity to mining, the range of diamond drilling equipment and power units developed for mining operations are generally utilised.

The same can be said of dam construction; this range of equipment is described in the next chapter on mineral development.

In addition to their actual use in blast hole drilling with solid bits, diamond core drills are used for sampling the rock through which the tunnel is to pass. A recent example of this has been the work undertaken in determining the route of the proposed Channel Tunnel. These cores were taken from the sea bed and from the land in the Folkestone area. The sea bed drilling was undertaken from drilling barges and platforms. Although the ground was relatively soft, tungsten carbide bits did not provide satisfactory cores of the chalk, gault and greensand. Diamond core bits produced smooth cores without scoring or distortion. The cores were taken at depths from 10–150 metres (30–480 ft.) below the sea bed in water depths of 6–65 metres (20–200 ft.). The land samples taken were of the order of 65–150 metres (200–480 ft.) below the surface.

DAM CONSTRUCTION

In many cases, diamond asserts itself even before the project is at the design stage. The suitability of a dam site depends very much on the nature of the rock adjacent to the ends of the actual dam structure. In order to investigate this factor, diamond core drills are used to obtain samples of the rock at whatever levels are

Example of dam with associated power house. Extensive diamond core drilling is undertaken to sample the rock before the site is determined. Diamond grout hole drilling follows in the course of ensuring a sound joint between the bed rock and the concrete retaining wall
(L. M. Van Moppes & Sons S.p.A.)

considered appropriate. When the site has been approved, further holes are drilled to key the barrage into the mother rock. If the mother rock is too weak, holes may also be drilled in order to inject cement. This strengthens the area sufficiently to withstand the stresses imposed by the water pressing against the finished dam. To test the strength of the dam itself, cores of concrete are cut from it by similar diamond drills at various intervals. These cores are then subjected to laboratory tests to confirm that the properties of the concrete are in accordance with the designer's specification.

In the course of construction, anchor holes are drilled in the concrete in order to fix cranes and other equipment used at various stages. Ultimately, inspection cores are cut at predetermined intervals for subsequent testing of the concrete structure and the joints between adjacent sections. Diamond saws are also used to section these cores. The sections are then subjected to alternative physical tests.

Grouthole drilling: It is the normal practice to seal the fissures in rocks beneath the foundations of dams by the injection of cement grout or sometimes chemical grout from holes drilled by rotary or percussive methods. The latter is normally the faster and cheaper, but the trend is away from it on the ground that the chippings produced tend to block the fissures, so preventing the full penetration of the grout.

The work is usually in two phases, that of the consolidation which entails a large number of short holes, and that of the curtain entailing a smaller quantity of longer holes. The average length of hole is about 40–50 metres (120–150 ft.) and the longest holes seldom exceed 100 metres (300 ft.). Totals of 20,000 metres (60,000 ft.) are not unusual nowadays and there are cases of 100,000 metres (300,000 ft.). The diameters of holes by the rotary method are normally smaller than 50 mm. (2 in.).

The movement of the drilling machines between their locations is frequently difficult owing to the environments, and, for this reason, the types of machine preferred are those that can be easily dismantled and when assembled weigh less than about 300 kg. (650 lb.). The working spaces usually prohibit the use of derricks, so the drillrods are normally hoisted by hand until their weight

Q

makes necessary the use of hydraulic rod-pullers. The drilling fluid is always water, and, as a rule, one delivery pump serves several machines. The keynote of grouthole drilling is the fast production of holes. This determines the amount of work that the contractors can undertake in programmes which are liable to be squeezed by unforeseen delays in the preparation of the sites. Depending upon the hardness of the rocks, the use of diamond bits is often essential to satisfactory production, and with them the adoption of techniques to minimise round trips.

When the grouting procedure requires the completion of holes before injection begins, it can be advantageous to use diamond full-hole bits, also known as non-coring or solid bits. It depends upon how frequently the bits have to be changed, the average length of run obtained when using core bits and the difference in the average rates of penetration between the two types of bit. The alternative procedure calls for the holes to be drilled in stages, often of 5 metres (15 ft.): the slower rates of penetration with full-hole bits make their value, as time savers, marginal in this case, as it is rarely necessary to make more than one round trip between stages when coring. Since the diamond contents of solid bits are naturally greater than those of core bits, any such advantages are usually cancelled out.

Contrary to the tenor in normal coredrilling practice, if, in grouthole drilling, the cores tend to break up and be washed away, it is so much the better, as, by doing so, it is possible to drill further than the capacity of the coretube and thus reduce the frequency of round trips. To this end, simple coretubes are preferred and corelifters are seldom used. The corelifter is a valuable asset when housed in inner tubes that rotate independently, but, otherwise, it is often the starting point of blockages; this is particularly so in the case of simple coretubes in which it also restricts the possibilities of clearing incipient blockages of cores. As the result of being able to avoid blockages, full coretubes are normally obtained unless drilling is interrupted by arrival at a grouting stage. The cores are retained either by blocking in the core at the bit by reducing the flow of drilling water or by wedging them in with chips of hard rock carried to the coretube by the drilling water. The former method has obvious perils; the latter often results in some cores falling into the hole during hoisting. When this occurs, the bit usually has to drill out the resulting debris on its next run as time does not often permit the nicety of cleaning the hole.

The grouting thus completed is designed to achieve the following ends:

a. To increase the resistance of the bed-rock to movement or sliding when the pressure of the dam and the water it supports are put upon it.
b. To improve the water holding properties of the rock itself.
c. To prevent water leakage at the junction of the concrete dam and the bed-rock on which it stands.

In addition to the exploratory and grouting applications, diamond drills are also used to provide a number of auxiliary openings, of which the following are some examples:

Drain holes: Into these are fitted pressure gauges which are then sealed in position. They are of particular importance when the basement of the dam is being filled. The gauges record any back pressure build-up and, at a predetermined point, operate safety valves which automatically restore the correct pressure.

Pendulum holes: Generally of the order of 250/300 mm. diameter (10–12 in.); they must be perfectly straight and vertical. These serve as control holes for the construction itself and are used for observation.

Peizometric holes: Are drilled to observe the behaviour of fissures and are generally of the order of 60–75 mm. (2½–3 in.) in diameter. They permit observation of the underground movement of water.

Control holes: In both the screen and the structure itself, including joints between the various concrete blocks which form the dam.

In addition to diamond usage in the actual barrage, similar applications also occur in the construction of the protective surround to the power house associated with hydro-electric schemes.

Diamond shares with tungsten carbide most of the drilling operations in dam construction, depending, for proportion, on the local rock structure and general conditions. The advent of sawtooth diamond bits has tended to extend the area in which diamond is considered an ultimate economy.

BRIDGE BUILDING

As in dam construction, diamonds are sometimes called upon to fill the drilling role in foundation sampling, grouting and concrete structure testing.

In addition to these fields in which mainly mining type diamond equipment is used, another range of thin wall bits is also used to modify these structures to suit changing conditions. The drilling work on London's Tower Bridge is described later in this chapter under the restoration of historic buildings. Another example was the drilling of a 400 mm. (8 in.) diameter drainage hole in Westminster Bridge. This provided an outlet in an area which, under changed traffic conditions, was liable to flooding. The hole was drilled at an angle of 45°, through about 300 mm. (12 in.) of limestone below pavement level. The smooth hole wall resulting greatly facilitated the contractors' installation of the conduit.

Range of diamond tube drills for masonry drilling (Holemasters Ltd.)

When the Water Board of the City of Geneva, Switzerland, wanted to link up the supply of a neighbouring quarter with the main passing under the Coulouvrenière Bridge, the engineers suggested mounting the steel pipe against one of the central pillars. The pipe was nearly 60 cm. (2 ft.) in diameter. The proposed method of fixing would have been technically simple, but aesthetically deplorable as it would have ruined the architectural harmony of this ancient bridge. Other suggestions proved impracticable for various reasons until diamond drilling was suggested. Finally, the Swiss company, Forbeton S.A., of Geneva, was called upon to drill a shaft down one of the pillars and into which the pipe was sunk. The 60 cm. (2 ft.) diameter hole was drilled to a depth of 6 metres (20 ft.) in three days. The bit was specially designed for the job and contained 1,500 diamonds weighing in total about 30 cts. The bit was rotated at 120 r.p.m. by a 5 h.p. motor.

One modern version of the bridge—the flyover—sometimes needs to have sub-surface heating elements fitted. The cutting of slots in granite kerbstones to allow for the connection of these elements to the central power cable on Hammersmith Flyover, in West London, was greatly facilitated by the use of segmental diamond saws. The 88 mm. ($3\frac{1}{2}$ in.) wide channels were cut through the 300 mm. × 150 mm. (12 × 6 in.) granite sections at approximately 6 metre (20 ft.) intervals. Each cut took about $1\frac{1}{2}$ minutes. These saws are basically of the same construction as those described in Chapter 7 on the stone industry, but with metal bonds modified to suit the conditions encountered. The saws for this purpose are mounted on mobile self-propelled sawing machines.

ROAD BUILDING

The extensive motorway building programmes, which have been such a feature of civilisation recently, have resulted in considerable application of diamond drilling with thin wall tube drills and diamond sawing with segmental saws.

The normal range of thin wall drill bits contains at least two sizes specifically designed for taking sample cores from concrete with reference to B.S.1881 'Methods of testing concrete', or parallel standards in other countries.

The requirement is for cores of 100 mm. (4 in.) or 150 mm. (6 in.) diameter and, to obtain these, tube drills having nominal outside diameters of 108 mm. (4¼ in.) and 159 mm. (6¼ in.) are used. The remainder of the range of bits is used for stitch drilling when removing slabs or making openings, making holes for fixings and passages for pipes and conduits. The following table indicates the diameters tabulated in B.S.4019: Part 2:1973. The barrel length quoted is 360 mm. and the effective drilling depth 300 mm.

| | Outside mm. | | Inside mm. | | B.S. Ref. (Nominal hole size) |
	Max.	Min.	Max.	Min.	
	36·33	36·07	29·33	29·07	2 (36)
	44·33	44·07	37·33	37·07	3 (44)
Diameter of thin	54·38	54·12	47·38	47·12	4 (54)
wall Diamond	82·13	81·87	75·13	74·87	5 (82)
Tube Drills	109·13	108·75	100·25	99·87	6 (109)
	159·13	158·75	150·25	149·87	7 (159)

Above this standard range, bits are made to cut cores up to 300 mm. (12 in.) in length, and extension tubes are supplied for longer holes and cores. Larger diameters are made to suit special applications. Some such large sizes cannot be made in one piece because of the limitation of production equipment, and, in such cases, the diamond bearing area is made in segments and brazed on to a steel tube of the requisite size.

This whole range of bit sizes is available in two basic cutting faces: the *surface set* type has individual hand set diamonds protruding from a sintered metal matrix; the *impregnated* type has a cutting face of coarse diamond grit mixed in depth in a sintered metal matrix. Generally, the surface set bits are to be recommended for the softer aggregates such as crushed sandstone, and the impregnated type for harder aggregates such as flint. Some of the worst conditions for diamond drilling occur in the lean-mix concrete sub-base for a road where Thames or Seine Valley gravel is being used and in coastal areas where beach aggregate is common.

The whole range of thin wall diamond tube drills is generally used on specially developed portable drill rigs driven by electric.

petrol or air motors and they generally incorporate the following
features:

1. Drilling pressure is applied by means of a hand lever through
   a spur gear and rack along which the carriage and power unit
   are advanced.
2. The rack can be pivoted through 360° and locks in any
   position to drill vertically up or down, horizontally or at any
   angle between.
3. The column bracket can be locked at any position along the
   column to give complete vertical adjustment.
4. The column can be removed from the base platform for
   otherwise inaccessible locations.
5. There is an extension tube which is tightened by a screw nut
   on the column for locking the stand between floor and ceiling
   or between wall and joists. Extension tubes of varying lengths
   are available.
6. The drill stand, even when fitted with a comparatively heavy
   power unit, is portable and easily positioned by virtue of
   castor wheels. Levelling bolts in the base ensure rigidity
   when drilling.
7. When not convenient to use an extension tube a vacuum
   suction pad is available for holding the drill stand to flat
   surfaces.
8. The stand may also be secured by means of Rawlplug bolts or
   heavy ballast when the position is in the open or on uneven
   surfaces.
9. The unit is operated by one man and is easily dismantled for
   manhandling over rough terrain and obstructions.

In addition to this range of machines, a number of trailer mounted
units have been developed with particular reference to roadway and
airport runway core cutting. They are, of course, more limited in
their range of application than the portable drilling machines, but,
in their own particular area, save set-up and moving time. They are
also more rigid and often incorporate their own water supply.
Eleven such machines, driven by 25 h.p. petrol motors, are in
constant use in the State of New York for taking some 5,000 cores

per year from concrete surfaces of roads, bridges and canal structures. These are submitted to the Bureau of Materials, at the New York State Department of Transportation, who monitor the general state of public structures.

The following notes are for general guidance in the use of the normal range of portable drill units: In setting up the drill, the angle of the feed rack should first be determined according to the hole direction required and the centre-line of the drive spindle positioned accordingly. The base of the drill stand should then be raised on the screw adjusters provided. This provides greater stability than if the base remains supported on the wheels. The assembly thus positioned should then be clamped between two fixed surfaces with the screw jack extension provided for the main column. This can be done between walls or from floor to ceiling. Where such clamping arrangements are impossible and the work is being done on a smooth surface, a vacuum hold-down arrangement is sometimes used. Failing these two alternatives, a certain amount of improvisation is necessary. The drill stand base can be held down with suitable weights loaded upon it and the base itself can be temporarily extended to take further weight. In extreme cases, retaining bars can be fixed across the base area held in position by Rawlbolt type fixings into the area being drilled. Rigidity of the set-up is of paramount importance.

The water flow should then be started. Too much water should not be used, but sufficient to ensure a visible flow back up the outside of the bit. The flow normally required to achieve these conditions is of the order of 1·1–1·7 litres (2–3 pints) per minute for bits up to 75 mm. (3 in.) diameter and 1·7–2·8 litres (3–5 pints) per minute for 75 mm. (3 in.) to 150 mm. (6 in.) diameter.

The drive motor should then be started and the bit rotated at speeds of the following order:

| Bit diameter range | | Speed range |
mm.	in.	r.p.m.
Up to 50	2	600–1,200
50–100	2–4	350–750
100–150	4–6	250–550
Over 150	6	350 max.

It is advisable to use the most powerful drill available for the job to ensure sufficient torque and to minimise vibration.

The diamond cutting face of the bit should then be brought gently in contact with the surface to be drilled. In many cases this particular part of the operation can be greatly assisted by passing the drill through a clearance hole in a wood-steady held in position where the hole is required. In drilling, sufficient pressure should be applied for the bit to cut without appreciably slowing the drive speed. The pressure required to drill will vary according to the material. Any pressure in excess of that at which the rotational speed begins to fall is wasteful. When reinforcing steel is encountered, the pressure should be reduced in order to conserve bit life as far as possible. When drilling in flint aggregate concrete, however, this tends in turn to premature 'polishing' or rounding off the diamond cutting points in the bit. For this reason it is recommended that, when cutting actual reinforcing, wherever possible an already worn bit should be used in place of the current one in use on the concrete itself.

That the steel has been severed will be indicated by an increase in rotational speed and a greater rate of penetration. At this point remove the diamond bit and extract the core. Ensure that the hole is now clear of all debris, especially steel fragments; a loose piece of steel remaining when the bit is re-introduced may cause it to jam and even stall the motor.

A close watch should be maintained on water return during drilling. The colour of this water is a good indication of the material being cut at any given moment. If the flow ceases, stop drilling immediately and ensure it is restored before restarting.

The advent of high speed concrete paving eliminated the possibility of pre-forming expansion joints in highways and these were then cut with diamond saws. In the case of the building of the Pomona Freeway, near Los Angeles, U.S.A., the high production concrete slip-form paver produced about $16 \times 1,600$ metres ($48 \times 5,000$ ft.) daily. In order to cope with this, the sawing contractor had to join together two specially designed sawing machines to span the total 16 metres (48 ft.) in order to keep pace with the paver and cut a 50 mm. (2 in.) expansion joint at an average spacing of 5 metres (15 ft.). Higher than usual cutting speeds also had to be employed. Up to about 350 joints per day were achieved.

A selection of machines and power units designed to utilise thin wall diamond tube drills and segmental diamond saws

When highway surfaces become uneven after a few years' use by heavy vehicles, diamond again comes to the rescue. Special machines have been designed to carry batteries of segmental diamond saws which are used to re-level the deformed road surfaces. In the case of U.S. Highway 80, between Albany and Richmond, diamond saws were first used to cut out particularly bad areas which had to be replaced, and to cut fresh expansion joints where necessary. The whole area, including 'stepped' joints from the original road building, was levelled with machines on which 360 segmental saw blades were used to grind a path 2 m. (6 ft.) wide. The blades were 350 mm. (14 in.) diameter and altogether contained some 7,000 cts. of diamond grit.

An alternative 'planing' machine employs whole diamond surface set cutter heads for levelling smaller areas to greater degrees of accuracy. With wider spacing of the individual diamond saws, a similar operation is carried out to groove the road surface and thus provide better water elimination to avoid 'aquaplaning', and improve tyre adhesion. The California State Highway Department started using this technique as long ago as 1959 and claim that, in some situations, the accident rate has been reduced by as much as 75% due to the improved road surface characteristics.

Where trenches have to be cut in existing road surfaces, restoration work is minimised by cutting through the bitumen and concrete layers with diamond saws. Conventional percussive and other equipment is only used to break out the material between the sawn edges and below the road level. The work is often done with two diamond saws suitably spaced on a common spindle and carried on a self-propelled sawing machine. The method can be used for comparatively wide trenches such as a 1·5 metre (5 ft.) for a replacement sewer, down to 12 mm. ($\frac{1}{2}$ in.) for a cable trench.

Both sawing and drilling techniques are also used to provide a 'key' when fixing lane markers in highways and bridges.

AIRPORTS

All that has been said about the use of diamond bearing equipment on road construction and maintenance is equally true of airports. In the latter case, however, even greater importance is placed on

Trailer mounted mobile drill for diamond core cutting in roads and airport runways (Kranbetrieb und Gerätebau Wiedtal)

the condition of the runway surfaces which are so critical in the high speed landing and take-off operations of modern jet planes. Examples of diamond levelling and grooving operations on runways have been reported from:

Germany:	Munich and Berlin.
Britain:	Heathrow—London, Lakenheath RAF, Prestwick, Birmingham.
U.S.A.:	Kansas, Atlanta, Kennedy, La Guardia, Newark, Boston, Seattle, Chicago, Washington National.
France:	Orly, Roissey-en-France.

There are doubtless many others which have not come to the author's notice.

In addition, the introduction of 'pancake lighting' has resulted in a further extension of the uses of both diamond tube drills and segmental saws. The drills are used to form the quite large diameter holes in which the light capsule is set and saws are used to cut the slots through which the necessary supply cables are routed. One such case reported is Abu Dhabi International Airport; in this case 225 mm. (9 in.) and 325 mm. (13 in.) diameter holes were required to house the lights and depths of 75–100 mm. (3–4 in.) were called for in 'black top' surfacing. A standard portable Holemasters HM1A drill stand was used with a 4 h.p. air motor as drive unit. A total of 258 holes of the smaller diameter was drilled at an average of less than 2 minutes per hole. The larger units were required only at key points, and 9 larger holes were drilled for these at an average of 3 minutes each. The overall average per hole, including the movement and resiting of the drill, was 15–20 minutes per hole.

Drilling for lights:

Britain:	Manchester, Prestwick.
U.S.A.:	Sacramento—California, Kincheloe and Selfridge Airforce Bases.
Abu Dhabi	
U.S.S.R.:	Moscow.
Finland:	Helsinki.

Diamond drilling and sawing are not confined only to the runways of airports. Orly's No. 3 runway and some of the buildings are

Special 200 mm. (8 in.) diameter drill bit developed for the 'pancake lighting' on Moscow and Helsinki airports (A.-B. Industridiamanter)

built over RN No. 7. It is a complicated reinforced structure, but the designers did not envisage the strain to which it will be subjected when the Concorde is in service. The supporting concrete beams needed to be strengthened; this was done by adding post-tensioned steel cables which were passed through the 550 mm. (22 in.) beams in 80 mm. ($3\frac{1}{4}$ in.) and 100 mm. (4 in.) accurately drilled holes. In all, 400 holes were drilled with appropriate diamond tube drills on air operated rigs.

Diamond drilling to reinforce the ceiling of the Eastern Tunnel of London's Heathrow Airport

Another example occurred later in 1968. It was found that the roof lining of the Eastern approach tunnel to Heathrow was becoming detached from the support structure under the main runway. It was decided to reinforce the lining support by inserting Rawlbolts on a 2 m. (6 ft.) grid over the whole area. Some 1,200 holes of 32 mm. ($1\frac{1}{4}$ in.) diameter were diamond drilled, each to a depth of 187 mm. ($7\frac{1}{2}$ in.). As the reinforcing of the mother structure had to remain intact, any hole which encountered steel had to be abandoned and re-sited—many holes came in this category as the reinforcing bars were only 50–70 mm. (2–3 in.) from the surface and generally at 113 mm. ($4\frac{1}{2}$ in.) centres. In order to complete the work in time for the tunnel to be re-opened for Christmas, nine air-powered Holemasters-Diatube rigs were put into use for two twelve hour shifts per day and the work completed in ten days.

In order to extend the facilities to cope with Jumbo Jet handling, it was decided by the authorities of Schiphol Airport at Amsterdam that it was necessary to remove a large slab of concrete wall to provide access between old and new buildings. Two diamond saws were used to cut out a slab some 170 mm. ($6\frac{3}{4}$ in.) thick by about 50 metres (150 ft.) long.

NEW AND EXISTING BUILDINGS AND OTHER STRUCTURES

There is now an extensive catalogue of the buildings in which diamond saws and drills have participated either at the time of construction or in subsequent alterations and modernisations. Some examples are:

Office blocks
Apartment buildings and hotels
Shops (particularly supermarkets and departmental stores)
Underground railways
Hospitals
Swimming baths and sports stadiums
Television masts
Power and pumping stations
Museums and exhibition buildings
Car parks and garages

Cutting pre-stressed concrete slabs with a Uni-Neven segmental diamond saw
(Impregnated Diamond Products Ltd.)

Nuclear reactor sites
Schools, universities and laboratories
Factories—the structure and for plant locating and fixing
Post Office buildings and telephone exchanges
Banks—general offices and strong rooms
Military establishments
Breweries
Railway stations and viaducts
Harbour quays and locks

Diamond starts to play its part even before the actual construction begins. Slabs of pre-stressed concrete are in increasing demand. Pre-cast lengths are cut to size with segmental saws similar to those

Diamond saw blade cutting off asbestos cement pipe (A.-B. Industridiamanter)

used so extensively in the stone industry. Stone cladding is, of course, cut in the same way. Bricks, tiles and other refractory materials are also cut to precise shapes using diamond saws on simple bench mounted saws. They are also used to cut to exact lengths such things as asbestos or pottery pipes.

At the next stage, it is being found more economical to make the building fabric complete without attempting to preform holes which can be diamond drilled for such things as pipe runs, central heating and air conditioning. The greater precision of location and allowance for modification are major attractions to the designers. In a large office development, in Liverpool, a two year contract has been placed for the drilling of all holes from 25 mm. (1 in.) to 350 mm. (14 in.) diameter through reinforced concrete walls and floors for all sub-contractors such as plumbers, electricians, etc.

In the same sense, a pair of diamond saws with a suitable spacer between can be used to cut two parallel slots, the material between

Drilling 200 mm. (8 in.) holes in the reinforced concrete roof of the podium of a Liverpool office development. Sample core in the foreground
(Holemasters Ltd.)

New opening being prepared by diamond sawing in an existing concrete retaining wall (Holemasters Ltd.)

is chipped away and a clean slot the required width has been formed to take supply conduit or other services.

At the next stage, diamond drilling is used to reduce noise in the neighbourhood of new, but already occupied, apartments. Two blocks were in this state at Champigny-sur-Marne, on the outskirts of Paris, some time ago. They were at 30° to one another and a decorative façade had to be fixed to cover the joint. The façade consisted of a series of concrete panels. A total of 84 holes of about 70 mm. ($2\frac{3}{4}$ in.) was drilled in the adjacent blocks and the panels attached by the inserted bolts.

At the Shell Centre in London, the nine approaches to the underground car park were slotted with diamond saws in order to

R

insert over 4,000 metres (14,0C0 ft.) of electric de-icing cable in the
38 mm. (1½ in.) deep slots. The grooves were at 150 mm. (6 in.)
centres.

In the construction of tile lined swimming pools, diamond drilling
greatly facilitates the fixing of grab rails. Spoiling of ceramic facing
is avoided and much greater accuracy of hole location is possible
than by any other method.

The new Bay Area Rapid Transit automatic rail system being
constructed in the San Francisco area needed additional ventilation
ducts between the second and third levels of the underground
stations; a special diamond bit of some 700 mm. (27½ in.) diameter
was made to drill through the 450 mm. (18 in.) thick reinforced
concrete dividers. The diamond tube drill method was adopted to
ensure smooth clean holes without patching. The drill rig employed
a 10 h.p. electric motor through a 10:1 reduction gear to turn the
bit at 175 r.p.m. Some of the holes included as many as twenty-four
reinforcing bars, each 22 mm. (⅞ in.) diameter and some even larger.
The forty segments, of 50 mm. (2 in.) length, each contained about
2·5 carats of 18/20 mesh diamond grit.

In the case of conversion work in buildings already in use or
evacuated for major alteration, there is often even greater reliance
on diamond techniques. New openings required in concrete walls
and floors can be speedily provided either by sawing, if accessibility

*Stitch drilling to remove a concrete slab in a power station prior to the
installation of new plant. Diamond was employed to minimise dust and
vibration*

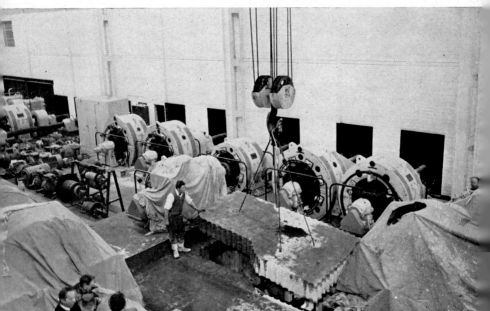

permits, or by stitch drilling with tube drills. This method is also used for controlled demolition in steel works and power stations when heavy plant has to be replaced.

As new skyscrapers dwarfed the 100 metre Euromast in Rotterdam some ten years after its construction, it was decided to add a further 75 metres to restore the structure as the tallest in Holland. To tie the new to the old, 32 anchorage holes were diamond drilled vertically downwards into the 30 cm. thick concrete walls of the lower section, to a depth of up to 2 m. The steel tie bolts were 55 mm. diameter. Other auxiliary work also utilised diamond drilling to modify ventilation and provide access to the tie bolt plates and nuts of the jointing arrangements.

The Blyth generating station in Northumberland had difficulty in clearing mussels which accumulated from the cooling water drawn from the neighbouring North Sea. In order to speed up the periodic clearing operation, 225 mm. (9 in.) holes were drilled through the 1·4 m. (54 in.) thick reinforced concrete floor to the culverts beneath. Through these compressed air could be introduced to reduce the time from two days to only ten hours.

In the modernisation of the Atlantic Hotel in Hamburg, large diamond drills were used extensively, and in modifications at the Royal Lancaster Hotel in London. In both cases the diamond drill technique was employed specifically to reduce noise and dust in the fully occupied hotels. One of the Royal Lancaster operations involved the provision of an access door to a lift shaft that had exceptionally bad acoustic problems. Impregnated diamond drills 100 mm. (4 in.) diameter were used to 'stitch drill' the opening through the 290 mm. (11½ in.) concrete wall. Depending on the incidence of reinforcing bars, each hole took 30–40 minutes.

Under financial pressure it was decided to convert Gorringes, the London departmental store, to a hotel, to be known as the Royal Westminster. One of the major phases was the conversion of the showroom to 136 bedrooms. The architect specified that access through the concrete floors for drainage, water and ventilation for these rooms should be provided exclusively by diamond drilled holes. Holes of 100–200 mm. (4–8 in.) diameter were required to a total of about 300.

The Ronan Point disaster resulted not only in a major reinforcement programme for the stricken apartment block but also for many others of similar construction. In order to install the various strengthening members, in many cases diamond drilling was employed. Special lightweight rigs of compact design were produced by drilling contractors and recirculation units provided to minimise water troubles in the often occupied flats. Tens of thousands of holes were drilled in the course of this major operation.

Underwater drilling is facilitated with diamond equipment and is utilised in work connected with quays and locks. At the Manchester Ship Canal's Eastham Locks one of the fast-end bolts had to be renewed in the 26 metre (80 ft.) wide lock. There are four parallel locks in the system, each having a pair of gates at both ends. The bolts 75 mm. (3 in.) in diameter and some 8 metres (25 ft.) long formed the anchorage for the winding gear needed to operate the gates. The existing bolts had been constantly under water and had deteriorated. A special cage was designed by the Canal Company and arrangements were made for intermittent drilling to suit the traffic flow. The operation was carried out by a skilled diver who had been specially trained in the diamond rig operation. Drill bits of 112 mm. ($4\frac{1}{2}$ in.) diameter were used with 1·5 metres (5 ft.) extension barrels driven by a $7\frac{1}{2}$ h.p. air motor.

At the Eisenhower Lock on the St. Lawrence, a 500 ton concrete sill became detached and an emergency repair had to be undertaken. Some 100 holes were diamond drilled, rods inserted and concrete surrounds poured to tie the sill back to the main structure.

Shields connected with nuclear reactors often require additional inspection or service entries, and diamond drilling is now the normal method employed.

THE RESTORATION OF HISTORIC BUILDINGS AND MONUMENTS

The restoration of Stonehenge some years ago employed diamond drilling to introduce strengthening bars to one of the uprights.

When the upper level walkway of the Tower Bridge in London needed to be replaced, diamond drills were used to form 300 mm. (12 in.) holes and house hawsers that needed to be attached to the granite tower walls.

The reconstruction of the 700 year old De Grey tomb at York employed diamond drilling. The canopy is supported by a number

The diamond tube drill and three of the four granite cores cut from the Tower Bridge, London

of Purbeck marble columns some 1·5 m. (4½ ft.) diameter by 95 mm. (3¾ in.) high. These needed to be strengthened by the addition of reinforcing rods. Despite the very decayed state of the stone, by supporting them in plaster of Paris bandages and employing special jigs, the vibrationless diamond drilling was successfully accomplished. A 45 mm. (1¾ in.) diameter hole was drilled through each of the ten columns.

The lid section of the granite sarcophagus used for Rameses III is at the Fitzwilliam Museum, Cambridge; other sections are at the Louvre in Paris and at a museum in Egypt. The Cambridge authorities decided to do some restoration work in the course of resiting the sarcophagus. The various sections were located on a wood base and jointed with epoxy resin. Twelve holes were then diamond drilled to take the 38 mm. (1½ in.) steel tie bars which varied in length up to 1·5 metres (4½ ft.). Special coolant disposal arrangements were made, and a 5 h.p. electric drive rig was utilised.

Although perhaps not strictly within the scope of this sub-heading, it is interesting to note that the holes used to house the fixings of the architectural feature depicting St. Michael and the Devil to the new Coventry Cathedral were also diamond drilled.

The church of the Abbey of Montier-en-Der, in France, was first built in wood in A.D. 672 and rebuilt in stone in A.D. 998; additions were made up to the 13th century. In the last war, German gunfire caused damage, particularly to the belfry. The French contractors, Entreprise Pradeau & Morin, were charged with the restoration. It was found that new foundations were needed and this was undertaken in collaboration with the Société Technique de l'Utilisation de la Précontrainte. The new foundation consisted of a raft supported on piles and tied to the existing foundations by cables. A total of more than 200 metres (600 ft.) of holes between 2 and 3 metres (6–9 ft.) were diamond drilled with a flexible drive electric powered machine. The hole diameters varied from 75 mm. (3 in.) to 175 mm. (7 in.).

Due to protests at the proposed demolition of the Queen's Tower when London's Imperial Institute was to be pulled down, this notable Victorian monument is now to be retained as a free standing edifice. The proof that the foundations were sound was provided by sample cores cut with diamond tube drills.

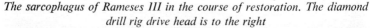

The sarcophagus of Rameses III in the course of restoration. The diamond drill rig drive head is to the right

'St. Michael and the Devil' is attached to the post-war *Coventry Cathedral* with fixings held in diamond drilled holes

Diamond bits and saws were also extensively used in the restoration of the famous Milan Cathedral.

REFERENCES

'Drilling through Reinforced Concrete'—S. Sinclair, M.I.C.W., *Civil Engineering*, January, 1963.
Published Papers of the Seminar of the Fédération Nationale des Bâtiments et Travail Publique—Reims, December, 1968.
Diamond Tools in Civil Engineering—De Beers publication L21.
Diamond Drilling in Dam Construction—R. Bolliger, Fino Mornasco, Italy.

9

Mineral development

UNDER this heading there are two main fields of application. The older is a development of the core drilling techniques said to have been invented by the Chinese, developed by the Egyptians and known to have been used by the Romans. Core drilling was said to have been started in the Durham coalfields in the 1600's. The use of diamond tipped core drills is now well established in the mining of metalliferous and other ores. In the search for oil, the principles were further developed to take account of the greater depths encountered and the different strata.

In addition to the coring function, bits are now made to cut complete holes also instead of cutting sample cores. The original core bits consisted of a length of steel tube, in one face of which holes were fashioned to retain the diamonds which were then caulked in with copper filling by craftsmen who were often the key to the whole economics of the operation. The current sequence of operations in producing drill bits is:

1. A suitable alloy steel blank is machined to the required dimensions.
2. A carbon mould is machined to the configuration decided upon for the diamond cutting area of the bit. To this broad pattern is added the pattern of 'flutes' and 'dimples' in the form of engraved recesses to determine the pattern to be followed by the diamond setter. In the case of 'impregnated' bits, this operation is omitted.
3. In the case of 'surface set' bits, a diamond is then located in each recess. In doing this the diamond setter takes into account the suitability of the profile of the diamond, which will eventually project from the matrix, and its orientation

in relation to grain structure. In the case of some oil-well drilling bits the diamonds are preset in hard metal inserts to provide added resistance to wear.

4. In the case of impregnated bits, the diamond grit is mixed with the metal powder which forms the matrix. In either case, the annular ring formed in the carbon mould is now filled with the metal powder. The latter ring consists of various mixtures of tungsten, tungsten carbide, iron, copper, nickel, zinc, cobalt and other metals.

5. Into this powder ring the prepared face of the steel blank is now pressed.

6. The whole assembly is then heat treated, not only to sinter the matrix, but also to weld the diamond bearing head to the blank. This may be done in a muffle furnace or on an induction heater.

7. Surplus alloy is then machined off, suitable waterways ground and the whole assembly machined to specification.

Impregnated bits are generally designed to be totally consumed without subsequent resetting, but surface set bits are normally returned to the maker for resetting. This operation follows the same sequence as for the production of a new bit, but is preceded by the following operations:

a. Electro-chemical extraction of the worn diamonds.

b. Sorting of the extracted diamonds to determine which are capable of further economic use. Where the diamonds were originally of the 'treated' variety, they are then 'reconditioned' before being reset.

c. To this re-usable salvage are added sufficient new diamonds to restore the original weight of the new bit.

MINING

The main uses in this field are core drilling, blast-hole drilling, methane drainage, drilling holes for fixings and other purposes in mines recovering such minerals as coal, iron, copper, nickel and pyrites.

The main factors in diamond drill bit design are very inter-

Working faces of typical diamond drill bits

Tongue type drilling bit
Designed for fast and trouble free drilling. Eliminates the usual dead centre portion of the concave type drilling bits.

Deflection or taper reaming shell
Can be threaded to fit core barrel or drill rods.

Bull nose deflection bit
Available in all sizes and with any thread.

Saw-tooth core bit
For use in soft and medium hard formations.

Impregnated type core bit
Specifications are available to suit all drilling conditions.

Face discharge saw-tooth type core bits
For use with Air Flush also manufactured for use with water or mud flush.

Casing shoe
Available for all Casing Standards with either Male (pin) or Female (box) Threads.

Diamond drilling and reaming equipment for mining

Surface set face discharge core bit
Having External or Internal Threads for D.C.D.M.A. Large Series B.S.I. 'F' Series Core Barrels.

Surface set core bit with internal thread
To fit Core Barrels such as metric type T & M Series.

Surface set core bit
Suitable for use in most Diamond Drilling Operations. Available in straight or bevel wall type, external thread, such as B.S.I.
D.C.D.M.A. Metric Types A, B, Y, Z, and K, also CDDA Stds.

Concave type drilling bit (non-coring)
Threaded to fit Drill Rods or Core Barrels.

Pilot type drilling bit (non-coring)
Threaded to fit Drill Rods or Core Barrels.

Surface set wireline core bits (stepped type)
For use with Wireline Core Barrels, Impregnated Wireline Core Bits also available.

Strip/panel type reaming shell
Suitable for use with Core Barrels or Casing.

Ring type reaming shell
Fluted Ring Type for use with single or double tube core barrels. Flutes ensure clearance for cuttings between blank and cutting points.

dependent and difficult to tabulate. The cutting medium or diamond content may vary not only in respect of bortz in various qualities and carbon, but also in the size range chosen. For the softer range of rocks, such as chalk, greywacke, marl, mudstone, shale and slate, a size range of 2 to 20 stones per carat is normal. In the medium range, for example, amphibolite, diorite, gneiss, limestone, sandstone and schist, the range would be of the order of 10 to 80 diamonds per carat, and for the harder range, such as dacite, gabbro granite, quartzite, rhyolite and syenite, 20 to 150 per carat would be more appropriate. In the case of impregnated bits, the diamond size range is usually smaller.

Matrices can be formed in a wide range of hardness from about Rockwell 18C to 60C. It must be remembered, however, that this hardness figure is not necessarily an absolute indication of the abrasion resisting properties of the matrix.

The form of the bit profile or 'kerf' can be selected from half-round, flat, quadrant and a number of composite curved forms. The diamond setting pattern can be varied, as also the size, number and form of waterways. This factor is now extended to cover the number and dimensions of the 'teeth' in sawtooth bits. The waterways can be reinforced to resist local abrasion and steel blanks can be given a 'hard facing' to counteract erosion.

The rock formation must be identified and, if possible, an indication given of whether it is expected to be uniform, broken, laminated or faulted and to what extent the strata is inclined. If the information is not available in this degree of detail, a brief description of known facts of the area geology will provide a working basis. The information can then be supplemented as drilling progresses and bit design modified where necessary. It is in this sense that close co-operation between the bit user and the bit manufacturer is most fruitful and can lead to considerable economies.

The next factor is the characteristics of the drilling machine. The design, performance and flexibility of this equipment have improved greatly, but one of the main elements in economic drilling continues to be the operator's ability to interpret from the machine's behaviour what is happening in the drill hole. Trials are currently being made of equipment designed to interpret automatically some of the equipment's responses.

The capacity of a drilling machine, in terms of the distance and diameter that it will drill, depends upon the power of the motor, the torque transmitting capacity, the thrust available and the efficiency of the hoist and brake systems.

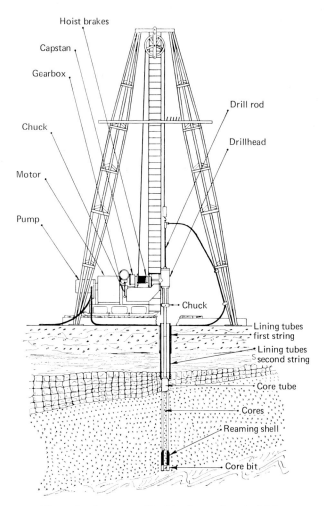

The main elements utilised in diamond rock drilling

The assembly of the transmission components of a modern heavy duty machine is similar to that coupling the drive between the front-mounted motor and the driven rear axle shafts of a conventional automobile, except that a simple straight-tooth bevel gear arrangement converts the drive through the right-angle to the hollow spindle in the drillhead. Twin hydraulic jacks, incorporated in the drillhead, control the longitudinal movement of the spindle, at one end of which (sometimes at both ends) and integrated with it there is a chuck having adjustable jaws. These clamp on to the drill rod passing through the spindle. Usually the motor also drives the hoist with which the core barrel and drill rods are pulled out of the hole, the pump of the hydraulic circuit and sometimes also the pump delivering the drilling fluid.

Lighter machines may be similarly constructed, or they may have a differential screw system, actuated either by a multiple disc clutch or by gearing, to control the longitudinal movement of the spindle. The light machines used in grouthole drilling and underground in mines are powered by electric or air motors, and frequently do not have either gear box or clutch in the interests of lessening bulk and improving mobility.

Apart from the basic machine, the equipment consists of one or more pumps to deliver the drilling fluid, the core tube which during drilling is situated behind the bit and so houses the cores as they are produced, and drill rods with which the core barrel is connected to the drillhead. When the drilling location is on the ground surface, a derrick is usually erected over the machine to facilitate the handling of the drill rods.

The selection of equipment depends firstly upon the minimum diameter of cores required, then upon the character of the rocks to be drilled and the lengths of the holes. In some situations the holes can be drilled entirely in the same diameter, but in others they have to be started larger than the minima required at completion owing to the need to line them. This is sometimes necessary to prevent the collapse of the surrounding rocks into the hole. It is not easy to decide what is wanted when the character of rocks is unknown; on the one hand the holes might not be completed, and on the other much equipment might never be used.

Clear water is the normal drilling fluid, but in some circumstances air or an emulsion of bentonite clays and water known as 'mud' is preferable. Mud tends less to erode the walls of holes than water, and thereby reduces the use of lining tubes (known also as casings). The mud has the same effect by supporting the walls of holes. This method is not widely applied in core drilling (except in the oil-fields) because its success depends upon obtaining adequate flow characteristics, which usually demand the use of larger diameter drill rods and thicker-walled bits than are necessary when using water, and these in turn often demand the use of more powerful machinery than is otherwise necessary.

The air flushing system has been found especially useful for coring in some coal measures and other soft friable formations.

In order to protect such friable cores and to facilitate their transport and examination, a transparent plastic sheath system was developed by the Turriff Construction Corporation Ltd., of Warwick.

In normal core drilling operations the majority of the time expended is in the round trips, comprising the removal of the core barrel from the holes and replacing it. During removal the drill rods are disconnected at suitable intervals, depending upon the working space, and they are reconnected during replacement. The speed with which round trips are carried out depends upon the length of hole, the length of drill rods that can be handled at a time, the speed of hoisting and the efficiency of the brake. The frequency of round trips depends upon the design of the core barrel and its length, and the character of the rocks drilled. Rocks that are compact rather than fissured, fresh rather than altered, strong rather than weak, are good from this point of view and the converses are bad.

Core barrels that are simply single tubes yield reasonably complete cores in really good rocks, but, if this type is used in bad rocks, much core is lost due to erosion by the drilling fluid and vibration. The most efficient type at the present time for obtaining complete cores has two tubes, the inner one being free to rotate independently of the outer one and extending almost to the front of the bit, the core lifter being housed in the extremity of the inner tube.

In earlier double tube types, still in service but diminishing, the inner tubes end some distance from the front of the bit, so exposing the newly cut cores to the drilling fluid over that distance; in such assemblies the core lifters are housed in the bits and may transmit

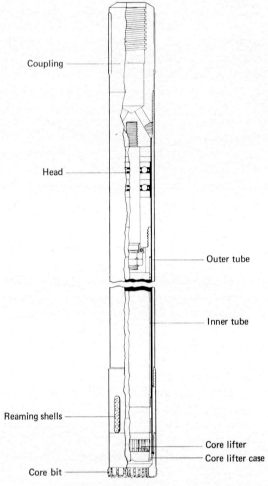

Coupling

Head

Outer tube

Inner tube

Reaming shells

Core lifter
Core lifter case

Core bit

Construction of typical core barrel assembly as used with diamond rock drills

sufficient torque to the newly cut cores to fracture them, before they enter the inner barrels.

The function of the core lifter is to grip the newly cut core and so enable it to be parted from the rock. It also retains the cores already inside the core tube. The common form of core lifter is a sleeve of tempered steel grooved to permit the passage of drilling fluid. It has parallel internal and tapered external sides and a slit of sufficient width to provide adequate grip when it is closed. It is in contact with the newly cut core during drilling, being then situated at the wider end of its bevelled housing, and is moved towards the narrower end by friction when the bit is pulled off the bottom of the hole.

In bad rocks the length of core tube is of little importance, given that optimum core recovery is the objective and to this end the best type of core barrel has been selected. The features of this latest type of core barrel that protect cores so well also make it virtually impossible to continue drilling once a blockage of cores has occurred.

The length of core barrel is important in good rocks and becomes more so with increasing length of hole, but there is a limit beyond which efficiency does not appreciably improve. This is governed by the diameter and wall thickness of the outer tube and by the thrust that is applied to it. These factors determine the distortion that occurs during drilling which is also influenced by the inclination of the hole. The limit for normal double core barrels of diameters smaller than 50 mm. (2 in.) is about 6 metres (20 ft.), but longer runs can be obtained in favourable circumstances.

Among the developments during the past decade aimed at speeding up round trips, the most notable has been the adoption of the wireline system known for many years in oil-well drilling. By this system the inner tube is removed and replaced through the drillrods. The E. J. Longyear Company, of Minneapolis, was the first to introduce a satisfactory device for hole diameters applicable in core drilling, which are much smaller than those obtained in oil-well drilling and so present more difficult engineering problems. In order to accommodate their latching mechanisms, the current wireline devices for core drilling require thicker-walled bits than are normally used. Higher levels of thrust are thus necessary to produce similar rates of penetration. Thus more diamonds have to be committed, and the tendency of holes to deviate, that is inherent in rotary drilling, is increased. Even so, there are many situations in which the wireline system is advantageous, particularly in bad rocks or where, as often is the case when drilling from locations underground, lack of working space prohibits the use of long core barrels. The wireline

S

core barrels have all the features of the best conventional ones that promote good recoveries of cores.

In determining the type of core bit required, it must, of course, also be taken into account what types of core barrel are to be used. This may be indicated by the barrel manufacturer's type or reference or a general description such as double tube, single tube, mud, bottom discharge and the size designation. Casing bit types are identified by their size and the alternatives 'flush jointed' or 'flush coupled'. If available, drill hole data will also have a bearing on bit design. Details of the type of over-burden, the average depth to bedrock, average hole depth and hole inclination may all influence the final specification.

Core drilling

The most common purposes of diamond drilling are to evaluate mineral resources and plan programmes of work in mines. The cost of bringing a mine into production may run into millions of pounds. All aspects of the project, therefore, justify thorough examination, and one of the most fundamental is the structure of the rocks.

The most reliable way of ascertaining the structures of rocks is by *in situ* examination, but this is seldom practical because the sinking of shafts of diameters sufficient for the purpose is both slow and very expensive. The nearest practical alternative is to examine the rocks displaced by the sinking of narrow shafts effected by drilling methods. Ideally, the samples so obtained should resemble in every respect the structures as they exist. This objective is still difficult to achieve in its entirety, but rotary drilling with annular bits is the only method yet devised to do so. The cylindrical sections of rock produced by this method are known as cores and the core bits with which they are produced have been described earlier.

Many rocks are sufficiently soft to be penetrated by materials other than diamond, but diamond requires the least thrust and so promotes the completeness of cores that otherwise could be impaired by vibrations at the cutting face.

Blasthole drilling

Under the mining and quarrying conditions encountered in such areas as Canada, Australia and South Africa it has been found, in many instances, that diamond drilling to take the explosive charges

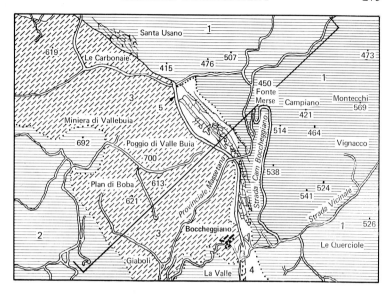

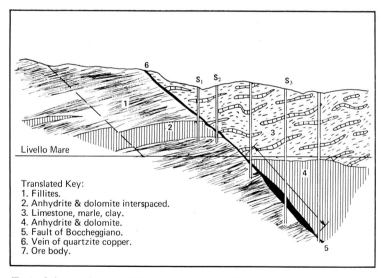

Translated Key:
1. Fillites.
2. Anhydrite & dolomite interspaced.
3. Limestone, marle, clay.
4. Anhydrite & dolomite.
5. Fault of Boccheggiano.
6. Vein of quartzite copper.
7. Ore body.

Typical diamond core drilling pattern used in Tuscany to develop the pyrite mine at Boccheggiano ('Costruzioni', October 1971) is more economical than the alternative methods. The latter usually consist of percussive or rotary-percussive drilling with tungsten carbide drillheads.

Many of the considerations in the choice of coring versus solid diamond bits that occur in grouthole drilling also arise in blasthole drilling. Some of the advantages of diamond drilled blastholes are a smooth straight bore of uniform diameter which is ideal for inserting the charge; better directional control; cleaner rock breaks; the use of smaller diameter holes with minimum vibration which prevents premature rock movements; the use of the most modern explosives is facilitated, providing better control of fragmentation.

Methane drainage and other uses

It has become standard safety practice in mining coal to drain methane from the vicinity of the seams that are being worked by means of holes, the essential aspect of which is their rapid completion. Since hard rocks usually do not occur in association with coal, diamonds are not often needed, but for use in those areas where they are necessary, full-hole bits, known as the tongue type, have been developed which produce holes 20% to 30% faster than hitherto has been achieved.

The matchless regularity of holes drilled by diamond bits makes their use obligatory in applications demanding this quality. One example is that of the photoelastic techniques devised by Rock Mechanics Limited, of London (now Soil Mechanics of Bracknell), to determine *in situ* stresses in rocks, which can cause the hazardous phenomena known as rockbursts.

In the installation of JORA raise lifts, a pilot hole of 80–150 mm. (3½–6 in.) is required from the level above. Through this is passed the supporting cable for the cage. Where the rock strata is suitable, as in the case of the Rio Tinto mines in Spain, this pilot hole is diamond drilled.

Common difficulties in core drilling

Deviation occurs in all holes drilled even by rotary methods, its extent in core drilling depending upon the inclination of the hole, the character of the rock drilled, the diameters of the core tube and the drill rods used and the clearance between the core tube and the wall of the hole. It happens quite often, particularly in near-vertical holes through homogeneous rocks, that the deviations cancel out to produce holes that are close to their desired positions. On the other hand, substantial deviations occur when the holes are started further from the vertical and the rocks produce eccentric loads on the bits. This occurs invariably on the top sides of the holes.

It is essential in many cases to know the nature and extent of the deviations, and this is made possible by instruments that are placed in the hole to record its bearing and inclination. Once the character of deviation has been defined, steps can be taken to nullify it in other and similar holes. Where the holes are short, it is the usual practice to start them in directions such that their deviations will take them to their planned targets. The same procedure may be adopted in the case of longer holes, but it is usually preferable to modify their starting directions, so as to produce shorter detours. Controlled deviations can then be introduced by adjusting the peripheral speeds of the bits and the thrusts applied to them. In some situations these methods fail, and it is then necessary to deflect.

There are various devices for deflecting holes, some being more suitable for steeply inclined holes than for shallow ones and vice versa. Some enable the secondary holes to be started in predetermined directions, being of particular value in countering deviations or where another cut is required through the target of a long hole. The basis of all these devices is a steel wedge having a tapered concave side, along which the bit travels and so penetrates the wall of the hole.

In cases when it is of paramount importance to have the straightest holes possible, a successful technique is to rotate clockwise and anti-clockwise in cycles of 1 metre at constant speed while maintaining constant thrust, using bits that are as nearly identical as possible and frequently changing them. For this technique special threading arrangements are necessary.

Metal fatigue and excessive torque (such as results from part of the surrounding rock collapsing into the hole or from the bit binding) are the causes of breakage of drill rods and core tubes. The tools designed to cope with such trouble are termed fishing tools, and, as with the real thing, to catch these 'fish' often needs the patience and skill born of long experience.

When there is insufficient drilling fluid passing through the bit, the cuttings commence to cake on to the surfaces of both bit and rock. If the condition persists long enough, the bit and rock become welded together. This can occur in a matter of seconds in some circumstances. The condition arises as the result of leakages from the joints of drill rods and, since there is normally one joint to 3 metres (10 ft.) or less, it is more likely to do so with increasing length of hole. It also arises due to carelessness on the part of the drill crew in assembling the drill rods or from pump failure.

Before further action is considered in such an event, an attempt is usually made to back off the core barrel, which in a downward hole is more often successful when the accident has occurred at the beginning of a run. The quantity of cuttings settling around the core barrel is then still small. If it is successful, the burned-in bit is then drilled out or chopped up and fished. If it fails, the course to take depends upon the value placed on the hole, the equipment available and the time and cost aspects of the possibilities open. If deflecting equipment is available and is suitable, having regard to the inclination of the hole, the obstruction can be by-passed. The alternatives are to drill out the core tube, to drill over it with lining tubes or to abandon the hole. This last alternative is frequently the cheapest in cases of short holes.

When a weak zone is encountered well beyond the end of the last string of lining tubes and it jeopardises the completion of the hole, it has to be sealed off. In such situations the further reduction in diameter of the hole, consequent upon the insertion of lining tubes to seal off the zone, is often out of the question. The alternative is to plug the cavity, formed by the recurrent collapse of the weak rock into the hole, with a cement-water mix or chemical grout which when set is drilled out. According to the length and inclination of the hole and the properties of the grout, it may be poured, or pumped through the drill rods, or ejected from a cylinder by means of

[continued on page 214]

Peripheral speed in feet per minute. British, American and Canadian standard corebits

Peripheral speed in metres per minute of Swedish system (Craelius)* corebits. (*Craelius is the trade name of Svenska Diamantbergborrnings A.-B., Stockholm, Sweden.)

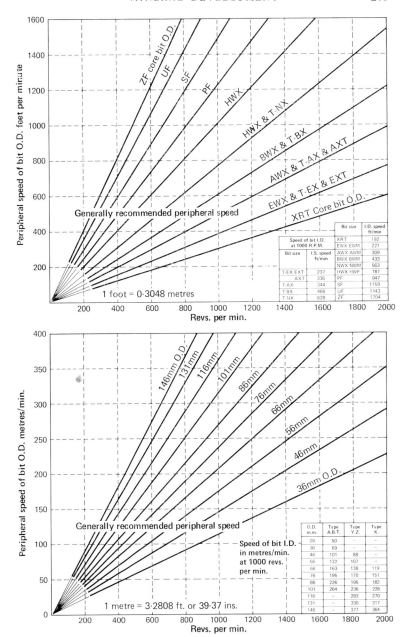

Top chart:

Y-axis: Peripheral speed of bit O.D. feet per minute
X-axis: Revs. per min.

Curve labels: ZF core bit O.D., UF, SF, PF, HWX, HWX & T-NX, BWX & T-BX, AWX & T-AX & AXT, EWX & T-EX & EXT, XRT Core bit O.D.

Generally recommended peripheral speed

1 foot = 0·3048 metres

Speed of bit I.D. at 1000 R.P.M.		Bit size	I.D. speed ft/min
		XRT	192
		EWX EWM	221
Bit size	I.S. speed ft/min	AWX AWM	309
		BWX BWM	433
		NWX NWM	563
T-EX EXT	237	HWX HWF	787
AXT	336	PF	947
T-AX	344	SF	1159
T-BX	466	UF	1143
T-NX	628	ZF	1704

Bottom chart:

Y-axis: Peripheral speed of bit O.D. metres/min.
X-axis: Revs. per min.

Curve labels: 146mm O.D., 131mm, 116mm, 101mm, 86mm, 76mm, 66mm, 56mm, 46mm, 36mm O.D.

Generally recommended peripheral speed

Speed of bit I.D. in metres/min. at 1000 revs. per min.

1 metre = 3·2808 ft. or 39·37 ins.

O.D. m.m.	Type A.B.T.	Type Y.Z.	Type K.
28	50	–	–
36	69	–	–
46	101	88	–
56	132	107	–
66	163	138	119
76	195	170	151
86	226	195	182
101	264	236	226
116	–	283	270
131	–	330	317
146	–	377	364

TABLE 1

BRITISH STANDARD 4019 PART 1, 1966

ALSO AMERICAN (DCDMA) AND CANADIAN (CDDA)

Core barrel assemblies

	Core bit				Reaming shell O.D.	Nominal size			Casing			
	O.D.		I.D.			Hole	Core		O.D.		Coupling I.D. min.	
Symbol	in	mm	in	mm	in / mm	in	in	Symbol	in	mm	in	mm
XRT	1·160	29·46	0·735	18·67	1·175 / 29·84	$1\frac{7}{16}$	$\frac{11}{16}$	XRT	1·437	36·50	1·190*	30·23*
EWX EWM	1·470	37·34	0·845	21·46	1·485 / 37·72	$1\frac{1}{2}$	$\frac{13}{16}$	EX	1·812	46·02	1·500	38·10
AWX AWM	1·875	47·62	1·185	30·10	1·890 / 48·01	$1\frac{13}{16}$	$1\frac{7}{16}$	AX	2·250	57·15	1·906	48·41
BWX BWM	2·345	59·56	1·655	42·04	2·360 / 59·94	$2\frac{3}{8}$	$1\frac{5}{8}$	BX	2·875	73·02	2·375	60·32
NWX NWM	2·965	75·31	2·155	54·74	2·980 / 75·69	3	$2\frac{1}{8}$	NX	3·500	88·90	3·000	76·20
HWX HWF	3·890	98·81	3·000	76·20	3·906 / 99·21	$3\frac{15}{16}$	3	HX	4·500	114·30	3·937	100·00
PF	4·720	119·89	3·625	92·08	4·750 / 120·65	$4\frac{3}{4}$	$3\frac{5}{8}$	PX	5·500	139·70	4·875	123·82
SF	5·720	145·29	4·437	112·70	5·750 / 146·05	$5\frac{3}{4}$	$4\frac{7}{16}$	SX	6·625	168·28	5·875	149·22
UF	6·845	173·86	5·500	139·70	6·875 / 174·62	$6\frac{7}{8}$	$5\frac{1}{2}$	UX	7·625	193·68	6·937	176·20
ZF	7·845	199·26	6·500	165·10	7·875 / 200·02	$7\frac{7}{8}$	$6\frac{1}{2}$	ZX	8·625	219·08	7·937	201·60

Thin-walled Canadian (CDDA) core barrels

	in	mm	in	mm	in / mm	in	in	
EXT	1·470	37·34	0·905	22·99	1·485 / 37·72	$1\frac{1}{2}$	$\frac{7}{8}$	Casing details as above EX
AXT	1·875	47·62	1·281	32·54	1·890 / 48·01	$1\frac{13}{16}$	$1\frac{9}{32}$	Casing details as above AX

Special thin-walled (T Series) core barrels (to suit B.S. hole size and casing)

	in	mm	in	mm	in / mm	in	in	
T-EX	1·470	37·34	0·905	22·99	1·485 / 37·72	$1\frac{1}{2}$	$\frac{7}{8}$	Casing details as above EX
T-AX	1·875	47·62	1·315	33·40	1·890 / 48·01	$1\frac{13}{16}$	$1\frac{5}{16}$	Casing details as above AX
T-BX	2·345	59·56	1·779	45·19	2·360 / 59·94	$2\frac{3}{8}$	$1\frac{3}{4}$	Casing details as above BX
T-NX	2·965	75·31	2·394	60·81	2·980 / 75·69	3	$2\frac{3}{8}$	Casing details as above NX

* XRT casing is flush jointed. Figures quoted are I.D. of casing.

Casing and casing barrel assemblies													Drill rods			
Casing bit				Casing reaming shell O.D.		Casing shoe						Rod coupling O.D.		I.D.		Symbol
O.D.		I.D.				O.D.		I.D.		O.D.						
in	mm	in	mm	in	mm	in	mm	in	mm	in	mm	in	mm	in	mm	
1·485	37·72	1·000	25·40	—	—	1·485	37·72	1·188	30·18	1·094	27·79	0·406	10·31			XRT
1·875	47·62	1·405	35·69	1·890	48·01	1·875	47·62	1·497	38·02	1·375	34·92	0·437	11·10			EW
2·345	59·56	1.780	45·21	2·360	59·94	2·345	59·56	1·902	48·31	1·750	44·45	0·625	15·88			AW
2·965	75·31	2·215	56·26	2·980	75·69	2·965	75·31	2·372	60·25	2·125	53·98	0·750	19·05			BW
3·615	91·82	2·840	72·14	3·630	92·20	3·615	91·82	2·992	76·00	2·625	66·68	1·375	34·92			NW
4·625	117·48	3·777	95·94	—	—	4·625	117·48	3·925	99·70	3·500	88·90	2·375	60·32			HW
5·655	143·64	4·719	119·86	—	—	5·655	143·64	4·837	122·86							
6·780	172·21	5·719	145·26	—	—	6·780	172·21	5·837	148·26							
7·810	198·37	6·781	172·24	—	—	7·810	198·37	6·899	175·23							
8·810	223·77	7·781	197·64	—	—	8·810	223·77	7·899	200·63							

TABLE 2

SWEDISH SYSTEM (CRAELIUS)*

Nominal size	Core barrel assemblies						Casing assemblies					Drill rods		
	Core bits	Thin-walled bits		Thick-walled bits		Reaming shells	Casing (flush jointed)		Casing shoe and casing bit	Casing bit	Casing shoe	Nominal Size	Rod O.D.	Coupling I.D.
	All types of barrel	Type B SW/MT/I Dis	Type T BW/FT/I Dis	Type Z / Type Y SW/MT/I Dis	Type K.3 / Type K.2 BW/MT/F Dis	All types of barrel	Tube O.D.	Tube I.D.	Set O.D.	Set I.D.	Set I.D.			
	Set O.D.	Set I.D.	Set I.D.	Set I.D.	Set I.D.	Set O.D.								
28 mm	28 mm / 1·102 in		16 mm / 0·630 in			28·3 mm / 1·114 in						24 mm	24 mm / 0·945 in	10 mm / 0·394 in
36 mm	36 mm / 1·417 in	22 mm / 0·866 in	22 mm / 0·866 in			36·3 mm / 1·429 in	35·2 mm / 1·386 in	29 mm / 1·142 in	36 mm / 1·417 in		28·85 mm / 1·136 in	33·5 mm	33·5 mm / 1·319 in	15 mm / 0·591 in
46 mm	46 mm / 1·811 in	32 mm / 1·260 in	32 mm / 1·260 in	28 mm / 1·102 in	24 mm / 0·945 in	46·3 mm / 1·823 in	44·15 mm / 1·738 in	37·15 mm / 1·463 in	46 mm / 1·811 in	35 mm / 1·378 in	37 mm / 1·457 in	42 mm	42 mm / 1·654 in	22 mm / 0·866 in
56 mm	56 mm / 2·205 in	42 mm / 1·654 in	42 mm / 1·654 in	34 mm / 1·339 in	34 mm / 1·339 in	56·3 mm / 2·217 in	54·15 mm / 2·132 in	47·15 mm / 1·856 in	56 mm / 2·205 in	45 mm / 1·772 in	47 mm / 1·850 in	50 mm	50 mm / 1·969 in	22 mm / 0·866 in
66 mm	66 mm / 2·598 in	52 mm / 2·047 in	52 mm / 2·047 in	44 mm / 1·732 in	38 mm / 1·496 in	66·3 mm / 2·610 in	64·25 mm / 2·530 in	57·15 mm / 2·250 in	66 mm / 2·598 in	55 mm / 2·165 in	57 mm / 2·244 in	60 mm	60 mm / 2·362 in	25 mm / 0·984 in

	76 mm	62 mm	62 mm	54 mm	48 mm	76·3 mm	74·25 mm	67·15 mm	76 mm	65 mm	67 mm
76 mm	76 mm / 2·992 in	62 mm / 2·441 in	62 mm / 2·441 in	54 mm / 2·126 in	48 mm / 1·890 in	76·3 mm / 3·004 in	74·25 mm / 2·923 in	67·15 mm / 2·644 in	76 mm / 2·992 in	65 mm / 2·559 in	67 mm / 2·638 in
86 mm	86 mm / 3·386 in	72 mm / 2·835 in	72 mm / 2·835 in	62 mm / 2·441 in	58 mm / 2·284 in	86·3 mm / 3·398 in	84·25 mm / 3·317 in	77·15 mm / 3·037 in	86 mm / 3·386 in	75 mm / 2·953 in	77 mm / 3·032 in
101 mm	101 mm / 3·976 in	87 mm / 3·425 in	84 mm / 3·307 in	75 mm / 2·953 in	72 mm / 2·835 in	101·3 mm / 3·988 in	98 mm / 3·858 in	88·3 mm / 3·476 in	101 mm / 3·976 in	86·5 mm / 3·405 in	89 mm / 3·504 in
116 mm	116 mm / 4·567 in	102 mm / 4·016 in		90 mm / 3·543 in	86 mm / 3·386 in	116·3 mm / 4·579 in	113 mm / 4·449 in	103·3 mm / 4·067 in	116 mm / 4·567 in	101·5 mm / 3·996 in	104 mm / 4·094 in
131 mm	131 mm / 5·157 in	117 mm / 4·606 in		105 mm / 4·134 in	101 mm / 3·976 in	131·3 mm / 5·169 in	128 mm / 5·039 in	118·3 mm / 4·657 in	131 mm / 5·157 in	116·5 mm / 4·586 in	119 mm / 4·685 in
146 mm	146 mm / 5·748 in	132 mm / 5·197 in		120 mm / 4·724 in	116 mm / 4·567 in	146·3 mm / 5·760 in	143 mm / 5·630 in	133·3 mm / 5·248 in	146 mm / 5·748 in	131·5 mm / 5·177 in	134 mm / 5·276 in

SW Straight wall bits
BW Bevel wall bits

MT Male thread (pin)
FT Female thread (box)

I Dis Internal discharge
F Dis Face discharge

* Craelius is the trade name of Svenska Diamantbergborrnings A.-B. Stockholm, Sweden.

a piston actuated by pressure of the drilling fluid. Fissures are similarly plugged if it is necessary to do so in order to continue drilling.

Equipment standards

A comprehensive B.S.I./I.S.O. standard on rotary drilling equipment is being drafted, but current practice is covered by B.S.4019: Part 1:1966, the publications of the Diamond Core Drill Manufacturers Association, of America, and the Canadian Diamond Drilling Association. In addition to these standards specifically related to diamond equipment, other standards are used as a basis for diamond bits such as the U.S.S.R. Gost 9431–60. The main elements of the British, American, Canadian and Swedish standards are shown in the preceding tables.

Core bit formulation and selection

Taking into account all of the foregoing relevant factors and assuming the 'surface set' bit as the standard, the following tabulation gives broad guidance on the relative merits of the alternative formulations. The rocks are listed in approximate order of resistance to drilling, but the composition, distribution and grain size of each mineral must be considered as well as the degree of weathering, the nature of any mineral bonding and the structural condition and attitude of the whole rock mass. Not only the predominant rock has to be considered, but also the inclusions and alterations.

Group	Rock type	Diamond size and comment
Soft	Chalk Marl Shale Tuff	2–8 diamonds per carat normal surface set or sawtooth. The latter is recommended for operations at 2·30 metres per second (450 ft. per min.) with a waterflow approx. 50% more than with a conventional surface set bit. The load should be of the order of 2·5–5 kg. (6–12 lbs.) per cutting diamond, to be increased to 12 kg. (30 lb.) in hard rock bands. Penetration rates of X2 to X4 can be obtained as compared to conventional bits.
Medium	Sandstone Limestone Siltstone Graywacke Slate Dolomite	8–16 diamonds per carat or sawtooth bits as above. 16–30 diamonds per carat.
Medium hard	Schist Gneiss Amphibolite Diorite	30–60 diamonds per carat or impregnated bits. The latter are recommended in broken strata. Can be used on light equipment at high speed and light thrust.
Hard	Quartzite Gabbro Syenite Granite Porphyry Andesite Rhyolite Basalt	60–150 diamonds per carat or impregnated type bits.

In addition to these tabulated variables, the following characteristics can be varied to suit the working conditions:

Diamond type:	Natural or treated bortz, Congo or carbonado and size of diamond grit.
Setting pattern:	Can be varied in surface set bit.
Concentration and depth of impregnation:	Can both be varied in impregnated bits and special protection provided in highly stressed areas.
Diamond protrusion:	In surface set bit.
Tooth angles and modules:	In sawtooth bits.
Profile shape:	In conventional surface set bit.
Waterways:	Number, size and special protection.
Number of waterholes:	In face discharge bits.
Matrix hardness	

To obtain optimum results from the harder matrix impregnated bits, sandblasting or grinding may be necessary after a period of use. Where sufficient information is available to the bit maker, this can sometimes be avoided by a properly balanced bit design. In all cases it is necessary to adjust water course depths as wear takes place.

To ensure uniform sandblasting, the following essentials should be followed:

Preparation:	Insert a soft wood or rubber plug to protect the inside diameter of the cutting area. Protect the thread by inserting in an old reaming shell or similar item.
Rotation:	Provide a small rotating platform on which the bit can be placed during treatment.
Abrasive:	Silicon carbide of 40–80 mesh at an air pressure of 36 kg. (80 lb.) through a nozzle of 5·5 mm. ($\frac{7}{32}$ in.) diameter.
Timing:	This varies with air pressure and condition of the abrasive, but is generally of the following order in relation to bit diameter:

Size	EX	AX	BX	NX
TIME/Seconds	10–15	15–20	20–30	30–40

In the work done by Messrs. James Paone and Dick Madson, for the U.S. Bureau of Mines, impregnated bits were evaluated under laboratory conditions on seven rock types and in the field on 21 different rock types. It was concluded that increases in thrust and r.p.m. improved penetration rates, especially in harder rocks. It was also indicated that more wear was apparent at higher rotational speeds. The trend was similar to that obtained with surface set bits for rock under 1760 kg./cm.^{2} (25,000 p.s.i.) compressive strength.

THE OIL-FIELDS

In 1878 the United States Patent Office granted Benjamin F. Asper and Robert Magill a patent 'Apparatus for Boring Oil Wells' which was described as a diamond set bit. These gentlemen were, no doubt, among the many other claimants to have been the first to introduce diamond to oil-well drilling. Drilling & Service Inc., of Dallas, Texas, claim to have successfully diamond cored the first oil-well in 1945.

As with other mineral drilling, diamonds were first introduced as coring tools for prospecting, but are now widely used for 'making hole' as well. The processes for making these oil-field bits follow closely the methods employed for other diamond bits used in mining, but they are generally of larger dimensions.

Round trip time always has been a crucial factor in oil-well drilling. This is due to the depths at which crude oil is usually found and to the high cost of the drilling machinery and equipment. The latter is on a massive scale—three or four prime movers are usual, having combined net ratings in the region of 350 b.h.p. per 1,000 metres (3,000 ft.) of hole—compared to that needed in core drilling. Even after the wireline system had been invented, coring was resorted to only when there were a priori reasons for doing so, but this position changed about the end of the Second World War with the introduction of diamond coreheads, firstly in the United States of America, which in many cases proved to be faster and cheaper to use than the conventional full-hole rolling-cutter bits. A decade later, efficient diamond drilling bits, as full-hole bits are known to the industry, had been developed in the United States of America. Since then the use of such bits has become widespread.

Previously, oil-wells were often completed at depths of 3,000 metres (10,000 ft.), but depths normally attained now are of the order of 7,000 metres (23,000 ft.). The range of diameters used progressively in holes of this depth start at 600 mm. (24 in.) for the initial drilling and then to 445 mm. (17½ in.) and 285 mm. (11¼ in.). At this diameter and smaller, the savings in the use of diamond bits become considerable as compared to the alternative 'tricone' bits. The reduction in diameter continues through 250 mm. (9⅞ in.), 215 mm. (8½ in.) and down to 103 mm. (4⅛ in.). In the last two diameters, because of the great depths, diamond bits are not only profitable but indispensable. In these smaller sizes, bits contain 80–100 carats of diamond, and, in the larger, up to nearly 1,500 carats. According to the operating conditions, the diamonds vary in size from 1·0 carat each down to coarse grit.

Coring bits used in the oil-fields are not made to any national standards nor are solid bits except that the taper threads on the latter are usually required to conform to the standards of the American Petroleum Institute specification for rotary drilling equipment. Copies of this are available from the Director of the Institute, Division of Production, 300 Corrigan Tower Building, Dallas 1, Texas.

The specification of the diamond bearing areas is dealt with in section 8 and states the tolerances on outside diameters shall be as follows (A.P.I. table 8·1):

Nominal bit size O/D		Tolerance O/D	
mm.	*in.*	*mm.*	*in.*
170 and smaller	6¾ and smaller	+0, −0·38	+0, −0·015
170–230	6¾ to 9 inc.	+0, −0·51	+0, −0·020
Over 230	Over 9	+0, −0·76	+0, −0·030

The standard also specifies the threads to be used for the various diameters of drilling bits (A.P.I. table 8·2):

Bit size range (O/D)		Size & type of rotary connection
mm.	*in.*	*A.P.I. threads*
94–114	$3\frac{11}{16}$–$4\frac{1}{2}$	$2\frac{3}{8}$
116–127	$4\frac{9}{16}$–5	$2\frac{7}{8}$ REG or IF
129–187	$5\frac{1}{16}$–$7\frac{3}{8}$	$3\frac{1}{2}$ REG–IF–FH
189–241	$7\frac{7}{16}$–$9\frac{1}{2}$	$4\frac{1}{2}$ or $5\frac{1}{2}$ REG–IF–FH
243–311	$9\frac{9}{16}$–$12\frac{1}{4}$	$6\frac{5}{8}$ or $7\frac{5}{8}$ REG
311 and larger	$12\frac{1}{4}$ and larger	$7\frac{5}{8}$ or $8\frac{5}{8}$ REG

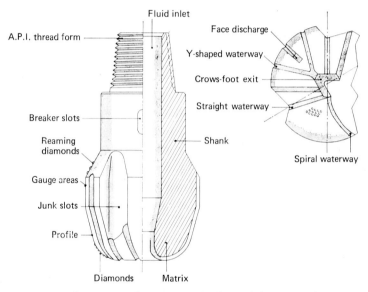

Diamond drill bit terminology in the oil fields (Drilling & Service S.A.)

Coring bits for use in the oil-fields are made in outside diameters to suit borehole conditions as the work progresses. Inside diameters and thread connections are made to suit individual core barrel manufacturers' designs. One range of such barrels is that originally developed by Mr. Carroll Deely and marketed by the Drilling & Service organisation. The range of bit sizes normally applicable to each barrel size is shown in the following table:

T

Core barrel reference number	Bit size			
	O.D. mm.	I.D. mm.	O.D. in.	I.D. in.
$4\frac{1}{2}$–50	121 146	60	$4\frac{3}{4}$ $5\frac{3}{4}$	$2\frac{3}{8}$
5	146 154	70	$5\frac{3}{4}$ $6\frac{1}{16}$	$2\frac{3}{4}$
$5\frac{11}{16}$	154 170 198	89	$6\frac{1}{16}$ $6\frac{11}{16}$ $7\frac{13}{16}$	$3\frac{1}{2}$
$6\frac{7}{8}$	198 217 221 227	89	$7\frac{13}{16}$ $8\frac{9}{16}$ $8\frac{11}{16}$ $8\frac{15}{16}$	$3\frac{1}{2}$
$7\frac{5}{8}$	217 221 227 268	124	$8\frac{9}{16}$ $8\frac{11}{16}$ $8\frac{15}{16}$ $10\frac{9}{16}$	$4\frac{7}{8}$
Wireline $4\frac{1}{4}$ and $4\frac{1}{2}$	111 143 154	31·75	$4\frac{3}{8}$ $5\frac{5}{8}$ $6\frac{1}{16}$	$1\frac{1}{4}$
Wireline $5\frac{3}{4}$	154 170 198	47·62	$6\frac{1}{16}$ $6\frac{11}{16}$ $7\frac{13}{16}$	$1\frac{7}{8}$
Wireline $6\frac{7}{8}$	198 217 221 227 268	47·62	$7\frac{13}{16}$ $8\frac{9}{16}$ $8\frac{11}{16}$ $8\frac{15}{16}$ $10\frac{9}{16}$	$1\frac{7}{8}$

For removing blockages encountered in drilling, 'washover shoes' are also made in a range of outside diameters from about 112 mm. ($4\frac{1}{2}$ in.) up to about 225 mm. (9 in.) and with inside diameters from about 75 mm. (3 in.) up to 225 mm. (9 in.).

Although the dimensions are on average larger than is the case with diamond bits used in mines and quarries, the methods of manufacture follow the same course. Harder matrices and larger diamonds tend to be used.

Drilling machinery and equipment for oil-wells

Most oil-well drilling is undertaken with 'rotary' drill rigs which impart the rotary and feed forces through a 'drill string' of lengths of metal pipes attached to each other with threaded 'joints'. In principle this is the same as for other mineral drilling, but the 'chuck' is replaced by a 'rotary table'. The clear water coolant normally used in other drilling is, however, replaced in oil drilling with a more viscous 'mud'. The latter has been the subject of intensive study by specialists and it has been shown that mud formulations play a great part in successful drilling, especially in difficult terrain.

Typical conditions for the use of diamond drilling bits are shown in the following tables:

A. *When starting a hole:*

Diameter				Fluid volume		
mm.	inches	Weight	R.P.M.	L.P.M.	G.P.M. (U.S.)
152	6	0·5–1t	60–70	606–719	160–190
216	8½	1–1·5t	60–70	606–1817	160–480
311	12¼	2–3t	60–120	2,195–2,498	580–660

B. *After 'bedding in', say 0·3 m. (1 ft.):*

Diameter				Fluid volume		
mm.	inches	Weight	R.P.M.	L.P.M.	G.P.M.(U.S.)
152	6	2 to 5t	60–140	719	190
216	8½	7 to 14t	60–140	1,400–1,817	370–480
	or 8½	15 to 18t	220–270	1,400–1,817	370–480
311	12¼	18 to 25t	180–240	2,195–2,422	580–640

Rotational speeds of up to 300 r.p.m. are available on modern machines.

Since 1964 the use of turbines has become widespread in many European oil-fields. In such installations the 'drill string' remains stationary and the drill fluid is pumped down the pipe to be used as the driving force of the turbine which in turn rotates the diamond bit at speeds 600/1,100 r.p.m. These higher speeds favour the diamond drill as an abrasive tool. Such equipment is capable of continuous operation for periods of up to 200–300 hours. The development is, of course, limited by the minimum diameter in which an effective turbine can be accommodated. This in turn dictates the smallest hole which can be drilled with the 'turbo-drill'.

Successful coring operations depend greatly on the core barrel performance. Regardless of how perfect the core bit may be, it cannot perform effectively unless the core quickly passes into the core barrel, away from the core bit area. To accomplish this, a core barrel should be designed to include the following features:

1. A non-rotating inner tube. If the inner tube rotates, torque will be applied to the core being cut, causing fractured cores and wedging. To ensure a non-rotating inner tube, the tube must be streamlined inside and outside and suspended on well lubricated anti-friction bearings.
2. An inner tube having a smooth bore to aid in prevention of core wedging by minimising core friction.

Diamond bit head designed for turbine or rotary table operation (Type OVBEL 72) (Drilling & Service S.A.)

3. Protection of the core being cut from the circulating fluid. The core should be exposed to the fluid only enough to flush away the cuttings before the core enters the inner tube.
4. A core catcher that will allow the core to pass with a minimum of disturbance. Otherwise, the core will be scrambled and will usually wedge in the inner barrel.
5. Allowance for full fluid circulation.
6. The barrel must be rugged enough to withstand oil-field use.

General recommendations on coring

Diameter				Fluid volume		
mm.	inches	Weight	R.P.M.	L.P.M.	G.P.M. (U.S.)
152	6 ⎱ bedding	1t	50	568	150
216	8½ ⎰ in	1–2t	50	719	190
152	6 ⎱ coring	3–6t	50–100	606–719	160–190
216	8½ ⎰	3–8t	50–100	908–1,211	240–320

Diamond bit selection

Some authorities recommend that, if a diamond bit follows immediately after a conventional tricone bit, it should be 1·5 mm. ($\frac{1}{16}$ in.) smaller in diameter than the latter. This is to avoid premature wear on the bit outside diameter due to the hole being undersize from a worn tricone. In practice, however, in Europe

Alternative diamond core cutting heads for the oil-fields
(Drilling & Service S.A.)

Type
TDP3DO

Type
ID9(H)

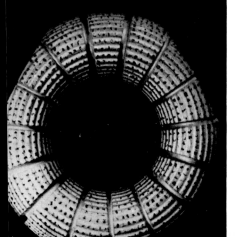
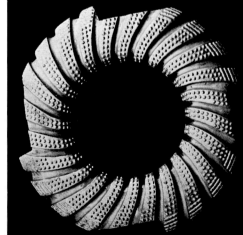

and North Africa this is now generally applied only to coring operations. The type of core barrel also influences bit design apart from the actual dimensions.

The type of rock formation and its condition constitute the main influence on bit design. Examples of the types of strata involved are:

Very hard: Quartzite or chert.
Hard: Limestone, dolomite.
Medium-soft: Sands, shales, salt and anhydrite.

A particular form of drilling mud is chosen by the drilling authority for many reasons and may consist of a water base, water base emulsion, water oil emulsion, oil base, straight water or crude oil. It is equally possible to drill with gas or air or aerated mud, that is to say, with mud in which minute bubbles of air are suspended so as to reduce its density.

The type chosen affects particularly the bit waterway design, as does the rate at which the mud circulates. This is usually quoted in gallons per minute. The hole depth at which the diamond bit is expected to be used and information on the type and performance of the preceding roller rock bit also provide useful background information to consider in diamond bit design.

Operational notes for oil-field drilling

The following paragraphs summarise the recommendations published by the Drilling & Service organisation for the use of their equipment:

Cost per unit of hole depth is normally based on the following formula:

$$\text{Cost per unit} = \frac{\text{(Rig operating cost per hour)} \times \text{(Trip hours + rotating hours)} + \text{Net bit cost}}{\text{Number of feet or metres drilled by the bit}}$$

In arriving at the 'net bit cost' it must be remembered that, with a carefully used surface set diamond bit, an average diamond recovery of up to 40 % can be expected when it is returned for resetting.

A clean borehole at the time of commencing operation with the diamond bit is absolutely essential if the full potential life of the bit is to be realised and, where applicable, the maximum amount of core recovered. Diamond bits are particularly vulnerable to metal scrap or 'junk iron' which may remain in the hole from previous operations. The following suggestions are intended to prevent this condition:

1. If the rock bit cones are lost, fish out the cones and all the bearings at that time; otherwise, the bearings will become embedded in the walls or stored in cavities. They may then fall to bottom during coring, damaging the diamond bit and core barrel or reducing core recovery.
2. Keep tong dies securely keyed in place.
3. Keep a wiper on the pipe when going in or coming out of the hole. An old wiper may be used when going in the hole.
4. Use a junk basket sub or a similar tool with the last two or three rock bits. This procedure has proved very effective in ensuring a clean hole ready for diamonds; however, if there is doubt whether or not the hole is clean, it may be advisable to use a magnetic tool or whatever method meets the operator's preference.

Sufficient drill collars should be used to exceed the weight required for the bit. The effective weight is controlled to hold the drill string in tension. Drill pipe in compression tends to 'wander' in the borehole and often induces vibration not conducive to optimum performance by the diamond equipment. However, the use of drill collars is not always feasible and their use should be influenced by:

a. Hole conditions.
b. Size of hole.
c. The related hazards involved.

Core barrel stabilisers should theoretically be used to such an extent that the core barrel is held absolutely concentric in the hole. To arrive at this degree of perfection, a series of stabilisers would be needed at about 3 metre (10 ft.) intervals with outside diameters about 0·25 mm. (0·010 in.) less than the diamond bit being used at the time. The objection to such a practice is that it materially increases the hazard of the barrel becoming jammed in the hole. As a compromise one stabiliser only is recommended. This should be about 300 mm. (12 in.) long and positioned directly above the bit. This stabiliser should be closely watched and, when it is worn to about 1·5 mm. ($\frac{1}{16}$ in.) under bit diameter, it should be replaced. Alternatively, of course, it may be built up and re-ground to a diameter about 0·40 mm. (0·015 in.) below that of the diamond bit to be used. If this degree of stabilisation is not used, the bit may be damaged or a wavy core cut. The latter will wedge in the inner tube of the barrel and reduce core recovery or the length of core runs. In turn this will call for more rig trips. Lack of stabilisation may also result in an undersize core being cut so that it cannot be picked up by the core spring.

When core barrels of more than one section are connected with a centre sub, the sub is usually equipped with protective ribs to control the wear by the walls of the hole. These ribs have the appearance of a stabiliser; however, they are well under the hole diameter and do not stabilise the core barrel. When these ribs wear down to the body of the sub they should be replaced or rebuilt to prevent wear and subsequent failure of the sub or core barrel. Core barrels without centre subs are often equipped with bands of hard metal near the centre joint to prevent wear.

In areas of difficult coring problems, due to the nature of the formation to be cored or the bit and core barrel size relationship, it might be helpful to increase the diameter of the protective ribs and let them act as a stabiliser.

The diamond bit diameter needs constant attention in relation to effective borehole diameter: A diamond bit will not always follow a rock bit of the same size unless the hole drilled by the rock bit was fast and easy drilling, leaving a straight full gauge hole. Reaming a rock bit cut hole can be a slow, costly and dangerous operation. The O.D. of the diamond bit can be damaged and worn, and would greatly reduce the diamond bit life. Selecting the diamond bit of an O.D. size that will not require reaming of the rock bit cut hole is most important. Reaming should be eliminated when at all possible.

The amount of gauge loss by the rock bits may be the most common measure of the necessary diamond bit O.D. reduction under rock bit size to avoid reaming. However, the loss in effective hole size or drift diameter may be the most prevalent problem. This loss in effective hole size is a common result from the rock bit drilling a spiral or helix shaped hole due to the action of the unstable drill collar string. Subsequent rock bits, by the design of their cutting cones, can roll through these spirals, whereas the diamond bit with its solid O.D. gauge section must ream such sections. In cases of the stabilised core bits, the possibility of having to ream is greater due to the increased O.D. area and increased length of the O.D. area in contact with the hole wall.

The drift diameter or effective hole diameter of a borehole cut with rock bits is influenced by the following factors:

1. Relation of drill collar O.D. and bit size.
2. Number, size and location of drill collar stabilisers.
3. Weight applied to the bit.
4. Rotary speed.
5. Penetration rate.

Any increase in stabilisation of the bottom hole assembly will increase the drift diameter of the hole drilled. A hole drilled with near-perfect stabilisation of the bottom hole assembly will have a drift diameter that approaches the rock bit size, and a diamond bit of a similar size could be run. As the stabilisation of the bottom hole assembly is reduced, the drift diameter of the hole drilled is reduced.

In rock bit drilled holes, drilled with moderate stabilisation of the bottom hole assembly, the diamond bit diameter may safely come within 1·6 mm. ($\frac{1}{16}$ in.) of the rock bit size. In holes drilled with no stabilisation of the drill collar string, and with a difference of 25–38 mm. (1 in. to $1\frac{1}{2}$ in.) between rock bit size and drill collar O.D., the diameter of the diamond bit may have to be 3 mm. ($\frac{1}{8}$ in.) under rock bit size to prevent reaming of the rock bit cut hole.

Re-reaming with a rock bit can be dispensed with provided the nominal dimensions of the latter are the same as those for the diamond bit and manufacturing tolerances are being observed:

Tricone rock bit: nominal O/D −0 mm. +0·3 mm. (0·011 in.)
Diamond bit: nominal O/D +0 mm. −0·3 mm. (0·011 in.)

It follows that in practice the diamond bit is slightly less in O/D than the tricone.

Pressure, speed and fluid circulation

It is impossible to predetermine the most efficient combination of weight and rotary r.p.m. to use in different formations. Many factors influence the best combination of weight and r.p.m. required. The action of a diamond bit, when properly employed, is similar to that of a 'drag' bit. The mechanical factors of 'making hole' deal with weight and repetition of moving the cutting elements over the formation being drilled. Therefore, for diamond bits to drill, sufficient weight must be applied to cause the cutting points of the diamonds to penetrate the formation. The degree of penetration depends on:

1. The hardness and characteristics of the formation.
2. Size and shape of the diamond point.
3. The applied unit weight. Weight causes the penetration and the rotation gives movement to the diamonds which removes the formation.

The mechanical factors of weight and rotary speed are directly related to the drilling rate. The provided hydraulic factors affect the drilling rate in direct relation to the efficiency with which these mechanical factors are applied. Hydraulically speaking, the 'jet principle' as applied to the diamond bit is the only efficient means of keeping the diamonds clean and cool so that new formation may be cut with each rotation, thus increasing the effectiveness and efficiency of the mechanical factors. Therefore, the 'jet action' to be effective on a diamond bit requires sufficient fluid velocity across its face satsifactorily to clean and cool the diamond points. The ideal fluid velocity is known, and usually other factors that may dictate a necessary change in this ideal velocity are also known. Therefore, for best performance, a diamond bit must be designed to meet the hole conditions and with waterways that will give proper fluid distribution at the ideal velocity, based on the fluid available to the bit. The available fluid may be limited by the capacity of the pump or pumps on the rig or by the fluid capacity of the diamond core barrel in use.

The fluid capacity of core barrels is determined by the annular space between the inner diameter of the outer tube and the outside diameter of the inner tube. When the circulation rate is sufficient to result in a fluid velocity in excess of twenty-five feet per second in this annulus, the fluid friction developed between the tubes tends to cause the inner tube to rotate with the outer tube, causing frequent core wedging and loss of core.

When approaching the bottom of the borehole with a diamond coring or solid bit it should be stopped at least 0·6 metre (2 ft.) off bottom. The pump strokes should then be regulated to deliver the volume rate at the fluid capacity of the bit in use. It should then be lowered to bottom, preferably without rotating. This should remove 'junk iron' or pieces of rock formation; (5,000 to 8,000 lb.) pressure should then be applied to ensure that the bit is seated on the hole bottom and not in cavings. The bit should then be raised 0·6–0·9 metres (2–3 ft.) and rotated slowly (40–50 r.p.m.). The bit should then be lowered to the cutting position again and say 2,250 kg. (5,000 lb.) weight applied. This pressure should then be gradually increased until the best penetration rate is achieved. At this stage the pump stroke figure should be checked. The pressure with this number of strokes should have increased about 14–19 kg./cm.^{2} (200 to 275 p.s.i.). This represents the pressure drop across the diamond bit. By increasing the rotary speed gradually until the best penetration rate is obtained, the most efficient combination of weight and rotary speed will be balanced with the fluid energy delivered to the bit.

The pump pressure must be watched constantly and changes corrected. The possible causes of pump pressure changes are:

a. Pressure increase or decrease may be due to a change in the pump volume. When the pressure changes, check the pump strokes first.

b. If the pressure increases and the pump volume is correct, it is possible that the bit has failed. As a rule, a ring of diamonds will have been destroyed, which will allow the formation to wear into the matrix, restricting the waterways and causing a pressure increase. If this is the trouble, the pressure will drop when the bit is picked off bottom, and, when set back on bottom, the pressure will immediately increase to the reading before being picked up. When these symptoms are definite, pull the bit to save further diamond damage and costly rig time.

c. Pressure increase may be due to a plugged circulatory system from debris in the mud, such as pieces of piston swabs, valve rubber, pipe protectors, soft rope, etc. If this is the trouble, the pressure will remain unchanged when the bit is picked off bottom. The coring might be continued if the trouble is definitely established as a plugged circulatory system, but it would be a rather blind and hazardous operation and the best practice is to come out of the hole to correct the trouble.

d. Increasing or decreasing pressue may be due to spotty, unbalanced mud. However, this mud condition is usually known and continued circulation will correct the situation. Meantime, with everything else normal, an allowance may be made for the pressure variations to compensate for the mud conditions until corrected.

e. Pressure decrease may be due to a wedged core holding the bit off bottom, such a decrease being accompanied by loss of torque and slow drilling time. This usually occurs when coring the harder fractured formations and it is a waste of time to try to force the bit to cut. It is better to withdraw from the hole.

f. Fluctuating pump pressure usually occurs when coring the softer fractured formations. When the fractures cause the core to wedge, the bit will quickly cut itself free, transferring the drilling weight to the core. At this point, the penetration rate will slow up noticeably until the weight crushes the soft core in the bit area. As the soft crushed core washes out through the small waterways, the pressure will increase 3.5 kg./cm.^{2} (50 p.s.i.) or more. As soon as the crushed core washes out through the small waterways, the pressure will return to normal and at the same time the penetration rate will speed up. When the pump pressure fluctuates and drilling time is erratic in a formation that is known to be soft and fractured, the core barrel should be pulled to avoid core loss.

In making connections stop the rotary table but maintain circulation. Pick the core barrel off bottom slowly, watching the weight indicator closely.

Most cores break off readily; however, in some formations the cores are tough to break. In such a case, pull at least 9,980 to 13,600 kg. (22,000 to 30,000 lb.) above the drill string weight, then set the brake and slowly rock into the core with the rotary until the core breaks.

When the core breaks, pick up at least 6 metres (20 ft.) off bottom and then slowly lower back to within 0·5 metre (18 in.) of bottom, feeling for any core that may have been lost out of the barrel. If the core is felt in the hole it is usually a comparatively simple operation to work over it.

When picking up lost core feel for the top of the core slowly and, when it takes approximately 225 kg. (500 lb.), agitate with the rotary table or slowly rotate. If the formation is not fractured and long cores have been cut, the core barrel should readily go over the core. If it does not, this usually indicates that a short piece of core has turned sideways in the hole necessitating redrilling. When redrilling over a piece of core, use a very light steady weight or the bit may be damaged. When available, it is advisable to use an old bit of doubtful further footage for lost core pickup.

In the world wide search for oil and gas, very large numbers of

Diamond preset in tungsten carbide inserts to resist erosion in operation
(Drilling & Service S.A.)

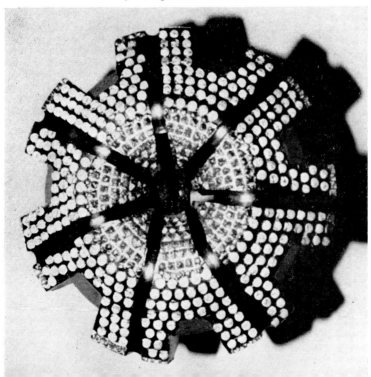

diamond bits have been used and extensive research undertaken. With rates of penetration of the order of 3 metres (10 ft.) to 18 metres (60 ft.) per hour in soft ground, the tool geometry still needs careful study. To obtain optimum rates of advance, the disposition and protrusion of the diamonds are of prime importance, and the whole diamond tool design conception has to be under continuous review to retain the industry's lead over the conventional tricone bit.

REFERENCES

Mining Annual Review 1971/1972.
'Diamond Drilling at Llanharry Iron Ore Mine—South Wales'—E. L. J. Smail.
'Drillability Studies—Impregnated Diamond Bits'—James Paone and Dick Madson, U.S. Dept of the Interior, Bureau of Mines, 1966.
'The Merits and Economics of Cored Exploratory Boring in Coalfield Development'—R. H. Allonby, B.SC., C.ENG., A.M.I.M.M., F.G.S.
British Standard 4019: Part 1: 1966—'Specification for Rotary Core Drilling Equipment'.
'How to Plan a Better Turbodiamond Program'—John Jeter, *World Oil*, February 1971.
'Drilling Equipment for Firedamp Drainage'—N.C.B. Information Bulletin 61/227.
'Anticipating Rockbursts by Photo-Elastic Methods'—*New Scientist*, December 1963.
'Jora Raise Lift'—'Chamber of Mines Journal', Salisbury, Rhodesia, August 1963.
British Patents 768,131 1957—838,570 1958.
Italian Patent 20/297 26.7.62.
Iran Patent 4870 14.7.63.
British Registered Design 904,443.

10

'Diamond cut diamond'—the jewellery and watchmaking industries

THE areas of production in which diamond plays its most significant role in the jewellery industry are broadly:

 a. Close tolerances of very often minute parts in sometimes intractable materials such as synthetic corundum, diamond or exotic metals.
 b. Highly polished finishes directly on precious metals or on base metals subsequently to be plated.
 c. A very flexible means of producing variations in component shapes and surface designs to follow current fashion.
 d. Methods to do all these things without the difficulties of employing highly skilled labour on operations such as hand polishing.

Diamond powder charged saws and laps have always been necessary tools in the shaping of precious stones, including diamond itself of course.

The skills learned in the ancient crafts utilising these tools were in due course adapted to the semi-precious stone industries in such areas as Idar Oberstein in West Germany and the Jura region of France. Refinements and extensions of these skills were then used to shape and polish the jewel bearings so essential to the accuracy of the watch industry. Changes in fashion and the wage spiral of the last twenty years extended diamond usage in the watch industry so that diamond tipped machining tools became essential to watch case and movement production. The tools, machines and techniques developed for this field are now extensively used in decorating many other items of jewellery such as rings, bracelets, tie-pins and cuff-links.

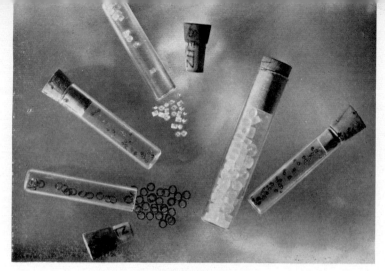

Synthetic jewel bearings

JEWEL BEARINGS

The methods used to produce the required dimensional accuracy and surface finish of synthetic jewel bearings still remain broadly:

First operation
Diamond saw semicircular slices from the 'boule' after splitting lengthwise.

Second operation
Use the same equipment to cut the plates into squares.

Third operation
Gang the square blanks into rods and feed into a small 'centreless' type grinder. The abrasive wheel consists of a copper roller into which diamond powder of about 150 mesh has been rolled. In the course of grinding the gap between the wheel, the 'control' roller is progressively reduced until the corners of the square blanks have been removed and circular discs eventually formed.

Fourth operation
The discs are then shellacked to a steel plate. The surface finish and flatness of the exposed faces are then improved by grinding on a copper lap charged with about 150 mesh diamond.

Fifth operation
The blanks are re-formed into a circular rod batch and again centreless ground using about 220 mesh diamond powder as the abrasive.

Last operation
The recess or other working area is formed. The roughing employs
either a solid diamond cutting tool of square based pyramid form
or an impregnated diamond 'broach'.

The high degree of surface finish required in these areas is achieved
by polishing operations using successively finer grades of diamond
powder down to less than one micron in some cases, although
some operating conditions produce a satisfactory finish with
$\frac{1}{2}$/3 micron. Whilst natural and other synthetic diamond powders
are used, the material produced by the Explosives Division of
Du Pont, U.S.A., has often been found to be superior in these
operations. It is marketed under the trade name 'SuperSyndia' and
covered by U.S. and other patents. Typical gradings for these
operations are:

Sawing from rough   85/100 to 120/150 mesh
Roughing   170/200 to 300/350 mesh
Final polish   2/4 to 0/1 micron.

The makers of the machines employed on these operations claim
very high production rates. The Boccadoro FBL7 automatic sawing
machine has a daily capacity of 6,000 carats of raw material sawn in
plates of 0·50 mm. (0·020 in.) thickness. The FBL8 is capable of
cutting 300,000 squares of 1·5 mm. (0·060 in.). On the centreless
operation, the FB40 can be used to produce 80,000 blanks of 1·2 mm.
(0·05 in.) diameter. On the face grinding operation, the FB60 flat
grinding machine has a production of 450,000 to 500,000, assuming
a stock removal of 0·10 mm. (0·004 in.).

Jewel bearings produced in this way are, of course, not only used
in watches but also in a very large variety of instruments used in
navigation, electronics and meters.

CASES AND OTHER WATCH COMPONENTS

The extent of diamond machining of many watch movement parts
has steadily increased. L. A. Hurwitz and R. A. Kurtz, of the Hamilton Watch Company, at an A.S.T.E. Symposium, in Chicago,
quoted as a yardstick the example of diamond turning a phosphor
bronze shell 50 mm. (2 in.) in diameter where the diamond tool path

U

cut was 1,250 miles long compared to 20·5 miles by a sintered carbide tool, and 5 miles by a high speed steel tool. The equivalent unit quantities were 25,000, 7,000 and 1,000 respectively.

The authors referred to diamond turning beryllium copper balance wheels as an aid to dimensional consistency. In this particular operation a set of six diamond tools was used. On a mass production basis, tolerances to 0·01 mm. (0·0004 in.) were maintained. Runs up to 100,000 were quoted for the facing of 14 carat gold balance wheel screw heads.

12% nickel silver plates and bridges, which position the gear train and jewel bearing mounts in brass, are also diamond machined.

Also employed in watch movement and other component production are, of course, form grinding techniques to produce punches and dies for stamping out gears and other movement parts, watch hands and watch cases. As in most profile grinding, diamond tools play an important part as the medium for truing the formed abrasive wheels.

The use of diamond machining techniques to produce the more visible components has also been widely developed. Particularly

Diamond turned plastic watch glasses

Lathe for turning watch cases. It is also made in a modified form to turn watch glasses. It provides for the machining of three faces at one setting (Alfred Jacoby [Machine Tools] Ltd.)

in Switzerland, specialist machine tool builders have emerged to satisfy the watch industry's needs. Examples of these are Dasa, Güdel, Mikron, Posalux, Sad, Schäublin, Sixis, Technica, Tornos and Tousdiamants. Examples from other countries are Benzinger of Germany and Wirth & Gruffat of France.

A typical lathe for these diamond machining operations is the Benzinger UDII which is also made in a modified form for watch glass turning. In that form it provides a set-up for turning three faces at one setting.

In this connection, the following information was supplied to the writer by Commonwealth Diamond Tools Pty. Ltd., of Sydney, Australia—their report quoted:

Operation:	Plunge cut angle on circumference of Perspex watch glass to provide fitting bevel to the watch case bezel.
Tool:	Approximately 6 mm. (0·25 in.).
Specification:	Cutting edge with 45° lead corner. Plan angle to tool centre-line 83°. Negative rake 5°. Primary clearance 1–1$\frac{1}{2}$°. Secondary clearance 10°.
Machine:	Small bench lathe.

Performance: High speed steel tools were used originally, but were replaced with tungsten carbide which produced the required finish, but tool life was of the order of only one hour. The diamond tool was in constant use for five weeks before relapping was necessary. Meanwhile the daily output of watch glass increased from 2,000 to 4,000 with much greater consistency of finish.

In common with most other diamond turning operations in the watch industry, this is a plunge cut application. In order to remain rigid during this operation, the fragile components are held between two pads with only the rim protruding.

The basic requirements of such machines are that they must be of rigid construction with well balanced spindles to avoid vibration. Generally, plain bearings are preferred. Adherence to the machine builder's oil recommendation is essential. The final drive is usually by endless belt. High spindle speeds and braking devices are essential to good machine utilisation.

The same type of lathe can be used to turn the conical faces of

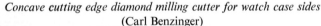

Concave cutting edge diamond milling cutter for watch case sides
(Carl Benzinger)

Diamond tipped milling tool for finishing watch case slides

brass watch cases. In some designs the lugs are a continuation of the same conical form and diamond cutting edges over 15 mm. (0·59 in.) in length are required to cover the whole area. With such tools, several thousands of parts can be machined and probably up to 20 relaps expected. This precludes the incidence of any serious damage. Where the lugs are curved, a shorter edge can be utilised, and the machine controls the tool path to form the curve.

For finishing the watch case sides, the lathe in effect is converted to a milling machine. Three diamond cutting tools are mounted on the lathe spindle by means of a balanced steel plate. The watch case is attached to a vertical column by a hydraulic cover plate interlocked with the spindle. This work holding assembly is fed automatically into the diamond cutters. Each cutter mills only one part of the form. The first mills the left-hand lug and forms the blend with the curved area of the case. To do this the tool edge is in the form of an obtuse vee. A second diamond of a reverse form mills the right-hand lug and blend. The third cutter is of concave form having a radius corresponding to the curvature of the watch case side. Such a cutter has a concave radius of 18 mm. (0·71 in.) corresponding to a watch case diameter of 36 mm. (1·42 in.).

Several thousands of components can be milled between relaps and, if carefully used, between 10 and 30 relaps can be achieved. It has been estimated that diamond tool edges, under watch case making conditions, have been known to turn or mill up to 40 or 50 times as many components as a corresponding tool in hard metal.

Plain watch bezels presented a straightforward diamond turning problem, but fashion decreed that patterned bezels were 'à la mode'.

The Posalux FCT150 miller was specially designed for this and similar diamond machining. The diamond carrying bar has a counterbalance for the mounted diamond tool. Where required, of course, two cutters can be mounted. Alternative heads to carry 3, 4 or 6 diamonds are also available. The component can be positioned by dividing head or by the setting microscope sighted through the milling head. The maximum speed of this head is 4,500 r.p.m. which, with a cutter describing a circle of 150 mm. (6 in.), gives a cutting speed of 2,120 metres per minute (6,955 ft. per minute). This operation is not only carried out on solid metal components, but also on formed sheet brass bezels with soldered wire lugs.

Timex Ltd. developed their own equipment for machining rectangular diecast bezels.

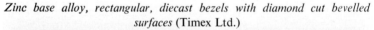

Zinc base alloy, rectangular, diecast bezels with diamond cut bevelled surfaces (Timex Ltd.)

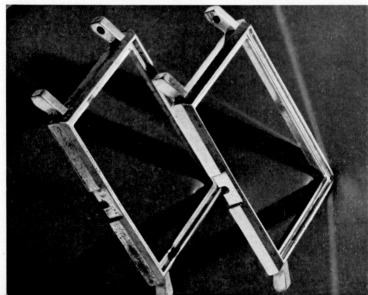

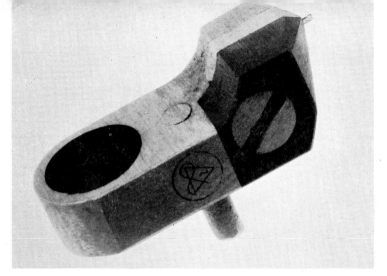

Diamond cutter with 0·3 mm. (0·12 in.) cutting face for watch dials. It would normally be used in a bar so that it described a cutting circle of 100 mm. (4 in.)

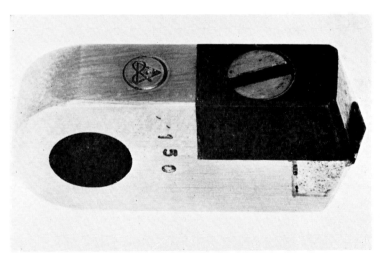

Obtuse vee form tool which, by tradition, is usually either 156° or 168°. In common with most other plunge cut diamond tools used in this industry, the primary front clearance is of the order of 1°–2°, and the negative rake 5°–8°. This particular tool is used for reproducing its vee form as a groove below the surface of the lacquered dial or on raised areas known as 'applique'

Six diamond cutters are used in 'scraping' or 'shaving' the bevels which vary according to pattern from 1·59 mm. to 3·18 mm. ($\frac{1}{16}$ in. to $\frac{1}{8}$ in.) wide. An average of approximately 0·13 mm. (0·005 in.) is removed per cut. No coolant is used. Production between relaps is of the order of 50,000–100,000.

Reverting now to the Posalux and similar milling type machines, they are also used in the finishing of watch dials. The diamond machining operations can be for purely decorative purposes.

The dials are held on a vacuum chuck so that they are positioned horizontally. The machined areas may be projections from the dial surface or grooves cut through the 'zapon' or varnish coating. Indexing of the dials can be by dividing head or by sighting through the microscope provided, if particularly accurate location is required.

Watch faces with diamond milled hour markings (Timex Ltd.)

The use of diamond tools provides a crisp, accurate marking, in keeping with the best traditions of the watchmaking industry.

Where the hour marks or numerals are raised above the varnished surface of the dial and the surfaces to be diamond finished are flat, they can, of course, be turned instead of milled. The edge lengths would normally be of the order of, say, 5–7 mm. (say $\frac{1}{4}$ in.). If the areas to be machined are curved to follow the shape of the dial, then they can still be turned by traversing a concave edge tool through a path to follow the dial curvature.

Ladies' watches finished and part finished showing not only the movements fitted into diamond machined cases but also attached to diamond decorated bracelets (Alfred Jacoby [Machine Tools] Ltd.)

Milling set-up for bracelets and other large patterned jewellery. The expanding mandrel holds the workpiece (Alfred Jacoby [Machine Tools] Ltd.)

DECORATIVE DIAMOND MACHINING OF METAL JEWELLERY COMPONENTS

The basic machine tools developed for general metal jewellery decoration are the same as, or similar to, those used in the watch industry. The actual work set-ups, however, are, of course, different.

One example is the set-up on a Posalux machine for decorating articulated bracelets in precious and base metals. One of the inherent difficulties in such an operation is the design of the holding device for the workpiece. Clamping in any form of chuck distorts the piece, lacquering to a plate is too time consuming for base metal blanks, and glue is difficult to remove from between the joints. These methods are still used but in many cases the two ends of the bracelet are joined and the band thus formed is held on an expanding mandrel. Other methods have been reported in the German technical press, at least on an experimental basis. One consists of freezing the component in a shallow water filled receptacle.

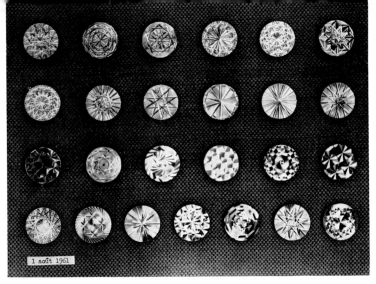

Cuff-links, diamond machined on a Posalux machine, showing the wide variety of pattern (Alfred Jacoby [Machine Tools] Ltd.)

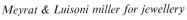

Meyrat & Luisoni miller for jewellery

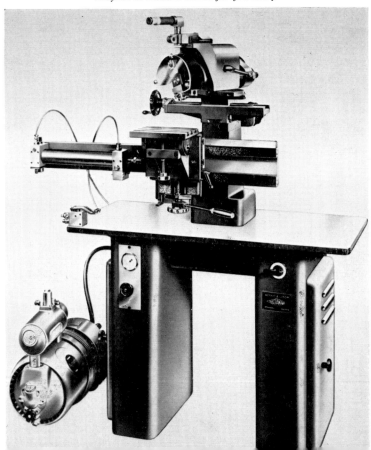

This is said not only to hold the workpiece securely, but also to provide a coolant for the diamond and to prolong life between relaps. A second takes the form of spraying a magnetic metal powder on to the contact surface of the workpiece and using a magnetic chuck as the holding element.

An infinite variety of patterns can be generated by various combinations of movements provided on the machine.

An alternative indexing work holding fixture is used to decorate cuff-links.

Other machines, such as the Posalux MUDIA Universal Automatic, are not only capable of milling geometric surfaces on flat components, but also of copying traditional patterns from masters.

The T2 series of machines from Meyrat & Luisoni, of Switzerland, is available in a wide range of component combinations. It can be used for horizontal and vertical machining of watch cases with

Posalux milling machine. The cutter path can be observed through the optical system (Alfred Jacoby [Machine Tools] Ltd.)

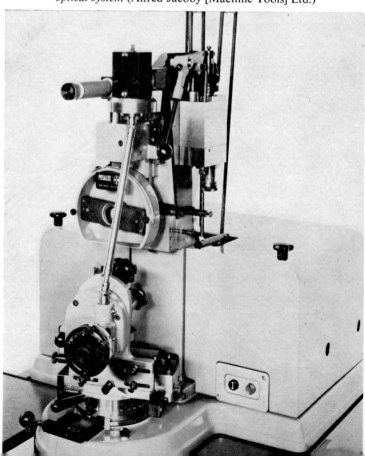

Diamond decorated wedding rings (H. Samuel Ltd.)

straight or lyre shaped lugs, milling between lugs and finishing their upper surfaces. It can be used for decorating jewellery in units up to 300 mm. (11·81 in.) long. The spindle speed range is 1,000, 2,000 and 4,000 r.p.m.

Included among the range of work, which can be accommodated on the indexing work holders available, are decorated wedding rings.

Even in jewellery production, diamond machining is by no means confined to the luxury class. A diamond machined key fob in Germany sells at DM.4.

SERVICING OF DIAMOND TOOLS

One of the obstacles to the economic application of diamond tooling in the jewellery industry is the resulting high inventory value. The wide range of specifications required when multiplied by the high unit cost can well result in a total counted in tens of thousands of dollars.

In an endeavour to assist diamond tool users to minimise this factor, the Swiss company of the Van Moppes Group took up the development of a patented design for a machine capable of carrying out much of the relapping work necessary. Such a machine is intended to be installed in the user's plant. This enables the user to reduce his tool inventory by the amount necessary to cover spare tools whilst others are being relapped. In most cases it also results in an actual cost reduction in respect of the repair charges. The

Triple diamond adjustable milling head (Meyrat & Luisoni)

multi-speed and reversing lap is diamond charged. The work holding fixture is sufficiently universal to accommodate most common tool shanks. It permits the tool to be orientated through 360° to arrive at the correct diamond grain to lap relationship. A crank device automatically traverses the diamond tool across the lap face.

GEM AND SEMI-PRECIOUS STONE WORKING

Several volumes have been published on the shaping, grinding and polishing of gems and semi-precious stones. All include extensive references to the use of diamond saws, grinding wheels and laps. It is, perhaps, not always realised that the same techniques are also used to produce larger items such as agate ash trays and similar articles cut in Idar Oberstein.

Handmade and mounted brooch. The natural stone has been diamond sawn and ground (Wessex Lapidary Society)

As is better known in America, the artistic and manual working of semi-precious and other stones has now become quite a popular hobby. In order to achieve results in a shorter time and thus make better use of their leisure, 'rock-hounds' are turning more and more to diamond tooling.

A typical set-up for amateur use incorporates a diamond saw, a peripheral diamond rough grinding wheel, two aluminium oxide fine grinding wheels and a lapping plate. On this diamond lapping compound is used to obtain high finishes.

A wide range of attractive jewellery can be made by these methods from a great variety of natural stones, many of which are quite inexpensive. Some are even picked up from the sea shore.

ALLIED FIELDS

Whilst, perhaps, not strictly coming within the scope of jewellery, there are a few other applications of diamond with artistic merit that give them a place in this chapter.

Engraving or 'engine-turning' techniques are widely used on such personal articles as cigarette lighters, and for decorating powder compacts. The design consistency depends on the wear

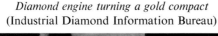

Diamond engine turning a gold compact
(Industrial Diamond Information Bureau)

Diamond machined anodised aluminium tableware (Conrah Products Ltd.)

resistant diamond tool that imparts the pattern to the metal surface. One example is the decorating of anodised aluminium serviette rings and flower vases.

Even the money we use to purchase these articles is coined in dies which are diamond lapped to ensure the high polish and sharp design contours.

REFERENCES

The History and Use of Diamond—S. Tolansky, F.R.S., D.SC., PH.D. University of London. (Published by Methuen, London.)

Gemcraft—Lelande Quick and High Leiper, F.G.A. (Published by Chilton Company, Philadelphia 39, Pa.)

'*Diamond Technology*'—Paul Grodzinski Dr. Ing., M.I.MECH.E. (Published by N.A.G. Press Ltd., London.)

Industrial Applications of the Diamond—N. R. Smith, C.ENG., A.M.I.PROD.E. (Published by Hutchinson, London.)

American Society of Tool Engineers—Paper 24T21–1—'The Use of Diamond Tools for the Turning and Shaping of Small Parts'—L. A. Hurwitz and R. A. Kurtz of Hamilton Watch Company.

'Die Uhr'—Nos. 6, 7 & 9/1963—'Diamond as a cutting tool—Mirror finish turning and milling with diamonds'—Alfred Reichard Pforzheim.

U.K. Patent 1,044,784—Toolmasters Ltd.

Swiss Patent 396,571—Meyrat & Luisoni.

Swiss Patent 419,884—Ragis S.A.

U.S.S.R. Gost 5448–70—'Diamond cutting watch tool. Requirements to the quality of certified products'.

11
Other uses

IN addition to the industries who form the major users of industrial diamonds, there is a number of other applications where the diamond consumption is small, but their importance considerable.

WOODWORKING

Tungsten carbide saws and other edge tools are now used extensively in woodworking. The grinding and re-grinding of the sharp tooth edges are generally undertaken with resin bonded diamond wheels on auto-indexing machines designed for this purpose. The basic requirements are similar to those for grinding edge tools such as milling cutters used in metal machining and described in Chapter 3.

PRINTING

Diamond tipped cutters are used to finish machine copper rolls used in printing. In this way they are reconditioned and prepared for further processing. Flexible printing plates of rubber and other materials are machined to the necessary degree of flatness with diamond milling cutters or diamond trued grinding wheels.

The engraving point in the Vario-Klischograph block and foil engraving equipment is diamond tipped to ensure consistent results in the production of high quality printing equipment.

TOBACCO

Some shredding and cut-off operations in automatic cigarette making plants are carried out with tungsten carbide knives. These

A2

knife edges are re-sharpened with specially designed electro-metallic diamond discs.

DENTISTRY AND OTHER USES IN MEDICINE

One of the earliest uses of electro-deposited diamond coated tools was in this sphere. The very free cutting durable working surfaces of these small tools proved to be a considerable advance over steel or tungsten carbide burrs. They have not only facilitated the dentist's work but appreciably reduced the pain suffered by the patient.

The diamond contributes to the manufacture of other surgical instruments and electric/electronic equipment used in medicine. Examples are hypodermic needles, for which the tube is drawn through diamond dies, and ultra-microtome knives employing diamond cutting edges. The uses of the latter are described on page 324.

DIAMONDS IN SCIENCE

Diamond lapping compound is extensively used in the preparation of metallographic specimens for subsequent study. The general procedure is on the following lines.

Samples for lapping should first be set in a mountant such as Bakelite or Perspex by normal methods, or cold set in Araldite casting resin or similar material. This step may be avoided if the samples are big enough, but edge preservation will be poor if it is omitted.

The samples should be ground flat, if possible, on a grinding machine, followed by lapping on metallographic silicon carbide paper down to 600 grit. It is important to change the grinding direction of the specimen at each grit change to be able to observe the complete removal of scratches from the previous operation. When an even surface has been prepared on a 600 grit, and all previous grinding marks removed, wash all traces of silicon carbide from the specimen and mount and proceed with diamond lapping.

The most generally useful grade of compound is 6/3 (Dialap code). A lap, charged in accordance with details given later, should polish out the 600 grit grinding marks in between 30 seconds and

2 minutes. The specimen should then be thoroughly cleaned and inspected. It may be found sufficiently polished for the purposes in mind. If not, a further polishing operation for between 30 seconds and 2 minutes on a lap containing 1/1 or ½/1 will improve the surface finish very considerably.

For the very finest metallographic photomicrography it may be necessary to follow with a further stage of about 30 seconds, with finest levigated alumina to remove the very smallest scratches. In order to preserve grain boundaries and reduce relief, it is essential that this latter operation be kept down to the minimum time.

These recommendations are for general application, some variation from them is to be expected for some cases. For example, if the surface is not quite flat after 600 grit, it may be necessary to undertake a preliminary diamond lapping operation with 8/4 or 14/5. Alternatively, in certain cases it may suffice to diamond polish only on 1½/1 which will yield a specimen of sufficient fineness for the purposes in view. This is particularly true of fairly soft non-ferrous materials, but it may be worth investigation in other cases.

Good results are obtained on a normal metallographic polishing machine using a lap of one of the following:

Nylon velvet	has long life, but tends to give relief.
Nylon sueded simplex	gives a relief free finish, although care must be taken to avoid tearing the cloth.
Beuhler micro cloth	gives a relief free finish and long life.
Photographic paper	gives the flattest finish but is very easily torn.

A new lap should be charged with compound over the working area, applying the compound in a series of dots about ½ in. apart in both directions. The compound should then be rubbed into the lap with a specimen, at the same time applying a little fluid to assist distribution.

Polishing can now be undertaken without dragging the compound off the lap. During polishing it may be necessary to add a small amount of fluid from time to time.

If the polishing efficiency starts to fall off, the lap can be recharged with further compound to regain the working efficiency.

Diamond knives

In many fields of research, it is often necessary to study thin sections of material. In medical research, for instance, it may be required to study thin sections of bone, muscle, tissue, etc., at very high magnifications, e.g. one hundred thousand times. This means that the samples have to be examined under the electron microscope and this instrument is best used with exceedingly thin slices of the specimen, since specimen thickness is one of the factors determining resolution.

In one particular case, the stomach of a mosquito had to be sliced into sections approximately 100 Å units thick (ten million Ångstrom units = one millimetre). It will be appreciated that these slices were indeed extremely thin. To do this slicing, diamond knives are used. The requirement is for a chisel shaped blade with a cutting edge from 1–2·5 mm. long. Obviously, the knife edge must be very sharp, since the slightest defect will damage the specimens so that they are useless when examined under these high magnifications. This is why diamond is used for these ultra-microtome knives; it is very strong, and therefore it can be polished to a very fine edge without the edge crumbling, as would happen with other materials, such as tungsten carbide.

The manufacture of these knives is a very skilled job, requiring equipment in perfect mechanical condition, high quality diamonds and virtually clinical working conditions.

Very similar knives are beginning to find a use in ophthalmic surgery for making incisions in the cornea. Some reports have indicated that the healing rates of incisions made with diamond knives are greater than those made with steel knives, but others quote similar healing rates. However, we do know that diamond can be polished to a much more perfect edge than steel, due to its characteristic properties. In certain surgical situations when small incisions are required and there is very little room to manoeuvre, this extra sharpness is at a premium, as the normal cutting action is virtually impossible. These problems are further aggravated when the incision has to be made in non-rigid material.

Diamond windows

As stated earlier in this book, diamond can be classified as Type I or Type II. It will be recalled that Type II diamond transmits infra-red and ultra-violet, and so it can be used as a window in instruments using infra-red and ultra-violet 'light'. One such instrument is the infra-red spectrophotometer. In this, infra-red from source is split into two beams; one beam is passed through the material being examined, the other goes through a reference cell, i.e. a blank. The sample will absorb some of the infra-red, to a greater or lesser extent, and a detector compares the two emergent beams, thus indicating the amount absorbed by the sample, together with the frequency of the absorbed radiation.

This information can be used for a variety of purposes, e.g. the material's molecular structure can be determined, its purity can be measured, the material can be identified, its concentration can be estimated and so on. The instrument is thus a very useful tool for the organic chemist, biochemist, etc.

Very few materials are transparent to infra-red at the required frequencies. Thus, whenever a small window is needed in the apparatus, as in the detector, and the infra-red beam has to pass through it, the choice of materials is very limited. Rock salt will transmit some of the infra-red, but clearly, if a window made of rock salt gets damp, it will rapidly become opaque. The other possible window materials are rather similar, Type II diamond being the exception.

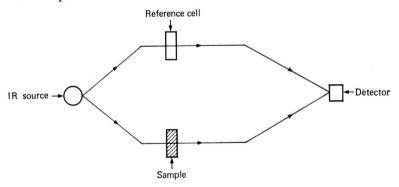

Schematic drawing of infra-red spectrophotometer incorporating a diamond window

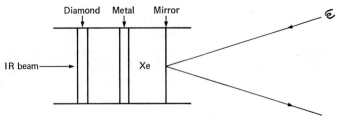

Schematic layout of Golay cell

From the very schematic representation of the detector, which is called a Golay cell, it will be seen that this is a tube in which xenon gas is sandwiched between a metal disc and a very thin plastic membrane. The latter is flexible and reflective on the outermost side. On the other side of the metal disc there is a window, and this is the part that must be made from Type II diamond. The radiation passes through the window and meets the metal disc which it warms. This causes the xenon gas to expand, which in turn deflects the membrane. A beam of light is arranged to shine on the membrane, and the deflection of this beam is a measure of the intensity of the infra-red being received. These detectors are very sensitive indeed; it is said that they can detect the heat of a candle that is half a mile away.

High pressure anvils

Another interesting use for both Types of diamond is in the study of materials at ultra-high pressures, i.e. tens of kilobars.

The problem is to find anvils which are transparent and strong enough to withstand the pressure. Glass would break, tungsten carbide is opaque, but diamond once again comes to our aid. It is strong enough and transparent. The diamond anvils are quite small, being made in the form of truncated pyramids, the working faces ranging from 0·5–1·0 mm. square. Adjacent is a schematic drawing of the high pressure apparatus, which is itself small enough to be mounted on the stage of a conventional optical microscope. Thus, a drop of whisky can be placed between the diamond anvils and seen to change into a crystal of whisky as the pressure is increased.

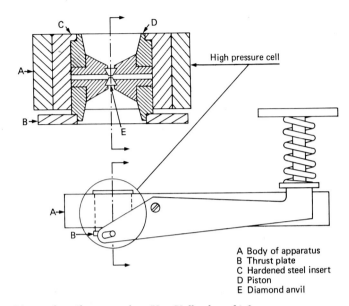

A Body of apparatus
B Thrust plate
C Hardened steel insert
D Piston
E Diamond anvil

Diamond anvils mounted on Van Valkenburg high pressure apparatus
(High Pressure Diamond Optics Inc.)

Direct observation of such transitions tell us a lot, but the infra-red spectrum is even more revealing, so we have to choose Type II diamonds which will trasmit infra-red.

Sometimes the physicist will use ultra-violet or X-rays instead of infra-red, and again suitable diamonds can be provided.

Weather satellites—diamond lens

As we are no longer content to live in caves, it becomes increasingly important to know what the weather will be like, both in the near and distant future, not only here, but everywhere, not only at ground level, but at all levels. The airline pilot wants to know the air density and temperature, wind direction and strength at ground level and perhaps at 10,000 metres (30,000 ft.) since these affect his take-off run, range, required fuel and permissible cargo load. Needless to say, it would be nice to know if he will be able to see through the fog when and if he eventually reaches his destination!

In this modern age of miracles, it is very easy to radio the distant airport for a weather report. It is not necessary to be a meteorologist to know if it is wet, dry, foggy or snowing, but what will it be like en route and on arrival, perhaps in 8 hours' time (depending on the weather, of course!).

How are we to plan for weather situations at altitudes and locations where there is no one to ask?

The need to be able to predict the weather is obvious. Away from the Earth's surface, the atmosphere gets thinner and the pressure drops. If there were no disturbing influences, the word 'weather' would not have entered our vocabulary, but there are disturbing influences. The Earth rotates about its own axis and is in orbit around the Sun; the Earth's surface is not smooth, it varies in composition and texture, it is not heated uniformly by the Sun, some parts are hot whilst others are cold. Thus, we get large air masses set in motion. These disturbances can be very local, or they can be global in scale. In essence, these disturbances result in what we call 'weather'.

We must measure to understand; in the case of weather, we are dealing with a global three-dimensional system, and the real problem is that of taking enough measurements, because the system is a dynamic one, and very complex. It is rather like trying to track the convection currents in a pan of water warming on the cooker.

Weather ships, rockets and balloons have all added enormously to our knowledge of meteorology, but there is obviously a limit to how many ships can be manned, and how many balloons and rockets can be launched. The latest tool, the satellite, is perhaps the most spectacular of all, because it can monitor such an enormous area, virtually the whole of the Earth's surface, and its instruments can take measurements at various altitudes.

One such instrument is the 'Selective Chopper Radiometer' (SCR), the first one being flown in the N.A.S.A. weather satellite, Nimbus 'D'. This instrument is a British one, designed by Dr. J. T. Houghton and Prof. S. D. Smith (now at Heriot-Watt University) and their colleagues at Oxford and Reading Universities. The satellite was launched in April 1970 into a circular polar orbit, at an altitude of 600 nautical miles, each orbit taking about 100 minutes. It will be appreciated that, as the satellite's orbit takes it close to the North and South Poles, and as the Earth rotates 27 degrees about its

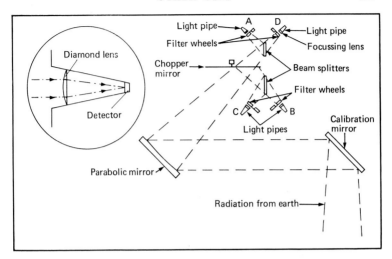

Selective chopper radiometer optics

own axis during one satellite orbit, the coverage is very comprehensive.

The SCR was designed to measure the temperature at six successive 10 km. thick layers in the atmosphere, from ground level up to 50 km. It does this by observing the intensity of the emitted infra-red radiation from the 15 micron absorption lines of atmospheric carbon dioxide, i.e. radiation from Earth.

This instrument has proved to be very successful, sending back daily temperature soundings for the whole Earth's surface. The instrument was designed to measure the temperature to an accuracy of 1°C.

An improved version of the SCR was accepted by N.A.S.A. for flight in Nimbus 'E'. The new instrument contains 16 channels, 10 more than the previous version, there being no increase in size or weight. This has been achieved by using a new optical system, using beam splitters and four position quick change filter wheels. The extra channels enable water vapour distribution and low and high cloud cover to be determined.

The schematic diagram shows how radiation from Earth is reflected from the calibration mirror on to the parabolic mirror. It then becomes a converging beam, which either passes through the chopping disc, or is reflected off its mirrored surface. Thus the beam is split into two. It is further sub-divided by the two beam-splitters which are wavelength dependent reflectors. These allow radiation of certain frequencies to pass through them, whilst radiation at other frequencies is reflected. The radiation then passes through one of the four filters in the filter wheel, through a focusing lens on the end of the light pipe and is focused down on to the pyro-electric detector, where it is converted into an electronic signal.

Ice particles and water droplets in Cirrus clouds are detected in one Channel. Together, the four filters in this Channel have a transmission range from 11 to 200 microns, and so the focusing lens has to accept radiation over this whole range; the only known material that has such a range is diamond.

Although diamond is the hardest material known, the hardness is not uniform, for it varies enormously with crystallographic orientation. A shift of only 2° can mean a tremendous difference in abrasion resistance. In general, diamonds are shaped by abrading them in the softer directions, using diamond impregnated grinding wheels, or laps.

When generating a lens form, the diamond has to be abraded in very many different hardness planes, or directions, and so to produce a surface of optical quality is very difficult indeed, as there is a tendency for the surface to be 'lobed'. To solve a problem like this requires very great skill and experience in diamond polishing techniques, including the right choice of diamond grinding wheels and lap conditions, plus that indefinable 'feel' for the job. It was difficult to know how to hold the diamond; both sides had to be polished, one plane, one convex, and any fixtures used had to be designed and manufactured so that the required optical geometry could be achieved, and there had to be no risk of damaging the diamond, i.e. it had to be held rigidly, otherwise the pressure from the wheel might have cracked it. The team at Reading University produced a vacuum chuck to hold the diamond, but this was only partially successful, and, in fact, it had to be complemented by using a few 'tricks of the trade'.

The outcome was entirely successful and, in fact, two lenses were produced.

Heat sinks

Diamonds are good conductors of heat and Type II diamonds are even better than Type I, being about five times better than copper at room temperature. This makes them very suitable for use as heat sinks.

In solid state electronic devices, such as transistors, the removal of heat from the device is most important and, in fact, the efficiency of the heat removal system can determine the usefulness of the device. A common technique is to mount the device on beryllia, a very good conductor of heat, and this in turn may be mounted on copper. The beryllia/copper assembly is called a 'heat sink', since it can be loosely thought of as soaking up the heat from the device.

For many applications, beryllia and copper are perfectly satisfactory, but there are some devices which require better heat sinks, since the rate of heat removal determines the power output and hence usefulness of the device. One of the first reports of diamond being used as a heat sink came from C. Burke Swan, of the Bell Telephone Laboratories Inc., U.S.A., who published results in the Proceedings of the Institute of Electrical and Electronics Engineers, in September, 1967. The device concerned was a silicon avalanche oscillator; a 0·014 cm. diameter silicon p–n diode was mounted on a polished Type IIa diamond, and the diamond was mounted on copper. The power output from the device was 4·7 watts of CW power at 13·3 GHz, approximately twice that from a device mounted on a copper heat sink cooled with liquid nitrogen.

In such cases, apart from increasing the utility of the device, diamond heat sinks will make installation and maintenance a more economic proposition, and this will help to justify the use of diamond.

The Gunn diode is another application where a diamond heat sink is advantageous. If a certain voltage is applied across a chip of gallium arsenide, an electrical oscillation is set up whose frequency is determined by the dimensions of the chip. If the chip is 0·1 mm. across, the frequency will be about 10^9 cycles/sec., a microwave radio frequency. Thus, with a battery connected to a very small piece of gallium arsenide, one has a microwave transmitter, and such devices are now in production. They can be used as burglar alarms, and in instruments for measuring velocity. To fully exploit this effect in radar and communications requires greater output power and, therefore, better heat sinks, and, once again, Type II diamond can supply the answer.

The Bell Telephone Laboratories have also found a diamond heat sink useful in a solid state injection laser. The active material is again gallium arsenide and its temperature must not exceed a certain limit. Because Type II diamond is such a good conductor of heat, the device can be operated by cooling to −68°C. with dry-ice, whereas, when it was mounted on copper, it had to be cooled to −132°C. with liquid nitrogen. Thus, the device can either dissipate more power for a given heat sink temperature or the heat sink can remain at a higher temperature for a given output power.

Thermistors

The Type II diamonds discussed so far are actually Type IIa and, like the vast majority of all natural diamonds, they are very good electrical insulators. However, there is a very rare kind of diamond called Type IIb which is a semiconductor; this diamond is generally very high quality blue gem material.

One interesting property of this diamond is that, as the temperature is raised, its electrical resistance decreases, and so Type IIb diamond can be used to measure temperature. In practice, two wires are

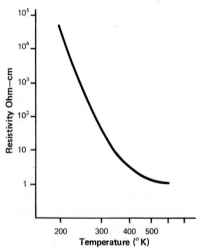

Type IIb diamond resistance versus temperature
(Prof. Mitchell, Reading University)

connected to the diamond and these are fed to a meter which measures the resistance of the diamond, but the meter is more convenient if it is provided with a temperature scale. These diamond thermistors are very sensitive; they can record a change in temperature of 1/500°C. Since the diamond has a very high thermal conductivity, these changes will be recorded almost instantaneously.

Although Type IIb diamonds are extremely rare in nature, synthetic ones are now on the market and are likely to find applications in medicine and in space research.

Diamond—one material which combines so many useful and extraordinary properties; it is this *combination* of properties which make it the pre-eminent material known to mankind.

REFERENCES

C. Burke Swan, Proc. Inst. Electrical and Electronics Engineers, Vol. 55, No. 9, Page 1617, 1967.
A. Van Valkenburg, 'Diamond Research 1964, Supplement to Industrial Diamond Review'.
R. Berman, 'Physical Properties of Diamond'—'Thermal Properties' (1965).

Index

(Compiled by F. D. Buck)

References in italic indicate an illustration or a table

INDEX